Evolution of
the Vertebrates

Evolution of the Vertebrates

A HISTORY OF THE BACKBONED ANIMALS THROUGH TIME

EDWIN H. COLBERT

Curator of Fossil Reptiles and
Amphibians, The American Museum
of Natural History
Professor of Vertebrate Paleontology
Columbia University

SCIENCE EDITIONS, INC., NEW YORK, 1961

Preface

This book is intended to be a general textbook on vertebrate pale-ontology, in which there is set forth an account of the evolution of backboned animals as based on the fossil record. It is written in language that tries to avoid as much as possible the use of highly technical terms. It is written for the general student rather than for the specialist, and for the lay reader.

An attempt is made in this book to present a very general review of vertebrate evolution, and to show how animals with backbones developed through more than 400 million years of earth history. Consequently, this is not a book upon the principles of evolution, even though principles are frequently mentioned or discussed in passing. Nor is it a book concerned with the mechanisms of evolution as revealed by genetics. As stated above, this is primarily a sur-vey of the fossil record of backboned animals.

A book such as this must inevitably omit a great deal; it must consider the most important facets of vertebrate history, and leave the details to other more comprehensive books. Therefore no at-tempt has been made to describe numerous genera in each family of vertebrates, or for that matter to discuss all the families. Rather, there are presented short but comprehensive descriptions of charac-teristic animals in the various orders of vertebrates, and these serve as examples to illustrate the group under consideration. Additional discussion of the group, whatever its rank, revolves around or de-velops from the description of the characteristic form. It is hoped that such a presentation may give a fair picture of the vertebrates without the confusion that might result from an attempt to tell the story in detail.

To follow the varied trends of vertebrate evolution through geo-logic time is not an easy assignment, because so many things were happening at once. Ancient fishes appeared during early Paleozoic times, 400 million years or more ago, and from them the fishes have evolved continuously up to the present day. Amphibians in turn sprang from fishes and have continued to recent times, while similarly reptiles evolved from the amphibians, and birds and mammals from reptiles. So it was that many vertebrates were evolving simultaneously in numerous separate lines through long stretches of geologic time. The author is confronted with the task of describing these evolutionary events, one by one, and of trying, somehow, to relate them to each other in the geologic time scale.

An attempt has been made in this book to maintain a feeling for the passing of geologic time through the story, partly by the order in which the various groups of vertebrates are discussed and partly by the insertion of chapters dealing with the relationships of faunas during certain phases of geologic history. Whether such treatment is successful remains to be seen.

Whatever the merits of the prose or of its arrangement in this book, there can be little doubt as to the excellence of the illustrations, practically all of them new, and drawn specifically for the book. This helps to give a fresh approach to the subject. The illustrations, as will be seen, consist of simple bone drawings, often grouped for purposes of comparison, of restorations and of pictorial phylogenies.

The bone drawings, so far as possible, are intended to illustrate characteristic animals (or their parts), and, like the text, do not pretend to be all inclusive. The restorations and the phylogenies, done with great skill and style by Mrs. Lois Darling, show what many ancient vertebrates looked like when they were alive. Here again, it has been necessary to select certain animals and to leave out many, for which similar restorations would be very desirable. Indeed, I wish there might have been many more illustrations made for this book, but limits had to be imposed and maintained if the volume were to be kept in hand.

Various people have helped in the preparation of the book. My particular thanks go to Mr. John Ostrom for assistance on the proof, and for his help in the preparation of the index.

Finally I wish to express my very deep appreciation to the several people who read the manuscript, or parts of the manuscript, and gave me the benefit of much-needed constructive criticism that has helped to improve the quality and the accuracy of the text. For their critical reviews and suggestions I gratefully acknowledge the help of Dr. Glenn L. Jepsen, who read the entire manuscript, of Dr. Bobb Schaeffer, who checked that portion of the manuscript devoted to the fishes, of Dr. Alfred S. Romer, who checked the section dealing

0

with amphibians, reptiles, and birds, and finally of Dr. George Gaylord Simpson, who checked the section on mammals. No author could ask for a more distinguished and authoritative panel of critics in the field of vertebrate paleontology.

EDWIN H. COLBERT

New York
January, 1955

Contents

14 · TRIUMPH OF THE DINOSAURS

15 · YEARS OF THE DINOSAURS

16 · SURVIVING REPTILES

17 · BEGINNING OF THE MAMMALS

18 · MARSUPIALS

19 · INTRODUCTION TO THE PLACENTALS

20 · UNGUICULATE MAMMALS

Fossil Hunters

I · Introduction

FOSSILS—THE EVIDENCE IN THE ROCKS

This is the story of vertebrate evolution as revealed by the fossil evidence. It is an account of vertebrate life through millions of years of earth history, as based upon petrified remains that are found in the sediments of the earth's crust. It is the paleontologist's interpretation of a record that begins with the primitive vertebrates of early Paleozoic times and extends, through vast expanses of geologic time, to the varied backboned animals of the great Pleistocene Ice Age. Fossils are the raw materials upon which the paleontologist, the student of ancient life upon the earth, bases his studies. Fossils are the remains or indications of life that is now extinct. They are generally the hard parts of animals that have been petrified, transformed from shell or bone into stone. But they may be the hard parts as they were originally constituted, preserved intact without benefit of petrification or fossilization. Sometimes the soft parts of animals or plants may be fossilized, although such preservation is not common. Indeed, extinct animals are occasionally preserved completely and without any change. Mammoths and other animals of the last Ice Age, frozen in the ice of the far north, have been preserved in this way.

Fossils are not necessarily direct evidence, in the form of preserved bones or shells, of the organisms they represent. They may be molds in the rocks—imprints left by the animal (or plant) or by some part of the organism. They may be footprints made by an animal. They may be the preserved structures that were built by an animal during its lifetime, such as nests or tubes. Indeed fossils are found in many varied forms, which, among other things, helps to make life interesting for the paleontologist.

The study of fossils is a comparatively new science. To the peoples of the classical civilizations the nature of fossils was hardly realized, and it was not until the days of the Renaissance that a true understanding of fossils was reached by (among others) that great and accomplished Florentine, Leonardo da Vinci. The scientific study of fossils, however, is barely more than a century and a half old, whereas the modern evolutionary interpretation of the fossil record really begins with the work of Charles Darwin, as crystallized in his epochal book *The Origin of Species*. In spite of the relative youth of paleontology as a science, an impressive amount of fossil material has been gathered together and studied by paleontologists all over the world. Consequently it can be said that our knowledge of the history of life as based upon the fossil record is now reasonably complete, and this is as true for the vertebrates as for other groups of organisms.

Of course there are many gaps still to be filled, and there are many new forms still to be discovered. Nevertheless the general aspects of vertebrate history are now known sufficiently well to make a connected and integrated story, and so far as lesser categories of backboned animals are concerned, the story is frequently preserved in the fossil record with considerable detail.

It is the possibility of finding entirely new organisms preserved as fossils that makes life for the paleontologist something like an extended treasure hunt. We never know what may be revealed in the next canyon or on the distant badland slope, and even in the laboratory things appear to surprise and delight the student of ancient life. But whether the fossils are new, or whether they represent animals already well known in the fields of paleontology, the collecting and preparing of fossils for study is more often than not arduous and difficult work. Only the person who has hunted for fossils in the field and worked on them in the laboratory can appreciate their true value in terms of the expenditure of human effort.

It takes much looking to find fossils, especially the fossils of the backboned animals. These generally are not so abundantly preserved as the fossils of sea shells and other invertebrates; consequently their discovery commonly requires much walking and climbing and some careful scrutinizing of rock exposures. Moreover, when they are found these fossils require special techniques of collecting if they are to be brought back to the laboratory with any degree of success. Very commonly it is necessary to expose the fossil carefully and to harden it with shellac as it is exposed, for although the bones or scales have been turned to stone and thus are hard, they are often at the same time as brittle as fine glass. Because such fossils may break of their own weight it is necessary to jacket them with casts of burlap and plaster of Paris before they can be removed from the ground.

Then in the laboratory the whole process must be reversed. The plaster jackets are removed, and the fossils are carefully and completely cleaned. Often they must be reinforced by wires or irons or by plaster, filling in the hollow cavities of the bones. Only then are they ready for study.

It is long and involved—often it is tedious—but when one becomes thoroughly interested in the subject, it is fascinating work. No antiquarian, poring over a lovely Greek vase, shows more care or solicitude for his treasure than the vertebrate paleontologist studying the fragile fossil bones of some animal that lived millions of years ago.

In the end a picture of this long extinct animal is reconstructed. Bones are compared with bones of other animals, either fossil or recent. Relationships are established. On the basis of our knowledge of modern animals, the soft parts of the fossil usually can be inferred. Muscles are mentally fastened to the bones, and the general patterns of nerves and blood vessels are indicated. Frequently even the nature of the outer covering of scales or skin is shown by the fossil, so that only such superficial features as color and accessory soft parts are left entirely to the imagination. Such are the methods of the paleontologist, and by their use, compounded many times over through the years, the vast picture puzzle of life in the past has been assembled.

ANIMALS WITH BACKBONES

The phylum Chordata includes those animals having, throughout their life or at some stage in their development, an internal supporting

(A)

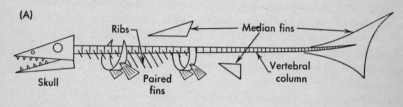

Ribs — Median fins —

Skull

Paired fins

Vertebral column

(B)

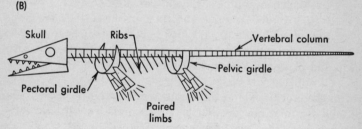

Skull   Ribs —   Vertebral column

Pectoral girdle

Pelvic girdle

Paired limbs

FIGURE 1. Generalized diagram of the skeleton in (A) an aquatic vertebrate and (B) a land-living vertebrate.

structure, in the form either of a continuous flexible rod known as a notochord or of a series of vertebrae, running dorsally along the midline of the body. The chordates having vertebrae are generally designated as the vertebrates, and they comprise by far the largest division of the chordates. Almost all fossil chordates are backboned animals, or vertebrates, so that virtually all our knowledge of the primitive chordates, in which there is only a rod-like notochord, is derived from a few surviving forms.

The vertebrate normally has the long axis of the body horizontally placed; any deviation from this position represents a specialization. There is a concentration of sense organs at the anterior end of the animal, and these are generally housed in a skull. The internal skeleton of the vertebrate is either cartilaginous or bony, and in the vast majority of forms it is bony. There is an axial skeleton, consisting of the vertebral column, with a skull anteriorly placed, and frequently with ribs extending laterally from the vertebrae. There may be median fins associated with the axial skeleton. In most vertebrates, but not all, there is also an appendicular skeleton, consisting of paired fins or limbs for steering and balance, or for propulsion, and these are attached to the body by bony girdles. There is a pectoral girdle in front and a pelvic girdle posteriorly. Moreover the vertebrate is characterized by the position of the spinal nerve chord above the notochord or vertebral column, and by the location of the circulatory system and the digestive system below the vertebral column. Respiration in vertebrates is either by means of gills, in which case oxygen is extracted from the water, or by lungs, in which case oxygen is extracted from the air. The gills are supported by arches—the branchial arches. In all but the most primitive vertebrates there is an upper and a lower jaw, which are formed by transformation of an anterior pair of branchial arches. The sense organs include paired eyes, paired nostrils in all but the most primitive types, and paired ears, which may be for balance and hearing, or for balance alone.

AMPHIOXUS

We shall probably never know what the first chordates were like, because it is unlikely that adequate indications of them are preserved in the fossil record. They must have been small, comparatively simple animals, and it is not likely that they had a hard skeleton, capable of being fossilized and preserved in the sediments of the earth. The first vertebrates appearing in the record of the rocks are characterized by highly developed bony armor, and for this reason it has been argued that bone is very primitive in the history of vertebrate evolution. Yet it seems logical to believe that there might have been a long period of vertebrate evolution preceding the development of bony armor so that the first ancient, bone-encrusted vertebrates in the geologic record in truth may be advanced far beyond the condition of the primitive chordates.

It so happens, however, that there is a modern chordate of such primitive form and organization that it approximates to a considerable degree our conception of the central ancestor for the backboned animals. This is the little sea lancelet known as *Amphioxus*. *Amphioxus*, which lives in the shallow waters along certain coast lines, and spends much of its life buried in the sandy bottom, is a trans-

lucent animal of fish-like form and rarely more than two inches in
length.   There are no vertebrae in *Amphioxus*, but rather a notochord
forming an internal support for the animal.   This support represents

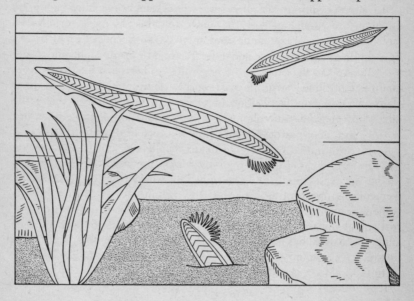

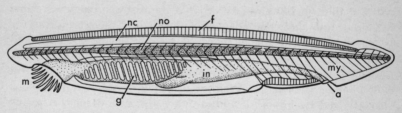

FIGURE 2.   The modern lancelet, *Amphioxus*, a simple chordate that lives in
shallow waters along seacoasts.   Abbreviations: a, anus; f, fin ray; g, gills; m,
mouth surrounded by tentacles; my, myotomes or segmented muscles; nc, dorsal
nerve chord; no, notochord.

the precursor of the backbone or spinal column.   Above the notochord
in *Amphioxus* is the nerve chord; below it is a simple digestive tube.
There is no real head or brain in this little animal, and no sense
organs, except for some pigment spots that seem to be sensitive to
light.   No matter how primitive and deficient *Amphioxus* is in these
respects, it is well supplied with gills, arranged in a long series down
either side of the front portion of the body.   These extended gills
serve to extract oxygen from the water; they also aid the animal in

feeding, by functioning as a sort of sieve to strain food from the debris of the ocean floor. Finally, although *Amphioxus* is a capable swimmer, it lacks paired fins of any sort. However, there is a small tail fin. All in all, *Amphioxus* is a very primitive chordate. The great development of the gill basket shows that this animal may be specialized in some aspects of its anatomy, yet in spite of this specialization the lancelet remains in a general way an approximate structural ancestor for the vertebrates. It is probable that there has been little change in the line of evolution represented by the lancelet since early Paleozoic or even pre-Paleozoic times. In *Amphioxus* we see in effect our chordate ancestor of five hundred million years ago.

GEOLOGIC TIME

Mention of the word Paleozoic and reference to a time span of such tremendous duration as five hundred million years bring us to the subject of geologic time. This is a consideration of prime importance to the paleontologist, because one of the great advantages that the study of fossils has over other branches of natural history is the possibility of projecting ourselves back through the fourth dimension of time into the past ages of the earth.

It is not easy at first to think in the immense units of geologic time. We are used to thinking in terms of years or centuries or millennia; geologic time is measured in millions of years. It seems almost incredible that there were rains and winds and volcanoes and the cycles of life and death on the earth as far back as one hundred million years or five hundred million years or a billion years ago, yet from the study of radioactive elements we know that such great time spans are necessary to measure the sequence of events that make up earth history. Careful studies of the disintegration of uranium into lead indicate that there are rocks on the earth almost three billion years in age, and there is good reason to think that the earth had existed for a long time before these rocks were formed. In terms of human experience this is a very old planet.

It is not possible at this place to go into the evidence for dating the earth or for drawing up the geologic time scale, but a few salient facts can be presented. As already mentioned, the first rocks that can be dated are almost three billion years old. Fossils first appear in abundance in rocks of Cambrian age, and they can be dated as about five hundred million years old. Although this is the beginning of an adequate fossil record, it is by no means any indication of the beginning of life on the earth, for there was probably a long time span before the Cambrian period when plants and animals were evolving as very primitive organisms. By the beginning of Cambrian times life was sufficiently advanced so that animals were highly organized, with hard parts capable of fossilization. Almost all the major groups of invertebrate animals are present in Cambrian rocks— an indication of the incredibly long evolutionary sequence during which life was differentiating and specializing to the comparatively high degree that is characteristic of the earliest Cambrian faunas. Perhaps a few other dates will help to indicate the long evolutionary history of life on the earth. The first vertebrates appeared in the Ordovician period of earth history, some four hundred million years ago. The dinosaurs began their long evolutionary history almost two hundred million years ago, and they continued for more than one hundred million years. They became extinct about seventy million years ago, and at that time mammals became the dominant animals on the earth. Man as such appeared less than a million years ago. In the last few hundred thousand years he has gone far.

Two geologic periods have been mentioned in the preceding paragraph. Earth history has been divided into a number of time divisions or *periods,* and these in turn have been grouped into longer time divisions known as *eras.*

Several eras mark the course of earth history prior to the beginning of the fossil record, but since this portion of geologic time is rather difficult to interpret, the general practice is to refer to it as "Precambrian times." The Precambrian portion of earth history is long, extending through more than 2500 million years of time. It need not concern us here.

With the beginning of the fossil record earth history can be measured and followed in considerable detail. As a result of cumulative studies carried on during the last century or so, three great eras of earth history are recognized by the sequence of the fossil record. They are, in the order of their age, the Paleozoic, the Mesozoic, and the Cenozoic eras respectively. The Paleozoic era, the time of ancient life, has been divided into seven periods, which in order from oldest to youngest are Cambrian, Ordovician, Silurian, Devonian, Mississippian, Pennsylvanian, and Permian. It is general practice among paleontologists outside North America to combine the Mississippian and the Pennsylvanian into a single period, the Carboniferous.

What are the bases for these names of geologic periods? For an answer to this question we have to go back to the early pioneers of geological science, who laid the foundations for the study of rock strata and their included fossils. The first four of the Paleozoic

periods were studied and named by English scholars. The name
Cambrian comes from Cambria the ancient name for Wales, where
rocks of this age are extensively exposed. Ordovician and Silurian are
names based on ancient tribes once living in southern England and
Wales, the Ordovices and the Silures, in whose one-time tribal terri-
tories there are extensive sequences of rock belonging to these two
ages. The name Devonian comes from the English county of Devon-
shire. As might be expected, the next two names in the geologic
column are based upon North American regions where Paleozoic
rocks are exposed, along the Mississippi River and in the Allegheny
Mountains of Pennsylvania. The older term, Carboniferous, comes
from the typically carbonaceous character of rocks of this age; this
was the period of great coal deposits over many continental areas.
The name Permian is based upon the province of Perm, in northern
Russia, where rocks of this age are especially well developed.

The Mesozoic, or period of middle life in earth history, is subdivided into three periods—the Triassic, the Jurassic, and the Cretaceous. The Triassic is so named because it was subdivided into
three units in central Europe, where it was first studied. The name
Jurassic comes from the Jura Mountains of the Alpine region. And
Cretaceous is based upon the Latin word *Creta,* meaning chalk, in
reference to the white cliffs of Dover.

Finally the Cenozoic, the time of recent life in earth history, consists of two periods under which are grouped six subdivisions, generally regarded as of lesser consequence, and therefore classified as
epochs. The periods are the Tertiary (originally considered as the
third great time division in earth history) and the Quaternary
(the fourth original time division). The epochs, from oldest to
youngest, are the Paleocene, the Eocene, the Oligocene, the Miocene,
the Pliocene, and the Pleistocene, names formulated in part by Sir
Charles Lyell, the great English geologist, as the result of his studies
on mollusks in the Cenozoic rocks of Europe. Of these epochs all
but the last, the Pleistocene, belong to the Tertiary period. In
Lyell's classification, Eocene was the oldest division—and the name
means "dawn of recent times." Then there come, in order, Oligocene,
a name meaning "little recent," Miocene, "less recent," Pliocene,
"more recent," and Pleistocene, "most recent times." The Paleocene epoch was recognized at a subsequent date, and even now its
acceptance is not universal. This name means "more ancient than
Eocene."

Such was the manner in which the names for the time divisions
of earth history became established. Let us now arrange them in

ERAS	Duration of periods	PERIODS	Epochs	Duration of epochs
CENOZOIC 70 million years duration	1	Quaternary	Recent	
			Pleistocene	1
			Pliocene	10
			Miocene	15
	69	Tertiary	Oligocene	10
			Eocene	19
			Paleocene	15
MESOZOIC 130 million years duration	60	Cretaceous		
	35	Jurassic		
	35	Triassic		
	30	Permian		
	25	Pennsylvanian		
	25	Mississippian		
PALEOZOIC 300 million years duration	40	Devonian		
	30	Silurian		
	70	Ordovician		
	80	Cambrian		

FIGURE 3. Chart of geologic time, and a simplified family tree of the classes of vertebrates, showing their range and relative abundance through time.

order, following the usual geological practice of placing the oldest period at the bottom of the list (since the oldest strata are at the bottom of the rock column), with each successively younger period above its predecessor in the sequence. The material can be set forth in tabular form, as shown in the figure.

THE SEQUENCE OF VERTEBRATES THROUGH TIME

As mentioned above, the first vertebrates are known from rocks of Ordovician age. However, the fossil evidence for these earliest

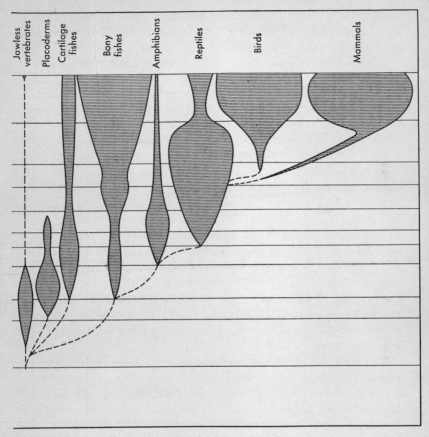

FIGURE 3 (*continued*)

known vertebrates is very fragmentary, and it is not until we reach the sediments deposited during late Silurian times that fossils are complete enough to give us some idea as to the form and relationships of the early vertebrates. Even here the evidence is scanty, so it is actually in Devonian rocks that the fossil record of the vertebrates becomes truly representative. Therefore, for our purposes the story does not begin until about the middle of the Paleozoic era. From then on, however, the history of the vertebrates is well known, as it is revealed in successively younger layers of the earth's crust. As will be shown in the succeeding pages of this book, we can see from the fossil record in the rocks how all the major groups of fishes had appeared by middle and late Devonian times, some of them to continue to the present day, one group to become extinct before the close of the Paleozoic era. We can see how during the transition from Devonian to Mississippian times the first land-living verte-brates, the amphibians, made their appearance as descendants of certain advanced fishes. The amphibians had their heyday, espe-cially during the final stages of the Paleozoic era, after which they continued to develop, but on a small scale as compared to the broad variety of their development at the time of their dominance.

In the course of their evolution the amphibians gave rise to the reptiles, an event that probably took place during Pennsylvanian times, and the reptiles were destined to rule the earth for many millions of years. During the Mesozoic era some reptiles, known as dinosaurs, became the dominant animals on the land, evolving along diverse lines that carried them to all the larger land areas of the earth and into most of the different environments that then existed. The dinosaurs were indeed the rulers of the earth for more than a hundred million years, but finally they became extinct. Today the reptiles that survive, although numerous and widely dispersed throughout the world, are but a remnant of the hordes that once ruled the earth.

Before the dinosaurs had become extinct, in fact during the earlier part of their long evolutionary history, two other groups of verte-brates arose from reptilian ancestors. Both these groups appeared during Jurassic times, to evolve, slowly at first and then with in-creasing rapidity and diversity, into the birds and the mammals of our present-day world. By Cretaceous times the birds had be-come highly specialized; by the beginning of the Cenozoic era they were populating the continents and the islands of the world in essentially their modern form. As long as the reptiles were domi-nant the evolution of the mammals was comparatively slow. But with the transition from the Cretaceous period into the beginning of the Tertiary period new opportunities were opened to the early mammals. The reign of the reptiles was at an end, and the "Age of Mammals" began. It has continued to this day, when one mam-mal, man, has developed within a comparatively short span of time to unprecedented heights. This is now the age of intellect (no mat-ter how despairing some people may feel about modern world trends), and because of his intellect the mammal known as man is able to look back through time to study the evolutionary history of his forerunners and forebears.

SOMETHING ABOUT CLASSIFICATION

The first vertebrates were fishes, if we use the word "fishes" in a very broad sense. Actually, the first vertebrates were primitive jaw-less animals known as *Agnatha*, a word compounded from the Greek roots *a*, without, and *gnathos*, jaws. From these early agnathous animals the gnathostomes or jawed vertebrates originated, first the fishes as we know them, and from certain fishes the early land-living vertebrates. After the vertebrates came onto the land, they evolved in time as several great groups. Thus the several classes of back-boned animals arose that can be grouped into two larger divisions or superclasses of vertebrates.

Subphylum	*Superclass*	*Class*
Vertebrata	Pisces	Agnatha, jawless vertebrates
		Placodermi, primitive jawed vertebrates
		Chondrichthyes, sharks
		Osteichthyes, bony fishes
	Tetrapoda	Amphibia, amphibians
		Reptilia, reptiles
		Aves, birds
		Mammalia, mammals

A logical study of the vertebrates, as is true of the study of any group of animals or plants, must be based upon an understanding of relationships. This means that we must understand the classifica-tion of these animals, if we are to obtain a clear-cut picture of them.

The list above gives the classes of vertebrates, and we need little if any zoological training to understand the reasons for dividing the backboned animals into the classes indicated. Most people may not be acquainted with jawless vertebrates or placoderms, but sharks are familiar to men the world around, and are identifiable by reason of certain characters common to all animals of this class. The South Sea native and the New England fisherman know that sharks are commonly elongated fishes, with strong jaws on the underside of the head and cruel teeth, with a large dorsal fin and an upturned tail, with large pectoral fins in the shoulder region and with an outer covering like very rough sandpaper. Of course not all sharks are like this, but such a description is general enough to outline the salient characters of these fishes.

Likewise, bony fishes are recognizable by certain characters common to the class as a whole; and the same can be said for amphibians, reptiles, birds, and mammals.

Frcm the major category of the class we proceed down through lesser grades of relationship to the order. There are several orders of sharks, two of which are the Selachii or common sharks and the Batoidea or skates and rays. The selachians fit pretty well the brief description given above. The skates and rays are specialized, being generally flattened, with crushing teeth, huge wing-like pectoral fins, and a much-reduced tail.

Several grades below the order is the family, in which are grouped closely related animals. Thus one family of sharks is the Lamnidae. Within the family is the genus. The genus *Isurus,* for instance, contains the various mackerel sharks. Below the genus is the species; the Mediterranean mackerel shark is *Isurus oxyrhynchus.* The species is the basic unit of 'classification. It represents a distinct, continuous population of animals, the members of which breed freely with each other but do not cross with members of other populations. Two such populations that are closely related to each other, but which do not interbreed, can be regarded as two separate species of a single genus. Thus the sharp-nosed mackerel shark of the Atlantic, *Isurus oxyrhynchus,* and the Pacific mako shark, *Isurus glaucus,* are distinct species of a single genus. They show many similarities. None the less they exist as separate populations, each with its own range, and the members of the two populations are genetically isolated from each other. Because of this there are constant, recognizable differences between them, the differences by which we distinguish and classify these two types of sharks as species.

These several grades of classification (class, order, family, genus and species) are the basic steps whereby an animal is assigned its proper place within the phylum. However, the relationships of species are so complex that it is necessary for modern students to use intermediate grades of classification, such as the subclass, superorder, suborder, superfamily, subfamily, subgenus, and subspecies, to express the proper positions of various forms with respect to each other. Together these systematic terms constitute the hierarchy of taxonomy, or scientific classification of life.

To the student of modern animals the species is of prime importance, and much of the significant work being done on recent vertebrates is concerned with species. But to the student of fossils, the species is of less importance. By the very nature of the materials, fossil species are generally very subjective; their definition cannot be established with so much certainty as the delineation of modern species. Therefore the paleontologist, especially the student of fossil vertebrates, is generally interested more in genera than in species. Genera in fossil materials are usually well defined, and serve as the common basis for evolutionary studies. In this book, the emphasis will be upon genera as the lowest category of practical value.

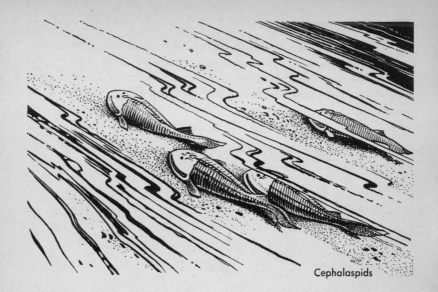

Cephalaspids

2 · Jawless Vertebrates

INTRODUCING THE LAMPREY

The lamprey is an elongated, naked, eel-like animal with a long fin on its back and around the tail, but without any other fins, with a nostril located on top of the head between the eyes, with seven gill openings behind the eyes on each side, and with a peculiar round, jawless mouth, containing sharp teeth. In the earlier stages of its life the lamprey lives on the bottom of streams and lakes, feeding upon small animals that it sucks up through its disc-like mouth, but as it reaches its full growth it becomes a parasite. It attaches itself to a fish by means of its vacuum-cup mouth, and then it proceeds to bore its way into the body of the victim with its sharp, rasping teeth, to suck the blood of its hapless host. The lamprey may abandon its host before the fish dies, or it may stay with the fish to the end.

This rather unpleasant animal is the highly modified survivor of some of the first vertebrates that lived on the earth. Even though the lamprey is specialized in many respects, such as its lack of a bony skeleton, perhaps the result of "degeneration" through the development of parasitic habits, it is nevertheless primitive enough in its general characters to give us some idea of what the first vertebrates were like. The lamprey and its relative, the hagfish, are jawless vertebrates, belonging to the class Agnatha, as did the first

16

vertebrates to appear in the fossil record. Moreover, the lamprey in particular shows some close resemblance to some of the early vertebrates that are known to us as fossils. When we look at a lamprey we get a partial glimpse of the ancient vertebrates that lived almost half a billion years ago.

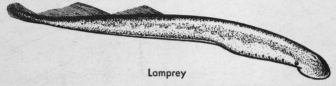

Lamprey

FIGURE 4. A modern jawless.vertebrate, the lamprey, *Petromyzon.* Notice the nostril on top of the head, and the laterally placed eye, behind which are the gill openings. About one-eighth natural size.

JAMOYTIUS

The first vertebrates known in the fossil record are indicated by scales that have been found in Ordovician fresh-water sediments in Colorado. These remains are very fragmentary and give no clue as to what the animals represented by them were like, yet they are sufficiently well preserved to be studied. When placed under a microscope they show a bony structure. Therefore it is obvious from these scales, unsatisfactory and tantalizing though they may be as evidence of the first vertebrates in the geological record, that in Ordovician times there were armored vertebrates living in shallow rivers and lakes.

The next evidence of vertebrate life is found in rocks of Silurian age. Within the last few years, E. I. White of the British Museum has described a small and seemingly a primitive, unarmored jawless chordate from the Silurian of England, which he has named *Jamoytius.* The fossil upon which the description is based is not easy to interpret, consisting in the main of an impression in the sediment. This impression shows a persistent notochord that gave support to the body, while around the sides are what seem to be elongated, lateral fin folds. There are indications of myotomes or muscle segments in this fossil, and they show a simple arrangement of the muscles, as in *Amphioxus.* If the interpretation of *Jamoytius* is correct we may utilize this knowledge to strengthen our assumption that the early primitive chordates were simple animals, not unlike the modern lancelet.

THE OSTRACODERMS

Although *Jamoytius* is an interesting and, as now known, an all too incomplete fossil of an upper Silurian chordate, it is not the only indication of chordate life in that particular stage of earth history, because in rocks of late Silurian age the record of the jawless vertebrates as preserved by the fossils of armored types becomes for the first time reasonably well documented. Here the jawless vertebrates appear as fairly adequate and identifiable fossils, and from late Silurian times on the evidence of the backboned animals in the rocks becomes increasingly complete and complex. Although the record of fossil vertebrates in upper Silurian rocks is good, it is in the sediments of Devonian age that the early vertebrates become really abundant. In Devonian times there was truly a great "explosion" in evolutionary development, a flowering of the vertebrates that established many evolutionary lines. Indeed the Devonian was a crucial period in the history of vertebrate life.

The earliest known vertebrates were, as we have noted, jawless animals belonging to the class Agnatha. They are designated collectively as ostracoderms, but in fact they can be classified in several orders that lived through late Silurian and Devonian times. The orders of agnathous vertebrates, including the modern forms, are:

Cephalaspida or Osteostraci. *Cephalaspis* is a characteristic genus.
Anaspida. *Birkenia* is a characteristic genus.
Cyclostomata. The modern lampreys and hagfishes.
Pteraspida or Heterostraci. *Pteraspis* is a characteristic genus.
Coelolepida. Poorly known forms, of which *Thelodus* is typical.

The ostracoderms, being agnathous vertebrates, lacked jaws, they lacked paired fins or at best had a single pair of fins behind the head, they lacked bony axial skeletons or vertebral columns, and they were typified by a rather well-developed armor of bony plates or scales. Except for these general resemblances, the several orders of ostracoderms were very different from each other; and it seems probable that they represent independent lines of evolutionary development, the result of a long period of phylogenetic divergence before their first appearance in the fossil record.

Among the best-known ostracoderms are the cephalaspids, typified by such upper Silurian and Devonian genera as *Cephalaspis* and *Hemicyclaspis*. These were small animals, generally not more than a foot in length. They were heavily armored, the head being protected by a strong, solid shield, and the body by vertically elongated, bony plates. The head shield was rather flat, but at its back margin it increased in depth where it joined the body. The body was elongated and of general fish-like form, terminating in a tail fin and bearing upon its dorsal surface a small median fin. At the lateral corners of the head shield was a pair of lateral fins.

The head shield appears to have been formed by a solid piece of bone, covering the top and the sides of the head and folded under

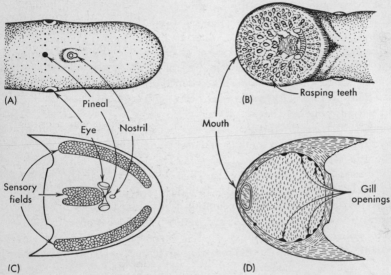

(A)

Pineal

Eye   Nostril   Mouth

(B)   Rasping teeth

Sensory
fields

(C)   (D)

Gill
openings

FIGURE 5. A comparison of the upper and lower surfaces of the head in jawless vertebrates. (A and B), the modern lamprey. (C and D), the Devonian ostracoderm, *Cephalaspis*.

around the margins of the shield. The front of the shield was rounded in outline as seen from above, and at the back it flared into two lateral projections or horns that pointed posteriorly. In some of the cephalaspids these lateral horns were very long, in others they hardly existed at all. On its dorsal surface the head shield was pierced by the openings for the eyes, situated close together and staring straight up at the heavens, while between the eyes and slightly in front of them was a single nasal opening. This is the relationship of eyes to nostril that is seen in the modern lamprey. Furthermore, immediately behind the nostril and between the eyes in the cephalaspids was a well-developed pineal opening, a median communication from the external surface to the brain that may have had a function as some sort of light receptor. There were three areas on the head shield that were depressed and covered by small, polygonal plates. One of these areas was an elongated surface between and behind the eyes, the other two were elongated surfaces on either side of the shield and more or less parallel to its borders. The significance of these areas of plates is unknown, but it has been suggested that they were electric or sensory fields of some sort.

The under surface of the head in the cephalaspids was protected, not by a single shield but by a pattern of fine plates that in life must have been rather flexible. They enclosed the lower surface of the head completely, except for a ventrally placed mouth opening at the front end of the shield, and a series of small ventral gill openings on either side that followed the line of junction between the solid margin of the head shield and the ventral armor plates. In *Cephalaspis* there were on either side ten of these gill openings, corresponding to ten gill pouches that occupied each side of the head shield. Except for *Amphioxus* this is a high number of gills among vertebrates. In the more advanced animals that we commonly designate as fishes, the gills range from seven in the sharks to five in the bony fishes.

In recent years the ossified cranial skeleton of the cephalaspids has been discovered and studied. It indicates that the brain in these early vertebrates was of a primitive type. As in the modern lampreys, there were only two semicircular canals in the ear region of the cephalaspids, in contrast to the three canals in higher vertebrates. Perhaps the most remarkable feature in the cephalaspid brain was the presence of large nerve trunks that radiated out on either side, to supply the supposed sensory fields on the lateral surfaces of the head shield.

As mentioned above, the back of the head shield joined the body armor; perhaps it might be said that the head flowed into the body with no joint between them. Immediately behind the head the body was rather triangular in cross section with a flat base, corresponding to the flat under surface of the head, and with the sides rising to a narrow dorsal apex. The body tapered posteriorly to the base of the tail, where it bent upward to form a strong dorsal support for the tail fin, which was formed of soft rays. Such a tail, known as a heterocercal tail, is characteristic of many primitive aquatic vertebrates. By analogy with modern fishes it is evident that the body and tail in the cephalaspids provided the force that drove these animals through the water. The body plates were arranged in vertical rows, thus giving the ostracoderm a great deal of side to side flexibility. Rhythmic waves produced by muscular action passed alternately down either side of the body, and were transmitted to the tail, swinging it back and forth. The combination of these movements pushed against the water and drove the ostracoderm ahead. In addition, the heterocercal tail drove the animal down as well as forward in the water.

To prevent the body's rolling from side to side there was a dorsal fin on the back, just in front of the tail. The front of this fin was stiffened by a spine. In the cephalaspids there were also paired fins that joined the body on either side immediately behind the "horns" of the head shield. These paired fins were scale-covered flaps, and nothing is known of their internal structure. Although it is doubt-

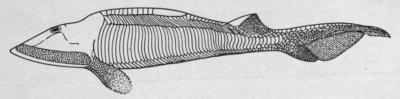

FIGURE 6. The ostracoderm, *Hemicyclaspis,* a very early jawless vertebrate of late Silurian age. About one-half natural size.

ful that these fins are to be homologized with the true pectoral or shoulder fins of the higher fishes, they probably served much the same purpose as do the pectoral fins in the fish, in that they very likely helped to control balance while the ostracoderm was swimming. It is quite possible, however, that they might have been used to help control the direction of movement as well. For instance, they may have functioned in part as elevator planes, to counteract on occasion the downward push of the tail. In this respect, the cephalaspids enjoyed an advantage over most of the other ostracoderms, which lacked paired fins.

No internal skeleton has been found behind the head shield in the cephalaspids, or in the other ostracoderms for that matter. Such skeleton as existed in these animals must have been cartilaginous, and therefore has not been preserved in the fossil record.

These are the salient characters of a cephalaspid. What were these ostracoderms like in life? It seems evident from the flattened head shield, from the dorsal eyes, from the flat under surface of the body, and from the ventrally placed mouth that the cephalaspids were bottom-dwelling vertebrates. They probably lived in the shallow waters of streams and lakes, possibly at times in estuaries, where they groveled in the bottom mud, sucking up small food particles through their vacuum-cleaner type of mouth. The food being passed through the throat region by the force of the water that entered the mouth was evidently directed into the esophagus, and from there into the digestive tract, while water and probably a great deal of detritus escaped through the gill openings.

There were many kinds of cephalaspids characterized especially by the wide range of differentiation in the shape of the head shields. *Cephalaspis* itself was a more or less central type. As contrasted with this genus, there were cephalaspids with elongated head shields, others with very short, broad shields, some with tremendous lateral horns on the head shields, others with no horns at all, some with long rostral spikes directed anteriorly from the front of the head shield, others with dorsal spikes sticking up from the back margin of the shield. But except for these differences the cephalaspids were essentially similar in their basic structure.

Having had a glimpse of the Osteostraci, as exemplified particularly by *Cephalaspis*, we turn now to a brief survey of some of the other ostracoderms. The order known as the Anaspida can be considered next since the ostracoderms of this group, like the cephalaspids, were covered with bony plates or scales. Among the anaspids the eyes were placed laterally, and between the eyes was the single opening for the nostril, and behind that the small pineal opening. Furthermore, there was a slanting row of about eight gill openings on either side in the anaspids, running down from the back of the head in the pharyngeal region; these can be compared with the gill openings of the cephalaspids.

In other respects, however, the anaspids were quite different in appearance from the cephalaspids. *Birkenia*, which can be described as a typical upper Silurian anaspid, was a tiny animal of rather fish-like form. It was not flattened for bottom feeding, as was *Cephalaspis*, but rather was comparatively narrow and deep bodied, as if it were adapted for active swimming. Instead of the solid head shield, so characteristic of *Cephalaspis*, the head region in *Birkenia* was covered with a complex pattern of small scales, many of them, especially those covering the throat, shaped somewhat like grains of rice. The mouth was terminal in position, not ventral, and was a transverse slit instead of a round, sucking opening. It had something of the appearance of a mouth, as we are generally accustomed to think of a mouth, yet even so it lacked true jaws. Behind the head the body was covered with a series of vertically elongated scales or plates, arranged in several longitudinal rows.

There were no paired fins in *Birkenia*. On either side, however, there was a small spine that projected from about the region where a pectoral or shoulder fin normally might be placed, and behind, on the ventral surface of the body, there were some additional spines. In addition to these appendages, there were in *Birkenia* several median dorsal spines, running in a row along the back. There was a fairly well-developed anal fin. The tail is of particular interest in that it was fish-like in form, but with the lower lobe of the tail larger than the upper lobe.

It was pointed out above that a fish tail having the upper lobe longer than the lower is known as a heterocercal tail, and such a tail pattern is primitive in many of the aquatic vertebrates. The tail in *Birkenia*, with the lower lobe more prominent than the upper, is accordingly known as a reversed heterocercal tail. The heterocercal tail of *Cephalaspis* would have tended to drive that animal down, as we have seen, and this would have been important for a bottom-feeding ostracoderm. Conversely, the reversed heterocercal tail of *Birkenia* would have driven the animal up, and this would have been an advantage for such a heavily armored vertebrate if it were an active swimmer. It would seem very likely that *Birkenia* swam near the surface of the water, feeding upon plankton there, and for such a mode of life the reversed heterocercal tail stood it in good stead. But one wonders how *Birkenia* managed to swim with any degree of efficiency, even with its well-developed reversed hetero-cercal tail acting as a propeller. The dorsal spines could not have been very efficient as stabilizers to prevent rolling (some sort of fin membrane is really needed for this), and the two "pectoral" spines were certainly not of much use as stabilizers to control pitching or up and down motion, and yawing or side to side motion. Perhaps *Birkenia* was not a very efficient swimmer, but nevertheless was good enough for the times in which it lived. We might say that the mechanics of vertebrate locomotion in the water were still in an "experimental" stage during late Silurian times.

In some of the anaspids there was a marked reduction of the body armor. For instance, the little Devonian anaspid, *Endeiolepis*, was almost devoid of external bony scales. It may be that anaspids such as this were trending in the direction that led eventually to the lampreys.

The earliest known ostracoderms belong to the Pteraspida or Heterostraci. This order differs from the ostracoderms that have been described in that the body armor, though well developed, lacked true bone cells. There is quite a range of adaptive radiation in the Heterostraci, some of them being rather small, fusiform, free-swimming types, others being large, flattened, bottom-living animals.

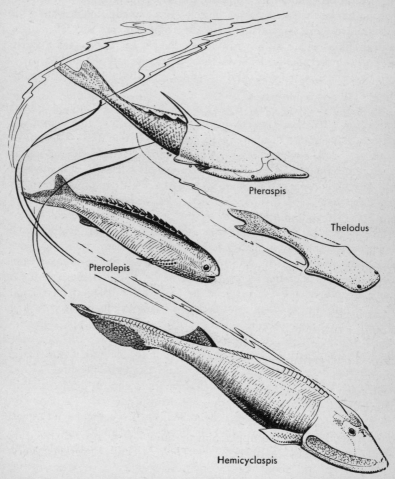

FIGURE 7. Ostracoderms, jawless vertebrates of Silurian and Devonian age, drawn to the same scale. *Hemicyclaspis* was a cephalaspid, *Pterolepis* (like *Birkenia*) an anaspid, *Pteraspis* a pteraspid, and *Thelodus* a coelolepid.

Of the former, *Pteraspis* of Silurian and Devonian age is typical. It was a small ostracoderm, heavily armored. There was a heavy head shield, but, instead of being flattened as was the head shield in the cephalaspids, it was rather rounded in cross section. At the front it merged into a separate element, a long, sharp beak or rostrum that extended far beyond the ventrally located mouth. This mouth was a transverse slit, placed near the front on the lower surface of the head shield, and stretched across it was a transverse series of slender plates that may have acted something like jaws. But they can in no way be compared with true jaws. The eyes were situated laterally, on either side of the head shield, and this lateral separation of the eyes is quite typical of the Heterostraci. There was frequently a well-developed pineal opening on top of the head, but there was no visible nasal opening, as in the cephalaspids. At the back of the head shield and on either side was a single exit for the gills, and on the dorsal midline a long spine projected up and back from the rear border of the shield.

The body in *Pteraspis* was covered with a pattern of small scales; and there was a reversed heterocercal tail, an indication that this ostracoderm, like *Birkenia*, may have been an active swimmer, feeding near the surface. But there were no well-developed median fins, and no paired fins at all. Once again, we are inclined to wonder how efficient a swimmer this little ostracoderm may have been.

The bottom-feeding Heterostraci are typified by such forms as *Drepanaspis*, a lower Devonian genus. These were among the largest of the ostracoderms, ranging up to a foot or more in length. *Drepanaspis* was very flat indeed and very broad. The eyes were set far apart on the sides of the broad head shield, and there was a wide mouth, located on the front of the shield and not in a ventral position. The head shield was covered by a series of plates of varying size, with a very large, oval plate taking up most of the middle region of the dorsal surface. The tail region was comparatively small as contrasted with the broad, flat head shield, a development that is characteristic of many bottom-living vertebrates.

The one other order of vertebrates that has been placed among the ostracoderms is the upper Silurian and lower Devonian Coelolepida, typified by such genera as *Thelodus* and *Lanarkia*. Very little can be said about these early vertebrates, because the fossils are very difficult to study, being little more than impressions in the rock. It is evident, however, that the coelolepids were flattened, with laterally placed eyes. The tail was forked, and apparently of the heterocercal type. The coelolepids differ from all other ostracoderms in that the body covering consisted of minute denticles, rather than flat plates. These denticles, though small, are to be considered as much-reduced plates and not dermal denticles such as those found on the sharks. Very little is known of the internal skeleton in the coelolepids. It is quite possible that these enigmatic little vertebrates were specialized ostracoderms in which there was a fragmentation of the head and body armor to form a sort of shagreen covering of minute denticle-like plates. Such ostracoderms would have been mobile as compared with their heavily armored contemporaries, squires in chain mail rather than knights in plate armor.

THE EVOLUTIONARY POSITION OF THE OSTRACODERMS

The geologic history of the ostracoderms is comparatively restricted, ranging as an adequate fossil record from the latter part of the Silurian period through the Devonian period. It may be that these vertebrates arose in Ordovician times, it may be at an earlier date, from unarmored ancestors, of which *Jaymoytius* is a possible relict. By Devonian times the ostracoderms had become adapted to varied modes of life and various ecological niches, as indicated by the wide divergence in the several orders now known from the fossil materials. And for a time they were successful.

In the end, however, they were unable to compete with the more advanced jawed vertebrates that were evolving rapidly and along many different lines during the Devonian period. So it was that at the close of the Devonian period the ostracoderms disappeared, and except for a few stragglers the agnathous vertebrates succumbed to competition from their more efficient contemporaries. A vertebrate without jaws was efficient after a fashion, but unless it became adapted to certain very specialized habits it was not well enough equipped for survival in a world where a pair of upper and lower jaws had evolved as a food-gathering mechanism.

Were any of the known jawless vertebrates of Silurian and Devonian times ancestral to the jawed vertebrates or gnathostomes? We would expect that among the great variety of ostracoderms there would be some group containing annectent forms, linking the Agnatha with the higher fishes. Yet the fossil record fails to show any such link. This is not surprising when it is remembered that the Silurian and Devonian ostracoderms were specialized and widely divergent animals. They were, in effect, the products of millions of years of evolutionary development, and in them we see animals approaching the end of their several evolutionary histories. Consequently it is to an earlier geologic age, possibly to a time as early as the Cambrian period, that we must look for the ancestors of the jawed vertebrates. So far the fossil record has yielded no information on this very important problem.

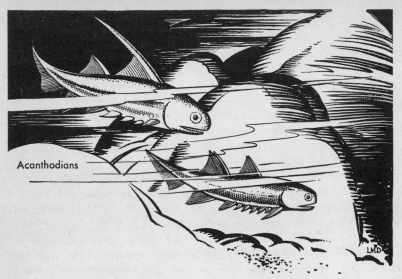

Acanthodians

3 · Placoderms

THE ORIGIN OF JAWS

The history of life, like human history, has been marked by certain great developments rising above the general level of events that collectively make up the record. These outstanding evolutionary developments are in the nature of revolutions, affecting profoundly the phylogenetic trends that follow them, just as great historical revolutions, like the American Revolt against Britain or the French Revolution, have affected the subsequent histories of the peoples concerned with them. A better comparison might be with the peaceful revolutions in human arts and industries, such as those brought about by the development of the printing press or the application of steam power to machinery.

One of the great events or revolutions in the history of the vertebrates was the appearance of the jaws. The importance of this evolutionary development can hardly be overestimated, for it opened to the vertebrates new lines of adaptation and new possibilities for evolutionary advancement that expanded immeasurably the potentialities of these animals. The jawless vertebrates were definitely restricted as to their adaptations for different modes of life, and it is possible that the ostracoderms of late Silurian and Devonian times had explored and virtually exhausted the evolutionary possibilities and the ecological niches open to animals of this type. Animals

without jaws can evolve as bottom feeders, as did some of the ostracoderms, or they can develop movable plates around the mouth opening that serve after a fashion as weak "jaws," as did some other
ostracoderms. Or they can become parasites, like the modern lampreys and hagfishes. Yet even under the most favorable conditions
they are denied the possibilities of development that are open to
animals with jaws; they simply do not have the structural mechanisms to exploit the opportunities that are available to jawed animals. So it is that the appearance of jaws marked a major turning
point in vertebrate evolution.

The appearance of the jaws in vertebrates was brought about by a
transformation of anatomical elements that originally had performed
a function quite different from the function of food gathering. Here
we see the working of a process that has taken place innumerable
times in the course of animal evolution; indeed, much of the progress
from earlier to later forms of animals has been brought about
through the transformation of structures from one function to another. The origin and evolution of the jaws are an excellent example
of this evolutionary principle.

The jaws were derived originally from gill arches. It will be remembered that the ostracoderms had a large number of gills, as many
as ten in *Cephalaspis*, and it seems probable that the presence of
comparatively numerous gills with cartilaginous or bony supports
was typical of the primitive vertebrates. At an early stage in the
history of the vertebrates at least one and probably two of the original anterior gill "arches" were eliminated, while another arch, probably the third one in the series, was changed from a gill support into
a pair of jaws. This transformation actually was not as radical a
shift as on first sight it may appear to have been. Each gill support
or arch in the primitive vertebrate was formed by a series of several
bones, arranged somewhat in the fashion of a V turned on its side,
with the point directed posteriorly. Imagine several such lazy V's
in series, thus: >>>. Imagine also the first of these (morphologi-
cally the third of the original gill arches) supplied with teeth,
and hinged at the point of the V, and you have the primitive vertebrate jaws, in alignment with the gill arches behind them. It is
immediately apparent that the transformation of a gill arch into jaws
was a natural evolutionary development, perhaps the simplest possible solution to the basic problem of developing a pair of vertebrate
jaws.

There are various facts that support such an origin for the jaws
in the vertebrates. For instance, a study of the embryological de-

velopment of certain modern fishes indicates this origin very strongly. Moreover the arrangement of the nerves in the head region of sharks shows that the jaws are in series with the gill apparatus. Thus the branching of the fifth cranial nerve in the fish, known as the trigeminal nerve, whereby one branch runs forward to the upper jaw and another down to the lower jaw, is identical with the branching of certain other

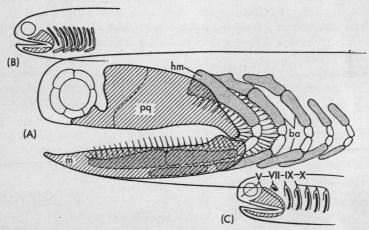

FIGURE 8. The head and gill region in primitive jawed vertebrates. (A) Diagram to show the relationships of the primary upper and lower jaws to the branchial arches in the primitive placoderm, *Acanthodes*. Notice the full gill slit between the back of the upper jaw, or palatoquadrate, and the dorsal element of the first branchial arch, the hyomandibular. For abbreviations, see page 449. (B) Relationships of the gill slits (solid black) to the branchial arches in an acanthodian. (C) Relationships of certain cranial nerves to the primary jaws and the gill slits in a shark. Here we see the first gill opening reduced to a small spiracle.

cranial nerves, whereby one branch runs forward in front of each gill opening and one down behind the gill opening. Finally, a simple inspection reveals that in various primitive jawed vertebrates the jaws are in series with and similar to the gill arches.

APPEARANCE OF THE PLACODERMS

The earliest of the jawed vertebrates, as revealed by the paleontological record, were the upper Silurian and lower Devonian animals that have been grouped in the class designated as the Placodermi. These ancient gnathostomes evolved along varied and divergent

lines during early and middle Paleozoic times, and for a time some
of them were the dominant vertebrates of the waters in which they
lived. But the dominance of the placoderms was of limited duration, because by the end of the Devonian period most of them
became extinct, and by the end of the Paleozoic era all of the placoderms had vanished from the earth. This, it should be noted, is the
one class of extinct vertebrates; all other classes are represented by
living animals in our modern world.

The placoderms were a rather heterogeneous lot, and it is quite
possible that taken together they are not a truly natural assemblage
of vertebrates. It is convenient, however, to combine in one group
the several orders of Silurian and Devonian jawed vertebrates that
were evolving along lines distinct from those of the early sharks and
bony fishes. We might regard the placoderms as ancient "experiments" in the evolution of jawed vertebrates. Perhaps the sharks
and the bony fishes of Devonian times were experiments too, but
at least they were successful, whereas the placoderms were evolutionary experiments that failed.

The orders of placoderms are:

Acanthodii. The most primitive and the most persistent of the placo-
derms, continuing until the end of the Permian period.
Arthrodira. For a time the dominant vertebrates of the Devonian
period. This order, like all the following orders of placoderms, be-
came extinct at the end of the Devonian period.
Macropetalichthyda. A restricted group of specialized placoderms.
Antiarchi. Small, bottom-living, heavily armored placoderms.
Stegoselachii. "Shark-like" placoderms.
Palaeospondyloidea. Represented by a single genus of very uncertain
affinities.

As will be seen from the descriptions that follow, the placoderms
were primitive vertebrates that, even though separated as different
evolutionary lines in early Devonian times, were nevertheless linked
by certain common characters. For instance, in addition to the lower
jaws, typical of these ancient gnathostomes, the placoderms had
strong upper jaws that were firmly fused to the skull. Behind the
jaws there was in most placoderms a full gill slit, as we shall pres-
ently see. And in these early jawed fishes there were always paired
fins.

In many respects the various placoderms were specialized, so that
we cannot look at any genus or even larger category as actually
ancestral to the higher fishes. Yet it is evident that the placoderms
evolved from very primitive gnathostomes, and when taken to-

gether they indicate many of the characters that we would expect
to find in the ancestral jawed vertebrates. Therefore by projecting
back from the known placoderms it is possible to visualize the stage
of evolution that vertebrates attained in their first steps beyond the
jawless condition.

THE ACANTHODIANS

Among the earliest of the placoderms were some small forms
known as acanthodians, or "spiny sharks," this latter name being
based entirely upon the general resemblance of these primitive
gnathostomes to sharks rather than upon any real relationship. The
acanthodians show very nicely the primitive upper and lower jaws
in early vertebrates, as can be seen in the figure of *Acanthodes,* a
middle and late Paleozoic genus. In these ancient fishes there was
an enlarged upper jaw known as the palatoquadrate, opposed by a
well-developed lower jaw, or mandible, provided with sharp teeth.
Immediately behind these scissor-like primary jaws was a full gill
arch, the hyoid arch, of which the upper bone, designated as the
hyomandibular bone, was enlarged. In the acanthodians there was
significantly a fully developed gill slit between the palatoquadrate
and the hyomandibular, and this relationship indicates how the jaws
and the hyomandibular (with an associated bone) were once V-
shaped gill supports in series with each other. In the higher fishes
the jaws crowd back upon the hyomandibular, so that the gill slit
between the palatoquadrate and the hyomandibular becomes .re-
duced to a small opening, the spiracle of sharks, or disappears completely as it does in most of the bony fishes. The hyomandibular is
then transformed into a prop that helps to hold the jaws.to the skull.
The acanthodians are therefore of particular importance by reason of
their primitive jaw structure. Here we see in the fossil record one
of the first steps in gnathostome evolution.

The early acanthodians are typified by the genus *Climatius,* of
late Silurian and early Devonian age, and it may be described as a
good example of these ancient gnathostomes. This was a small
vertebrate, only a few inches in length, with a fish-like body tapering from the front portion to the tip of the tail. In the posterior
region the body was turned up, and there was a fin beneath this up-
tilted portion forming a heterocercal tail—the type of tail that seems
to be so commonly developed in primitive swimming vertebrates. In
addition to the tail fin, however, *Climatius* was well supplied with
median and paired fins. Thus there were two large, triangular dorsal

fins on the back, each consisting of a web of skin supported along
its front or leading edge by a strong spine. Below the more posterior
of the dorsal fins, and balancing it, was an equally large and similarly shaped anal fin, also supported along its front edge by a spine.
Then there was a pair of anterior or pectoral fins immediately behind the skull and another pair of posterior or pelvic fins in front
of the anal fin, while between these two there were five pairs of
smaller fins, running along either side of the ventral portion of the
body. All these fins had spines, like the spines in the median fins.
The presence of "extra" paired fins is characteristic of the acantho-

FIGURE 9. The acanthodian, *Climatius*, about natural size. In this restoration
the scales are cut away behind the operculum, to show some of the elements of
the branchial arches. Note the several pairs of spines along the ventral surface
of the body.

dians, although the number of such fins varies from one genus to
another. It has been suggested that these numerous paired fins in
the acanthodians represent the remnants of ancestral continuous
lateral fin folds, but a more probable explanation is that they were
evolved as independent and separate structures.

Climatius was protected by a dermal armor of small rhombic or
diamond-shaped scales that covered the entire body and continued
over the head, where they took the form of regularly arranged plates
of small size. The head plates were never expanded into large units
like the skull bones or head shields in most other vertebrates.

Climatius had large eyes, each surrounded by a ring of bony
plates, and the eyes were placed very far forward, so that there was
a very restricted nasal region in front of them. It would therefore
seem evident that the sense of sight was dominant in these early
placoderms, whereas the olfactory sense played but a minor rôle in
their life. The upper jaw or palatoquadrate was generally ossified
in three separate pieces, and it commonly was devoid of teeth. The
mandible, as we have seen, was well supplied with teeth. On the
sides of the head were gill coverings or opercular flaps, one to each
of the five gill arches, and over these there was a larger opercular

covering of stiff, bony rods. In effect, therefore, *Climatius* had an operculum, somewhat similar to the operculum in the higher fishes but quite different in structure and origin.

This description of *Climatius* gives a picture of the early and generalized acanthodians. Evolution in these placoderms, through the remainder of Paleozoic times to the close of the Permian period, was marked by variations on the primitive pattern as exemplified in *Climatius*. The later acanthodians evolved by changes of proportions so that some of them became long and slender, others rather deep bodied. In some there was a loss of fins, both median and paired; in others, like the Devonian form *Parexus*, there was a tremendous exaggeration of the dorsal fin spines, especially the anterior one, to form great spikes on top of the body, stretching far back over the tail region.

The significance of these spines in the acanthodians is not clear; perhaps they were to some extent protective characters that helped their bearers to survive the attacks of large vertebrate and invertebrate predators. However that may be, it would seem that the spines (and the opercular cover) were rather specialized features in animals otherwise comparatively primitive.

It is not surprising that these vertebrates were primitive in many respects, for the geologic record indicates clearly that the acanthodians were among the first of the known gnathostomes, appearing in late Silurian times. By early Devonian times the acanthodians had reached the peak of their evolutionary development and from then on until the close of the Paleozoic era theirs was a declining history. These were fresh-water animals, living in rivers, lakes, and swamps of middle and late Paleozoic times, and although they were doomed to eventual extinction they were for the time of their existence characteristic elements of the ancient vertebrate faunas of the continental regions.

THE ARTHRODIRES

Certainly the most spectacular of the placoderms were the arthrodires, often known as the armored fishes or the joint-necked fishes of the Devonian period. These placoderms achieved a position of dominance during late Devonian times, and for a brief spell they were in some respects the most successful of all vertebrates. But their success was short lived, and with the close of the Devonian period the arthrodires became extinct.

A rather typical arthrodire was *Coccosteus*, found in the Old Red Sandstone beds of northern England and Scotland. This was a comparatively small vertebrate, ranging from about one to two feet in length. The body in *Coccosteus* was of fish-like form. But here ends the resemblance to fishes as we know them, for in front the head and shoulder region of this early gnathostome was heavily armored, whereas in the back the body would seem to have been completely naked.

The skull in *Coccosteus* consisted of a series of large bony plates, firmly joined to each other along sutures. These plates can in no way be compared directly with the skull bones of the bony fishes; consequently they have been designated by a series of names that is peculiar to the arthrodires. In many of the arthrodires the skull was quite deep, and strongly arched across its top from side to side. The eyes were large and situated near the front of the skull, and each eye socket contained a ring of four plates, the sclerotic plates, that protected the eyeball. The nostrils were small and placed at the very front of the skull.

There was a very strong lower jaw, hinged to the back of the skull. This lower jaw consisted of a single bone on each side, designated as the inferognathal bone, and anteriorly the upper edge was scalloped into a series of points, superficially like teeth. Opposing the lower jaw were two plates of bone on either side, attached to the front margin of the skull; and these bones, known as the anterior and posterior supragnathals, were also tooth-like in shape. Thus this arthrodire had exposed bony plates that functioned as teeth. In some of the more advanced arthrodires, such as *Dinichthys,* these plates were nicely shaped to form scissor-like cutting edges. They must have been very efficient shearing mechanisms.

At the back of the skull on either side was a strong plate known as the external basal plate, and on its free surface it carried a strong socket. Behind the skull was a ring of heavy shoulder or thoracic plates, encircling the front of the body, and on one plate on either side of this ring there was a strong "ball" or condyle that fitted into the socket of the external basal plate of the skull. In this manner the skull was hinged on either side to the shoulder armor, and since the two hinges were aligned from side to side the skull could be moved up and down on a horizontal axis. In *Coccosteus* as in many of the arthrodires there was a considerable gap between the back of the skull on its dorsal surface and the front of the body armor, which would seem to indicate that there was freedom for strong upward movements of the head. It is generally assumed that these arthrodires opened the mouth, not only by dropping the jaw, as is normal among jawed vertebrates, but also by raising the skull with relation to the body, which would have allowed for a very wide gape. A widely gaping mouth is most advantageous to aggressive carnivores, such as the arthrodires would seem to have been.

There was no gill cover or operculum in *Coccosteus,* so it would seem probable that the gills were located in the "cheek" region of

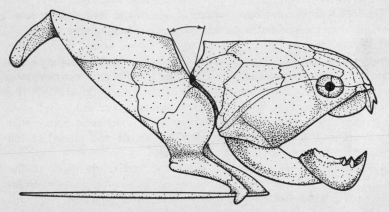

FIGURE 10. The gigantic upper Devonian arthrodire, *Dinichthys.* The head and thoracic shield, shown here, may be eight or ten feet long. Notice in this placoderm the bony plates in the upper and lower jaws that functioned as cutting blades. The hinge between the head shield and the thoracic shield allowed the head to be raised as the lower jaw was dropped, thus making possible a large bite.

the skull on either side and that they opened at the back of the skull. Since there was no spiracular opening, it is probable that the hyoid arch in the arthrodires was primitive, something like that already described for the acanthodian fishes.

The heavily armored head and thoracic region of *Coccosteus* is in striking contrast to the naked back portion of the fish. No dermal covering is known from the posterior body portion or the tail in any of the arthrodires. There was a well-developed supporting column, with a cartilaginous notochord, bordered above and below by spines, but without any vertebral discs or centra. The tip of the column was turned up somewhat, so it appears that the tail was of the heterocercal type. In addition to the tail fin there was a median dorsal fin, as indicated by fin rays projecting up from the spines of the vertebral column. Paired fins were not well developed in the arthrodires, but in *Coccosteus* there is evidence that a pair of pectoral fins was situated close behind the skull, and posteriorly there was a pair of pelvic fins, much smaller than the pectoral fins.

The earliest known arthrodires, from rocks of late Silurian and early Devonian age, were small and somewhat flattened vertebrates. They had the well-armored head shield hinged to a thoracic shield that is typical of the arthrodires, but in some respects they were very different from the more advanced forms, such as *Coccosteus*. These early arthrodires, as exemplified by the Devonian genus *Arctolepis*, frequently bore very long, strong pectoral spines solidly attached to the body armor. The jaws were rather weak. All in all the evidence would seem to indicate that these earliest of the arthrodires were bottom-living animals, perhaps competing to some extent with the early ostracoderms. The greatly enlarged pectoral spines of the early arthrodires are puzzling; it has been suggested that they served as anchors, to hold the animal steady against rapidly flowing currents in the streams that they may have inhabited.

From such a beginning the trend in arthrodiran evolution was generally toward an increase in size and an increase in mobility. By middle and late Devonian times the trend had progressed to such a degree that the arthrodires had become fast-swimming, aggressive predators, of which *Coccosteus* was typical.

However, the peak of arthrodiran evolution was reached by the giant genera *Dinichthys* and *Titanichthys,* found in the upper Devonian Cleveland shales of Ohio. These were enormous fishes with huge skulls and strong jaws, equipped with large cutting plates. *Dinichthys* attained lengths of thirty feet. The giant of its day, it probably preyed upon any other upper Devonian fishes that it could catch. *Dinichthys* was the ruler of its environment.

Before the arthrodires became extinct in middle and late Devonian times, several aberrant lines had evolved. The ptyctodonts, typified by such genera as *Rhamphodopsis,* were very small arthrodires with reduced head and thoracic armor and with a large dorsal spine in addition to the pectoral spines. The dental plates were heavy, and it would appear that these little arthrodires were adapted to a diet of mollusks. The phyllolepids such as *Phyllolepis* were medium sized, but very flattened, arthrodires, with ornamented plates. They were probably bottom-living forms.

THE ANTIARCHS

In the upper Devonian rocks of the Gaspé peninsula, Quebec, skeletons of a small placoderm known as *Bothriolepis,* a representative of the antiarchs, are found, sometimes in considerable numbers. *Bothriolepis* was heavily armored anteriorly, having a head shield, with a body shield behind it. The head shield was short, and was composed of large plates; in contrast, the box-like body shield was rather long.

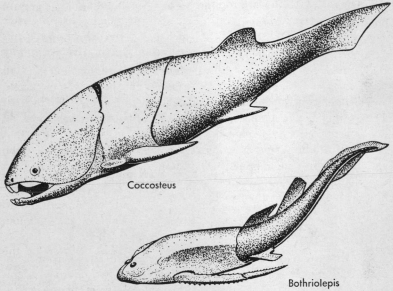

Coccosteus

Bothriolepis

FIGURE 11. Two Devonian placoderms: *Coccosteus*, an arthrodire, and *Bothriolepis*, an antiarch. Drawn to the same scale, each about one-third natural size.

In *Bothriolepis*, as is usual among the antiarchs, the eyes were situated very close together on the top surface of the head shield, and between them was the pineal opening. On the bottom of the head shield was a small mouth, equipped with very weak lower jaws. With dorsally located eyes and with a ventral mouth *Bothriolepis* superficially resembles some of the ostracoderms, the result of convergent evolution toward similar modes of life in the two classes of vertebrates.

Impressions of portions of the soft anatomy that have been preserved in *Bothriolepis* show, among other things, that this early vertebrate had well-developed and probably very functional lungs, opening from the pharynx. Here is one of the many lines of evidence to show that lungs were primitive in the early vertebrates and were common to almost all the principal lines of piscine evolution in the Devonian period.

This antiarch had long, pointed, armored pectoral appendages, attached to the front portion of the body shield by a joint that permitted free motion. Moreover, these "arms" in *Bothriolepis* were hinged in the middle so that they might have been bent to some degree. Evidently they were useful to the animal in getting about; possibly they served like movable hooks to pull *Bothriolepis* around on stream or lake bottoms.

Behind the body shield the body was naked in *Bothriolepis,* although in some other antiarchs, such as *Pterichthys* from the Old Red Sandstone of England, the posterior body region and the tail were covered with scales. In *Bothriolepis* the body was elongated and slender back of the thoracic shield, tapering posteriorly to form a sort of heterocercal tail. In addition to this tail there was a median dorsal fin. It is evident that the general plan here is similar to that of the arthrodires, and it would seem logical to suppose that the antiarchs represent a branch separating from an ancestry held in common with the arthrodires, and evolving along a trend toward bottom living and bottom feeding.

THE MACROPETALICHTHYDS

The three remaining orders of placoderms are known from comparatively few genera. For instance, the order now under consideration is based to a large degree upon the single genus *Macropetalichthys,* although some other genera, notably *Lunaspis,* belong to the group.

Macropetalichthys of Devonian age had a strong, bony head shield, generally comparable to the head shield in the arthrodires. The ossified brain case within the head shield has been described within recent years, and from this description it has been possible to reconstruct the brain of *Macropetalichthys,* which was similar to the brain of the arthrodires. Behind the head shield there were thoracic plates and a pair of pectoral spines. In *Lunaspis,* also of Devonian age, there were also well-ossified head and thoracic shields, the two separated by a joint but not by a highly mobile hinge. The thoracic shield bore very large spines. In this animal there was external armor behind the thoracic shield, consisting of large scales. The macropetalichthyds obviously were related to the arthrodires, but it is evident that the two groups diverged at an early stage in their histories to follow separate evolutionary paths.

THE STEGOSELACHIANS

The group of placoderms known as the stegoselachians show certain resemblances to the sharks, and for this reason it has been suggested by some students that these ancient Devonian vertebrates were early relatives of the sharks. The genus *Gemuendina*, from

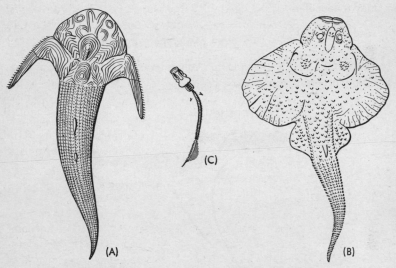

FIGURE 12. Three Devonian placoderms from Europe. (A) *Lunaspis*, about one-third natural size. (B) *Gemuendina*, one-third natural size. (C) *Palaeospondylus*, about natural size.

Devonian sediments of central Europe, is the best known of the stegoselachians and may be taken as a typical representative of the order. This ancient fish was flattened, with a broad head, and a tapering body covered with small tubercles, much like the denticles that cover the body in modern sharks. However, these tubercles represent the surface ornamentation of plates that were small over much of the body, but became enlarged in the forward region. There was a terminal mouth, equipped with pointed teeth, and the eyes and the nostrils were located on the dorsal surface of the head. Perhaps the most striking feature of *Gemuendina* was the enlarged pair of pectoral fins, giving to this animal an appearance remarkably similar to that of some of the modern rays and monkfishes. Yet the jaw structure of *Gemuendina* is of the primitive placoderm type, so that there is every reason to think that the resemblances of this vertebrate to rays were the result of evolution along similar lines in two separate animal groups. One might say that *Gemuendina* antici-pated in Devonian times the *habitus,* the mode of life and adaptations to environment, that was followed in later times by the bottom-living skates and rays. This is an excellent example of convergence in evolution—the similar development of unrelated animals for a par-ticular mode of life.

PALAEOSPONDYLUS

In the Old Red Sandstone at Achannaras, in northern Scotland, a little vertebrate known as *Palaeospondylus* is found. It is an

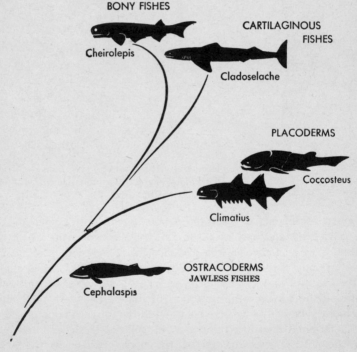

FIGURE 13. Evolution of the primitive fishes.

enigmatic little fossil for, although it is known from hundreds of specimens, it is so difficult to interpret that no clear idea of the details of its structure or of its relationships can be gained. It is placed among the placoderms more as a matter of convenience than anything else, but what it may be is still a matter of much debate.

Palaeospondylus had a peculiarly shaped skull, many elements of which are difficult to homologize, and a well-ossified vertebral column. Some students have regarded *Palaeospondylus* as a larval vertebrate of some type, but the bony vertebrae make such an interpretation doubtful. It may be possible that it was a very small placoderm that had lost completely the external dermal armor; it is probable that *Palaeospondylus* will always remain a paleontological question mark.

Sardines

4 · Success of the Fishes

DESIGN FOR SWIMMING

Many of the primitive vertebrates that we have surveyed up to this point have been designated as early experiments in the evolution of animals with backbones. We might compare them in a general way with the first weird and wonderful automobiles that managed to get along and survive because there were at the time no automobiles of better design to compete with them. The early vertebrates, like the early cars, followed various lines of development, of which many were doomed to quick failure. For a time the ostracoderms were reasonably successful vertebrates, as were many of the placoderms, especially the acanthodians and the arthrodires, but as other patterns of vertebrate organization became established, and evolved, these earlier vertebrate patterns were suppressed. The ostracoderms became extinct, and today only two types of cyclostomes survive as relics of the jawless vertebrates that once had been so abundant throughout the world. The placoderms also became extinct, so that today there are no survivors of this once briefly successful class of vertebrates.

Many factors were probably contributory to the disappearance of the ostracoderms and the placoderms, but it is likely that the rise and development of the first bony fishes and sharks, the vertebrates that we generally think of when we speak of *fishes,* was the principal cause for the decline of the pioneer vertebrates. Among the "higher" fishes designs for life in the water evolved that were definitely superior to any of the plans developed among the ostracoderms or among the placoderms, with the result that these fishes prevailed. What are the factors of design and of life processes that have made the sharks and the bony fishes so eminently suited for life in the water? A simple answer to this question is that these fishes, from the beginning of their evolutionary history, have been primarily very active swimmers. Of course there are many of them that have departed from the active life, but the central types have been and are good swimming vertebrates. It was probably because of their superior design for swimming that the early sharks and bony fishes took a lead over their ostracoderm and placoderm contemporaries.

The typical shark and bony fish is streamlined, as of course were many of the ostracoderms and placoderms, with a body well adapted to rapid movement through the water. The head of the fish acts as an entering wedge, to cleave through the dense medium in which the animal lives, whereas at a point not far behind the head the body reaches its maximum size. From here back the body decreases in its dimensions to the stem or peduncle of the tail, and this decrease in body height, width, and girth from front to back allows the animal to slip through the water with a minimum amount of disturbance, or turbulence. So far we can see little evidence that such a fish is better adapted for active swimming than were numerous ostracoderms and placoderms; it is only when we consider the fins that the superiority of this fish becomes apparent. The ostracoderms and placoderms had fins variously developed, but in none of these early vertebrates was there a complete array of fins so well perfected as in the higher fishes.

In a typical modern fish there is a large and efficient tail fin or caudal fin, the function of which is to help drive the animal through the water by a back and forth sculling action. Rhythmic and alternate muscular waves pass down the sides of the body and are transmitted to the tail, and these pulsations push back against a column of water, thereby thrusting the fish forward. In addition to the caudal fin there is a median dorsal fin, or frequently two dorsal fins, on the back of the fish. These fins are stabilizers that prevent the animal from rolling as it swims through the water, and they also function as a dorsal keel to prevent side slip. Likewise, there is generally a median ventral fin, the anal fin, also functioning as a stabilizer and keel.

Finally there are the paired fins, consisting of an anterior or pectoral pair and a pelvic pair that may be either anterior or posterior in position. These fins are mobile in the advanced fishes and are important for controlling movements. They may act as planes or elevators to assist the fish in going up or down through the water, they may act as rudders to assist the fish in turning sharply right or left, and they may act as brakes enabling the fish to stop quickly. Indeed, the paired fins can be used in many fishes for "backing up."

So with a combination of median and paired fins the fish is well adapted for active life in the water. In addition, modern fishes have evolved along many lines for efficient feeding and for protection, and are generally abundantly endowed for reproducing themselves. Consequently these are at the present time the most numerous of the vertebrates, and, if success is to be measured in numbers, fishes are undoubtedly very successful animals. The species of modern bony fishes outnumber by far all other species of recent vertebrates combined, and in numbers of individuals some of the marine fishes reach population figures of almost astronomical magnitude.

THE HYOID ARCH

The rise of the higher fishes was marked among other things by an important anatomical development that contributed to the advancement of these vertebrates beyond the placoderms with which they were contemporaneous. We saw that in the placoderms the jaws (derived from gill arches) were followed by the functional gill arches, all of which were very much alike. In the more advanced fishes there was a specialization of the first arch behind the jaws, the hyoid arch, so that the upper bone of the arch was transformed into a sort of prop or connecting element, to join the jaws with the brain case. This transformed bone is known as the hyomandibular, and it has played an important rôle in the evolution of the fishes and of the land-living animals that evolved from the fishes. Since the hyomandibular was connected to the back of the skull at one end and to the back of the jaws at the other end, the gill slit that originally had occupied the space between the skull and the hyoid arch was greatly restricted. In the more primitive of the modern fishes this restricted gill slit remains as the spiracle, a small, dorsally placed opening in front of the first full gill slit, but in the highly advanced fishes the spiracle disappears completely.

THE CLASSES OF FISHES

The higher fishes are divisible into two large classes, the Chondrichthyes or sharks, and their relatives, and the Osteichthyes or bony fishes. Both these groups appeared in the Devonian period, and it is possible that they may have originated at some time in the Silurian period, although there is no fossil evidence to prove this.

The sharks evolved rapidly in Devonian times and continued their expansion through the Carboniferous and Permian periods of earth history. At the close of Paleozoic times many lines of shark evolution died out, but these fishes have nevertheless continued to the present day in comparatively restricted numbers. Throughout their entire evolution the sharks have been primarily marine fishes. The bony fishes also evolved rapidly through the Devonian and the later Paleozoic periods, but, whereas the history of sharks was circumscribed after the end of Paleozoic times, the evolution of the bony fishes continued in an ever-expanding fashion. Many lines of bony fishes evolved through the Mesozoic era, and toward the close of the Mesozoic, in the Cretaceous period, one group of bony fishes, the teleosts, began a remarkable expansion in their evolutionary history that has continued from that time to the present. In evolving through time, the bony fishes have become adapted for many environments, both fresh water and marine.

EVOLUTION OF THE SHARKS

Sharks are generally considered to be "primitive" fishes, but it is doubtful whether they are more truly primitive than the bony fishes. Certainly they appear in the fossil record at a stage somewhat later than that at which the first bony fishes appear. Perhaps the allocation of sharks to a primitive position in the sequence of vertebrate life has grown out of the view that the cartilaginous skeleton, so typical of the sharks, is more primitive than the bony skeleton found in other fishes. Yet it is quite reasonable to think that the opposite is true— that the cartilaginous skeleton of the sharks is a secondary development and that the bone seen in the skeletons of ostracoderms, placoderms, and the first bony fishes is truly primitive.

However that may be, the fact is that the sharks are and have been cartilaginous through the extent of their history. The teeth and various spines are the usual "hard parts" in the shark skeleton, and most of the fossil sharks are known from such remains, although occasionally there has been sufficient calcification in the brain case or the vertebrae for these skeletal elements to be preserved as fossils. In spite of such qualifying statements it is still correct to speak of the sharks as having a cartilaginous skeleton.

Certain other characters are typical of the sharks as a large group. Internal fertilization of the eggs is usual in these fishes; consequently the males bear clasping devices on their pelvic fins. Furthermore, the sharks are characterized by an absence of lungs or air bladders; and in this respect they differ markedly from the other Pisces, for, as we have seen, lungs were early developed in the history of aquatic vertebrates. Most sharks, but not all of them, have separate gill openings, with a small spiracle or reduced gill opening in front of the first full gill slit. Finally, as mentioned above, the sharks have been predominantly marine fishes throughout their history.

Cladoselache

FIGURE 14. The primitive sharks of late Devonian times were generally similar to many modern sharks.

One of the first sharks known to us from fossil evidence is the genus *Cladoselache*, found in the upper Devonian Cleveland shales, along the south shore of Lake Erie. This shark was fortunately fossilized in black shales, derived from fine-grained mud, and as a result it is unusually well preserved. The body outline is frequently indicated, and even such soft parts of the anatomy as the muscle fibers and the kidneys are fossilized. From this remarkable material it has been possible to derive a rather accurate picture of *Cladoselache*.

In certain aspects *Cladoselache* was similar to some of the living sharks that are familiar to us. It was rather small—three feet or so in length—and it had a typical "shark-like" or torpedo-shaped body. There was a large heterocercal tail, in which the two lobes were outwardly equal. In addition there were two dorsal fins, pectoral and pelvic fins, and a pair of small, horizontal fins, one on either side of the base of the tail. The paired fins had very broad bases whereby they were attached to the body, and because of this the fins could not have been very mobile. The pectoral fins were very large, however, and must have been of great importance to the fish as balancing and steering controls.

Cladoselache had very large eyes set far forward in the skull. The jaws of this ancient shark were attached to the brain case by two articulations: one immediately behind the eye, the postorbital articulation, and one at the back of the skull, in which region the hyomandibular bone formed a connecting rod between the brain case and the back of the upper jaw. Such a jaw articulation, known as an amphistylic method of suspension, is relatively primitive among the jawed fishes. In this shark the upper jaw, thus supported at its front and back from the brain case, consisted of a single element, the palatoquadrate, and opposed to this was the single element of the lower jaw or mandible. Each tooth of *Cladoselache* consisted of a high central cusp, with low lateral cusps on each side. This is an early form of tooth structure among the sharks, and is found among many of the ancient fossil forms. Behind the jaws were six branchial arches or gill bars.

The structural pattern seen in *Cladoselache* is in most ways primitive for the sharks, so that this fish may be considered to approximate the central stem from which later sharks evolved. From such a beginning the shark-like fishes evolved in five directions, indicated by five orders: the pleuracanth sharks, the "typical" sharks, the skates and rays, the bradyodonts, and the chimaeroids or rat-fishes. As a result of these evolutionary developments the cladoselachians were destined to be replaced in time by the more advanced sharks that sprang from them, yet even so they were sufficiently well adapted to their environment that they could survive until the end of the Paleozoic era. Here we see a phenomenon that is common in the evolutionary history of life—the persistence of primitive forms; the grandfather living on in association with his descendants.

The pleuracanth sharks, named from the typical genus, *Pleuracanthus*, evolved during Carboniferous and Permian times. They were in a sense an aberrant offshoot from the evolutionary tree of sharks, for in contrast to almost all the other sharks these were freshwater fishes, living in shallow rivers and lakes of late Paleozoic times. The pleuracanths were like their cladoselachian ancestors in that they had the primitive amphistylic type of jaw suspension, but in various other respects they evolved in rather specialized directions. Thus these sharks had an elongated body, with a long dorsal fin running along most of the length of the back. Posteriorly the tail extended straight back in line with the body, to terminate in a point. Such a caudal fin is known as a diphycercal tail, and this tail in the pleuracanths was obviously secondarily derived from a primary heterocercal tail. The paired fins, too, were unlike the paired fins in other sharks, being composed of a central axis from which fin rays radiated on either side. One of the most striking features of these strange sharks was the presence of a long spine, projecting backward from the back of the skull. The teeth were composed in each case of two long divergent cusps or blades, with a small cusp in between them.

While the pleuracanth sharks were invading the fresh waters of the continental regions, the more successful and persistent lines of shark evolution were developing in the oceans around the globe. Our modern sharks arose from cladoselachian ancestors during the transition from Devonian to Mississippian times. In the early phases of their history they remained comparatively primitive, having many ties that linked them to the ancestral cladoselachian types. With the advent of the Mesozoic era, however, and particularly during the Jurassic period, the modern sharks began a series of evolutionary steps that established the foundation for their success in later geologic periods. In these advanced sharks the primitive amphistylic method of jaw suspension was replaced by the hyostylic suspension, whereby the jaws were attached to the skull only at the back by means of the hyomandibular bone. This type of suspension allows for increased mobility in the development and the functioning of the jaws, and it is characteristic of the advanced fishes.

From Mesozoic times to the present the evolution of the higher sharks has followed two general lines. On the one hand there are the "typical" sharks, streamlined, elongated, fast, aggressive, and highly predaceous. The head is pointed and provided with a widely gaping, ventrally placed mouth, equipped with sharp teeth. On each side there are five separate gill slits, with a round spiracle in front of the first gill. The torpedo-like body tapers back into the strong, heterocercal tail. On the back are one or two dorsal fins. The strong paired fins have narrow bases, making them rather mobile and effective in controlling the motion of the animal through the water. On the pelvic fins of the males are claspers. In this group of sharks are the common sand sharks, the mackerel sharks, the tiger sharks, and the dreaded white sharks or man-eaters. Also there are certain divergent types, such as the huge basking sharks and whale sharks and the flattened angel fishes.

The other line of evolution among the higher sharks is that of the skates and rays. These are highly specialized sharks, adapted for life on the bottom. In these fishes the pectoral fins have become greatly enlarged and are used somewhat like wings, so that the fish "flies" through the water. The tail is generally reduced to a small pointed appendage, often a mere whiplash. The gills are ventrally placed in the skates and rays, and water is taken in through a greatly enlarged, dorsally situated spiracle. The teeth are highly modified to form large crushing mills, well fitted for cracking the shells of the mollusks upon which these fishes feed. In this group of sharks we find the banjo-fishes, the sawfishes, the skates, the various rays, and the torpedoes, these last provided with electric organs in the head.

There exist today some sharks that are persistent connecting links between the modern sharks, described above, and the primitive cladoselachians. These "living fossils," if so they may be called, are the Port Jackson shark, *Heterodontus,* of Australia, and the genera *Hexanchus* and *Chlamydoselache* (the frilled shark); in all of them the amphistylic type of jaw suspension is retained.

Two other orders of shark-like fishes that have never been particularly numerous can be set apart from the sharks so far considered as a separate subclass, the Holocephali. One order of the Holocephali, the Bradyodonti, is known mainly from tooth plates that indicate for the most part a crushing type of dentition. The other order, derived from the bradyodonts, is that of the chimaeras or rat-fishes, which persist at the present time in deep oceanic waters. The chimaeras are active fishes, with an elongated, pointed rostrum on the head, and with the upper jaws firmly fused to the brain case in an autostylic type of jaw suspension. The pectoral fins are large and fan-like, and the tail is elongated into a long whiplash. Various chimaeras are known in the fossil record, which extends as far back as lower Jurassic times.

There should be mentioned at this place peculiar whorls of fossilized teeth, obviously selachian, which have been classified among various groups of sharks according to the individual views of the students who have worked on them. These whorls, commonly designated as edestid teeth, from the upper Paleozoic genus *Edestus,* are in the form of flat spirals, with the smallest teeth on the inner curves of the spiral, the largest on the outer curves. It has been generally supposed that these are whorls from the symphyseal portion of the jaws, that is, where the two halves of the jaws join, and that they represent some peculiar type of tooth replacement. They are largely a mystery, giving us practically no clues as to the morphology or the evolutionary history of the sharks represented by them; but they are beautiful and striking fossils, and as such have attracted much attention.

The history of the sharks as revealed by the fossil record is not broadly documented. In many respects the fossil evidence is tantalizing and disappointing, often consisting only of isolated teeth or spines, and less frequently of poorly fossilized jaws and brain cases. Yet from the fossil evidence as we know it, and from our knowledge of

Figure 15.   A tooth whorl of the Permian edestid shark, *Helicoprion,* about one-half natural size.

modern sharks, it is quite apparent that sharks have been very successful vertebrates.   They have never been numerous in genera and species as compared with other vertebrates, but the forms that have evolved have been extraordinarily well adapted to their environments.   There were sharks in late Devonian times and there are sharks today, and through the intervening geologic periods, from the beginning of the Mississippian period to the present day, sharks have lived in the oceans of the world, successfully holding their own against, and even dominating, the "higher" types of life that have shared this habitat with them.   In spite of competition from the bony fishes, from aquatic reptiles such as the ichthyosaurs, and from aquatic mammals such as the whales, the sharks have carried on in a most successful way.   The sharks have succeeded because, with the exception of some of the bottom-living skates, they have been very aggressive fishes, quite capable of taking care of themselves in spite of earth changes, changes in food supply, and competitors. It looks as if sharks will continue to inhabit the seas for a long time.

BONY FISHES—MASTERS OF THE WATER

Of all the animals that have lived in the water, none have been so successful as the bony fishes. Even the most completely aquatic and highly developed of the invertebrates, such as the various mollusks, particularly the complexly evolved ammonites of Mesozoic times, cannot be rated as equal to the bony fishes in their adaptations to life in the water. For the bony fishes have invaded all the waters of the earth, from small streams, rivers, lakes, and ponds of continental regions to all levels of the ocean. They have evolved species showing a remarkably wide range in size, from tiny animals a fraction of an inch in length to huge fishes like the tunny. Their diversity of body form and of adaptations is remarkable indeed. The bony fishes are in many respects the most varied, and as mentioned they are certainly the most numerous of the vertebrates. At the present time they have reached the culmination of their evolutionary history.

What are the characters that distinguish the bony fishes? In the first place, these vertebrates are, as the name implies, commonly highly advanced in the ossification of the skeleton. This is true not only of the internal skeleton, the skull, vertebrae, ribs, and fins, but also of the external skeleton, the outer covering of plates and scales. In the primitive bony fishes the scales were heavy and generally of rhombic shape, and were of two basic types, the cosmoid scales typical of the early lungfishes and crossopterygians and the ganoid scales of the early actinopterygians. The cosmoid scale consisted of a basal portion formed by parallel layers of bone. Above this portion was a middle layer of spongy bone, richly supplied with blood vessels. Finally there was an upper layer of hard cosmine formed around numerous pulp cavities, above which there was a thin layer of enamel. In the ganoid scale the same layers were present, but the enamel was very thick and formed a heavy shiny surface on the scale, known as ganoine. As the bony fishes evolved there was a general reduction in thickness of the various layers comprising the scales so that finally they were composed only of thin bone. Nevertheless the body in most bony fishes has been and remains completely covered by an armor of scales.

In the skull the brain case is completely ossified, whereas the outer bones of the skull are numerous and well formed. Generally speaking, these bones form a complex pattern of several series of related elements, covering the top and the sides of the head, extending back over the gills, and comprising the two halves of the lower jaw. This dominance of bone is carried over into the gill region, so that the several gill arches are composed of articulated chains of bones, whereas the entire gill region is covered by a single bony flap or operculum. Consequently there is a single gill exit at the back or free edge of the operculum as contrasted with the separate external gill openings in the sharks. Moreover, the spiracle is greatly reduced or even suppressed in the bony fishes. The hyomandibular bone is an important element in the skull, forming in most bony fishes the hyostylic support for the jaws from the brain case.

Behind the skull the vertebrae are highly ossified, with spool-shaped central bodies or centra that form an articulated shaft for support of the body. From the centra extend spines directed up (the neural spines) and in the tail region spines directed down (the haemal spines), and from the sides of the vertebrae the ribs extend out and down, to enclose the thoracic region of the body.

There is a compound shoulder girdle, often attached to the skull, and to this the pectoral fins are articulated. All the fins, the pectoral and pelvic fins and the median dorsal, anal, and caudal fins, have bony rays for internal supports.

In the primitive bony fishes there were functional lungs, but in most of these fishes the lungs have been transformed into an air bladder that helps to control the buoyancy of the animal. The eyes are generally large and important in the life of the fish, whereas the olfactory sense is of secondary consequence. Other characters can be listed as typical of the bony fishes, but these are the features of particular importance to the student interested in their evolution as revealed primarily by fossil materials.

Bony fishes are of ancient ancestry, first appearing in fresh-water deposits of middle Devonian age. These first-known bony fishes were of small or modest size, and were characterized by their heavy diamond-shaped or rhombic scales. The skull showed the basic osteichthyan cranial pattern that was to be the starting point from which the complex skulls of later bony fishes evolved. Thus there was a series of rostral bones that covered the nasal region; behind these bones were paired bones forming the skull roof. Around the eyes were several bones, the circumorbitals, and behind them and on either side of the roofing bones were the bones of the temporal region. Around the edges of the skull were the marginal tooth-bearing bones, and these were joined ventrally and medially by the various bones of the palate. Opposed to the tooth-bearing bones of the skull were the bones that formed the two rami of the lower jaws.

In these ancient bony fishes the eyes were very large and the mouth was often long, extending the full length of the skull. Behind the skull the fusiform body tapered back to the tail, which was of heterocercal type, with a long upper lobe and a much smaller lower lobe. There was a single dorsal fin, far back on the body, and balancing it on the ventral surface an anal fin. In addition there.

Cheirolepis

FIGURE 16. An ancestral bony fish, or palaeoniscoid. About one-third natural size.

were the paired fins, the pectoral fins in front and the pelvic fins farther back. In these early fishes the vertebrae were incompletely ossified, and the notochord was still strongly developed.

These first bony fishes belong to an order known as the Palaeoniscoidea (the palaeoniscoids), which are particularly well exemplified by the Devonian genus *Cheirolepis*. From an ancestry illustrated by *Cheirolepis* the main line of bony fishes, the actinopterygians, evolved and in evolving they passed through three general stages of development. These three stages of actinopterygian evolution can be indicated by three superorders.

	Superorder	*Time*
Primitive	Chondrostei	Devonian through Permian, with a few forms surviving into the Recent
Intermediate	Holostei	Triassic through Cretaceous, with a few forms surviving into the Recent
Advanced	Teleostei	Cretaceous to Recent, culminating in recent times

The general characters of a primitive palaeoniscoid chondrostean have been described above. From such a beginning certain definitive evolutionary trends can be followed in tracing the rise of the actinopterygian fishes through the higher chondrostean fishes, through the holosteans, and finally through the teleosts. The bony fishes have

such a complex history that the details of their evolutionary development include numerous diverse adaptations, too involved for description at this place. It may be useful, however, to set down the
general trends that typify the successive stages of evolution in these
vertebrates.

Chondrostei	*Holostei*	*Teleostei*
Heavy, rhombic scales	Rhombic scales contin-ued	• Thin scales, of rounded shape
Internal skeleton part-ly cartilaginous	Internal skeleton part-ly cartilaginous	Internal skeleton com-pletely ossified
Spiracular slit present	Spiracle lost	Spiracle lost
Eye large	Eye large	Eye large
Hyostylic skull	Hyostylic skull	Hyostylic skull
Maxilla fastened to cheek	Maxilla freed from cheek, reduced, and jaws shortened	Maxilla free, trans-formed into a "push-ing" bone; cheek re-gion opened; jaw shortened
Hyomandibular strong	Hyomandibular en-larged	Hyomandibular en-larged
Tail strongly hetero-cercal	Abbreviated hetero-cercal tail	Tail homocercal
Pelvic fins usually pos-terior	Pelvic fins usually pos-terior	Pelvic fins move for-ward in many forms
Lungs not transformed	Lungs transformed into air bladder	Air bladder usually completely hydro-static

Although the chondrosteans have been described as comparatively
primitive actinopterygians, it must not be thought that all these fishes
were of the generalized type, as exemplified by *Cheirolepis*. In fact
there was an early stage of branching out, of adaptive radiation,
among the chondrosteans that took place even in the most ancient
order of the bony fishes, the Palaeoniscoidea. So it was that in
evolving through late Paleozoic times the palaeoniscoids followed
many lines of adaptation that led to a considerable variety of body
forms. The climax of this evolutionary history was attained during
the Pennsylvanian and Permian periods, when the palaeoniscoids
were perhaps the most abundant of all fishes.

Some of the palaeoniscoids followed the generalized line of adaptation that had been established by *Cheirolepis* and other stem forms.
For instance the genus *Palaeoniscus* itself was essentially a very
primitive actinopterygian, showing few advances beyond *Cheirolepis,*
yet it lived many millions of years later in the Permian period. On
the other hand, some of the Pennsylvanian and Permian palaeonis-

coids were highly specialized. *Amphicentrum* was a deep-bodied fish with elongated dorsal and anal fins, and with a tail that was superficially homocercal, although in structure it was heterocercal.

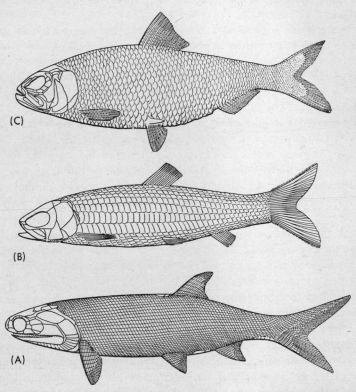

FIGURE 17. Three stages in the evolution of the actinopterygians or bony fishes. (A) *Palaeoniscus*, a Permian chondrostean. (B) *Pholidophorus*, a Jurassic holostean. (C) *Clupea*, a Cenozoic teleost. All one-third natural size. In the sequence from A to C, notice some of the evolutionary changes, as outlined on page 54.

Dorypterus was another deep-bodied fish, with fin developments similar to those described above for *Amphicentrum*, but with the anterior part of the dorsal fin tremendously high. It is interesting to see that in this fish the pelvic fins had migrated forward to a position beneath the throat and actually in front of the pectoral fins— a type of fin placement that is especially characteristic of the higher teleost fishes, as we shall see. Other late Paleozoic chondrosteans underwent great reductions in the scaly body covering. In one very aberrant genus, *Tarrasius*, there was not only a loss of scales but also a loss of the pelvic fins and a fusion of the median fins to form a continuous fin along the back, around the tail, and along the ventral surface of the body.

During their evolutionary development, the palaeoniscoids gave rise to three other orders of chondrostean fishes, two of which have survived to the present day. One of these surviving orders is the Polypterini, now represented by the genera *Polypterus* and *Calamoichthys* of Africa, for many years supposed to be of crossopterygian relationships. The other modern order of chondrostean fishes is the Acipenseroidei, represented in modern faunas by the widely distributed sturgeons and by the paddlefishes of North America and China. In these recent chondrosteans there has been a great reduction of bone, both in the endoskeleton and in the outer armor.

During the Triassic period still another order, the Subholostei, sprang from palaeoniscoid ancestors. These were progressive chondrosteans, showing an abbreviation of the upper lobe in the heterocercal tail, a reduction in the middle layer of each scale, and a shortening of the jaws. These fishes, of which *Redfieldia* is a typical example, were abundant in Triassic fish faunas, and they can be regarded as truly intermediate between the chondrosteans and the next higher group of fishes, the holosteans.

As the chondrostean fishes declined at the end of the Triassic period they were replaced by the Holostei, which, having arisen from several subholostean stems, carried farther the specializations already initiated by their immediate ancestors. In the holostean fishes the upper lobe of the heterocercal tail was even more abbreviated than it had been in the subholosteans, there were specializations in the skull and jaws, there were frequent ossifications of the vertebral centra, there was a considerable reduction in the fin rays, and the scales showed structural reduction beyond that of the earlier fishes. The spiracle was lost.

The first holosteans were of comparatively generalized form and are well exemplified by the early Mesozoic genus *Semionotus*, but at an early stage in the evolution of this group specializations took place that imitated in a remarkable way many of the specializations that had occurred earlier among the chondrostean fishes. For instance, deep-bodied genera such as *Dapedius* or *Microdon* evolved during the Jurassic period, showing evolutionary trends similar to those exhibited in the evolution of deep-bodied chondrosteans in late Paleozoic times. Other holosteans were elongated fishes, like the Jurassic form *Aspidorhynchus*.

The culmination of holostean evolution was reached in Jurassic and early Cretaceous times, after which there was a decline. However, two genera of these fishes have persisted into recent times; they are *Lepisosteus*, the garpike of the Mississippi River, and *Amia*, the bowfin of the northeastern United States.

With the progression of the Cretaceous period the holosteans were replaced by the expanding teleost fishes, and so began the great development in fish evolution that has continued unabated to the present day. As is apparent in the tabulation presented above, the teleosts continued many evolutionary trends that had already been established among the holosteans. In the skull there was a general shortening of the jaws, with a specialization of the maxilla in the highest types as a toothless bar, and with a concentration of the teeth upon the premaxilla. The extension of the vertebral column into the upper lobe of the tail was suppressed, so that the caudal fin became completely symmetrical or homocercal. The internal skeleton became highly ossified. There were varied specializations of the dorsal fin and the paired fins, marked especially by the frequent migration of the pelvic fins to an anterior position close to the skull. The scales became very thin, and were generally of rounded shape, rather than rhombic.

The first teleosts are represented by the genus *Leptolepis*, appearing definitely in Jurassic times. This generalized teleost makes a very good intermediate between the holostean fishes and the teleosts, so nice an intermediate form in fact that it has been variously placed by different authorities in both these large categories. By Cretaceous times the teleosts were well established, and from that time on they have followed numerous lines of adaptive radiation that have established them as the masters of all waters, continental and marine. Because of the vast expanse of the oceans, covering the greater part of the earth's surface, most teleosts are marine forms.

A simplified arrangement of the multitudinous array of teleost genera and species may be outlined, by orders, in the following manner:

Isospondyli. The first and least specialized teleosts, with soft fin rays and a primitive position of the pelvic fins on the middle or posterior part of the body. Herrings, salmon, trout, and such fishes as the giant Cretaceous isospondyl, *Portheus*.

Ostariophysi. A group of predominantly fresh-water fishes, characterized by a chain of small bones, the Weberian bones, that connect the ear with the air bladder. Characins, suckers, carp, and catfishes.

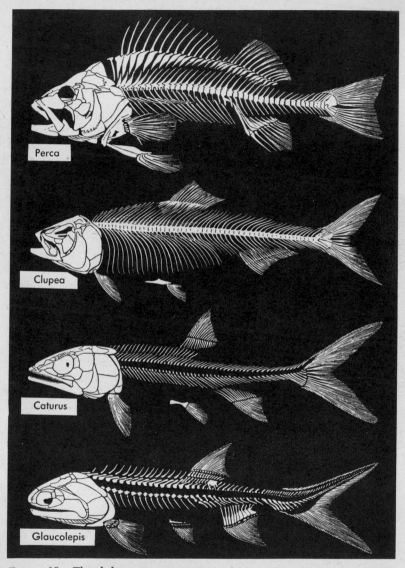

FIGURE 18. The skeleton in actinopterygian fishes. *Glaucolepis* was a Triassic chondrostean, *Caturus* a Mesozoic holostean, *Clupea* a generalized teleost, and *Perca* an advanced teleost, the last two of Cenozoic age. In the sequence from chondrostean to advanced teleost, notice some of the successive evolutionary changes, as outlined on page 54.

Apodes. Elongated fishes in which the paired fins are frequently suppressed, the scales reduced or absent, and the mouth peculiarly specialized, with the premaxilla bones missing. The true eels.

Heteromi. Deep-sea fishes with long heads and bodies, and with the true caudal fin suppressed.

Mesichthys. The intermediate teleosts. Here is a variety of fishes showing various progressive features. The premaxilla often is elongated and excludes the maxilla from the mouth. Pike, needlefishes, seahorses.

Acanthopterygii. The spiny teleosts. These are the most advanced and by far the most numerous of the teleost fishes. The maxilla is excluded from the mouth and becomes a bone that pushes the toothed premaxilla forward. The scales are very thin and rounded. The pelvic fins migrate to an anterior position beneath the skull, frequently in front of the pectoral fins. The dorsal fin is divided into an anterior spiny portion and a posterior soft portion. The entire endoskeleton is very highly ossified. These are predominantly marine forms that show an enormous range of adaptations, and include such fishes as the perches, sunfishes, bass, snappers, porgies, weakfishes, sailfishes, blennies, triggerfishes, butterfly fishes, flounders, sculpins, toadfishes, and anglers. They may be regarded as representing the culmination of fish evolution.

Body forms and adaptations in the teleosts and particularly in the spiny teleosts are well known and too numerous to consider here. It is enough to say that in form they run the gamut from small to large, from elongated to deep and short, from narrow to round to flat, and in adaptations they range from speedy swimmers to slow swimmers to almost sedentary forms, from dwellers in the open ocean to bottom-living types to lake and river fishes, and from highly carnivorous feeders to scavengers to plant-eating types. It is probably safe to say that no other vertebrates show such wide ranges of adaptation as the teleost fishes.

REPLACEMENT IN THE EVOLUTION OF BONY FISHES

One of the striking features in the evolution of the bony fishes is the predominant rôle that replacement has played during the long history of these vertebrates. It was pointed out above that the chondrosteans were the first bony fishes to evolve and that they were dominant during late Paleozoic times. Then it was shown that during early and middle Mesozoic times the chondrosteans were replaced by the holosteans, and during the last phases of the Mesozoic era and the Cenozoic era the holostean fishes were replaced by the

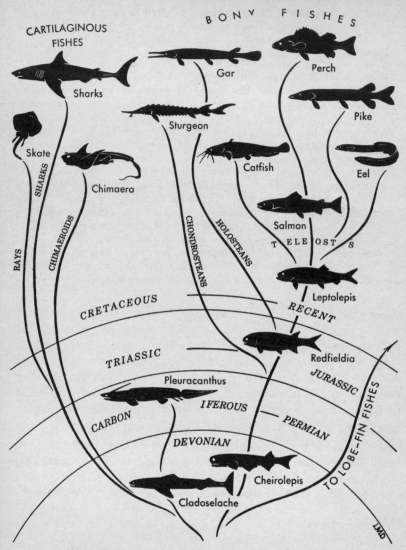

FIGURE 19. Evolution of cartilaginous and bony fishes.

teleosts. Replacement of one large group by another has been the characteristic pattern in the evolution of the bony fishes.

In the development of this pattern we can see the repetition of many details through time by some remarkable examples of parallel evolution. For instance, the chondrostean fishes evolved some short,

deep-bodied forms in Permian times. Then among the holosteans
in the Jurassic period remarkably similar fishes were developed.
Finally the same pattern of evolution was repeated among the teleosts
in Cenozoic times. Examples might be multiplied at great length.

Why should this be? Why should the chondrosteans have waned,
to be replaced by holosteans, many of which evolved in ways that
were remarkably similar to the adaptations previously established
by the chondrosteans? And why did the same process take place

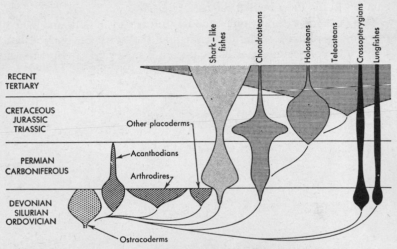

FIGURE 20. Range and relative abundance of fishes through geologic time.

as between the holosteans and the teleosts? The answer is probably
complex, but it would seem likely that the factor of competition was
of primary importance. Competition among the fishes must have
been intense through time, as it is today. As new forms evolved
by means of genetic processes and natural selection, increasingly efficient mechanisms arose for coping with environments and for meeting competition from other fishes. Thus there were trends toward
ever "higher" types—from chondrosteans through holosteans to
teleosts.

But the restrictive qualifications for life in the water are very
severe. Streamlining is essential for fast fishes. Deep bodies and
essentially homocercal tails are important for fishes that live among
coral reefs. Large mouths are important to many carnivorous fishes.
Consequently, as the more advanced and more efficient fishes evolved
they "swamped" their less efficient predecessors, so that finally the

more primitive forms disappeared. Yet all the fishes, whether of primitive or advanced structure, were confronted by similar evolutionary problems that were of necessity solved in similar ways. Consequently the replacement so characteristic of fish evolution was marked by repetition of similar types in successively later geologic ages. The deep-bodied chondrosteans were well adapted to their environment at one time, but eventually they gave way to the deep-bodied holosteans that were even better adapted to the same type of environment. And the deep-bodied holosteans eventually succumbed to the deep-bodied teleosts.

This is the key to an understanding of fish evolution, and when this key is utilized with discrimination the story of bony fishes through time loses much of its confusing complexity. It becomes a logical story, and a highly interesting record of evolution.

Latimeria

5 · From Water to Land

AIR-BREATHING FISHES

With the rise and the almost fabulous increase of the teleosts during the seventy-million-year lapse of time from the Cretaceous period to the present day, the evolutionary history of the fishes has reached its climax. The modern bony fishes that populate the waters of the earth have reached the pinnacle of evolutionary success among the water-living vertebrates, and it seems probable that this culminating phase in the long phylogenetic development of the fishes may continue for an appreciable time into the geologic future. In outlining the story of the fishes we have arrived at the high point, and anything more that is said is likely to be an anticlimax.

Yet when we look at the whole picture of vertebrate evolution we see that the adaptive radiation of the teleosts is in some respects a very complicated side issue. It is a most fascinating side issue, to be sure, for it is important to keep in mind the fact that the modern teleost fishes represent a branch of vertebrate development in many respects as significant in the history of life as any other branch of vertebrate evolution. Nevertheless the teleosts are off the main line of evolution that led to the so-called higher vertebrates, so that in order to follow the history of backboned animals beyond the fishes it is necessary to turn to lines of phylogenetic development quite separate from any that have so far been considered. These are the lines of evolution represented by the air-breathing choanate fishes—the lungfishes and their cousins, the crossopterygian fishes.

The lungfishes or dipnoans and the crossopterygians comprise a subclass of the Osteichthyes or bony fishes set apart from the subclass of actinopterygians, which we have reviewed in the preceding chapter. Moreover, the choanate fishes can be regarded as making up a phylogenetic group equal in rank and importance to all the other bony fishes, even though they have always been restricted in numbers of genera and species as compared with the vastly multiplied actinopterygians.

The first choanate fishes appeared in Devonian times, as did so many of the aquatic vertebrates, and in their early manifestations these fishes were in many respects rather similar to the first actinopterygians. We might say that *Cheirolepis*, the stem actinopterygian described above, had various characters in common with *Dipterus* and *Osteolepis*, representing rather generalized ancestral types of dipnoans and crossopterygians, respectively. For instance, all these fishes were of fusiform shape, and all of them were covered with heavy scales. They all had the primitive heterocercal type of tail, and in all of them the paired fins were located in their primitive positions, with the pectoral fins close behind the head and the pelvic fins far back on the body. In these fishes the skull was covered by a pattern of bony plates.

But there were significant differences that divided these early fishes into two groups, with the ancestral actinopterygians in one group and the ancestral choanates in the other. Even though the early crossopterygian and dipnoan each had a heterocercal tail, it differed from the tail of *Cheirolepis* in that there was a small epichordal lobe above the body axis, a feature not present in the primitive actinopterygian. Again, the internal structure of the paired fins was basically quite different in the two types. In the primitive actinopterygian the fins were supported by parallel fin rays, as we have seen, but in the early choanates there was an arrangement of supporting bones that consisted of median or axial elements with lesser bones radiating either on the sides or distally from these central members. This type of fin has been called the archipterygium. The primitive actinopterygians had but a single dorsal fin; the first choanate fishes had two dorsals. There were important differences in the skull, too. In the early choanates a pineal opening was present on the top of the head, between the two parietal bones, whereas in the early actinopterygians the pineal was generally absent. The two groups can be additionally contrasted in that whereas the early actinopterygians like *Cheirolepis* had large eyes, the eyes in the choanates were not particularly large. Of particular significance, the choanates had internal narial openings, which may have been important for air-breathing vertebrates. No such internal nostrils are

found in the actinopterygians. Finally, in primitive choanate fishes
the scales were of the cosmoid type, with a thick layer of cosmine
above the basal bony layer of the scale, a contrast to the primitive
actinopterygian scale, in which the cosmine was limited and the
surface of the scale was covered by a heavy layer of enamel or ganoine. These differences indicate that as early as middle Devonian

FIGURE 21. A comparison of the Devonian ray-finned fish or actinopterygian,
(A) *Cheirolepis*, with the Devonian lobe-finned fish or choanichthyan, (B)
Osteolepis. *Cheirolepis* about one-fourth natural size, *Osteolepis* about one-half
natural size. This figure shows the differences in the proportions of the skull
bones and the contrast in the position and the size of the eyes in the two types
of fishes. It also shows the single dorsal fin, the long rays of the paired fins,
and the heterocercal tail without an upper or epichordal lobe in *Cheirolepis*, as
contrasted with the two dorsal fins, the lobed paired fins, and the heterocercal
tail with an upper or epichordal lobe in *Osteolepis*. On the upper surface of the
tail of *Cheirolepis* are heavy ridge scales.

times there was a basic divergence between the two lines of bony
fishes, even though they had been closely related to each other at the
beginning of their evolutionary development.

THE LUNGFISHES

There are three genera of lungfishes living at the present time:
Epiceratodus in Australia, *Protopterus* in Africa, and *Lepidosiren* in
South America. The Australian lungfish, which closely resembles
the lungfishes of Triassic age, is almost certainly the most primitive
of the three modern types. It lives in certain rivers of Queensland

that become reduced during the dry season to stagnant pools. At such times *Epiceratodus* is able to survive by coming to the surface and breathing air, for which purpose it uses its single highly vascular lung. This fish cannot live out of the water.

The South American and African lungfishes, on the other hand, are able to live for months at a time when the rivers that they normally inhabit are completely dried up. At the beginning of the dry season these fishes burrow into the mud and encyst themselves, leaving an opening or openings from their burrow to the outer air; they breathe through these openings. These two lungfishes are characterized by a pair of lungs, in contrast to the single lung of the Australian lungfish.

The ability of the lungfishes to breathe air is certainly suggestive of an intermediate stage between fishes and land-living vertebrates. (In this connection it is interesting to note that the Australian lungfish is able to "walk" along the bottom of the rivers or pools in which it lives by using its paired fins like legs.) Yet in spite of such specializations in the lungfishes directed toward a method of living out of the water, the total evidence points quite clearly to the fact that these vertebrates are not and never have been on the direct line of evolution leading from fishes into the first land-living vertebrates. Briefly the lungfishes show too many specializations, even in the earliest known stages of their evolutionary history, for vertebrates that might occupy an intermediate position along the line from fishes to amphibians.

The earliest lungfishes are represented by the genus *Dipterus,* as mentioned above. *Dipterus,* a fish of middle Devonian age, possessed many of the generalized choanate characters that were outlined above for the primitive air-breathing fishes, such as a long, fusiform body terminating in a strong, heterocercal tail, paired fins of the archipterygial type, with a strong central axis down the middle of each fin, and with subsidiary bony rays diverging on either side of this axis, and two dorsal fins. The large, heavy rounded scales were of the cosmoid type.

Contrasted with these primitive characters there were various specialized features that indicate even in as early a form as *Dipterus* the trends that were to take place in the evolution of the dipnoans. For instance, there was considerable reduction of bone in the internal skeleton of this fish, and such a development is found in all of the later lungfishes. The brain case, too, was poorly ossified, although in those Devonian lungfishes in which the brain case has been preserved a certain amount of bone is present. Subsequent to Devonian times the ossification of the brain case was to be completely suppressed. The jaws were partially ossified, yet even here a process of chondrification was beginning that was to become typical of later dipnoans. The earliest of the lungfishes had already begun to specialize in the reduction of the bony skeleton.

The skull was composed of numerous bony plates. In general there was a great multiplication of bones covering the head in *Dipterus*, and because of this it is almost impossible to indicate any

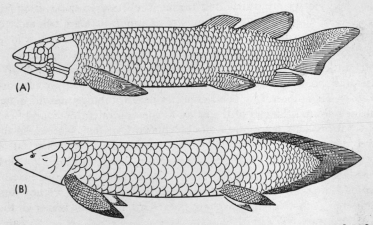

(A)

(B)

Figure 22. Ancient and recent lungfishes. (A) *Dipterus*, a Devonian lungfish from Europe, one-fourth natural size. (B) *Epiceratodus*, the modern Australian lungfish. This fish may grow to be five feet or more in length.

homologies between the bones of the skull in this fish and the skull bones in other bony fishes. Likewise, the dentition in *Dipterus* had become highly specialized. The marginal teeth were suppressed in both the upper and lower jaws, and mastication of the food was effected by large, tooth-bearing plates, those above being formed by the pterygoid bones of the palate and those below by the prearticular bones of the lower jaw. On these plates the teeth were arranged in a fan-shaped fashion, a pattern that was to be carried on through the evolutionary history of the lungfishes. Obviously such teeth were adapted for crushing hard food, and it is probable that the food of the Devonian lungfish, *Dipterus*, was rather similar to that of the modern Australian lungfish, consisting of small invertebrates and vegetable matter.

From *Dipterus* the lungfishes evolved as inhabitants of continental waters during the long lapse of time between the Devonian period and the present day. The lungfishes seemingly were never very numerous, but from the evidence at hand it would appear that they reached their greatest variety of forms in late Devonian and late Paleozoic times. The earlier lungfishes were for the most part variants of the *Dipterus* theme, but as time progressed these fishes evolved along the major lines that have already been indicated, following evolutionary directions marked by progressive chondrification of the skeleton and by modification of the median and paired fins.

The central line of dipnoan evolution led to *Ceratodus,* a genus that became widely distributed during the Triassic and subsequent periods of the Mesozoic era, when this lungfish inhabited most of the continental regions of the world. The modern Australian lungfish *Epiceratodus,* a direct descendant of *Ceratodus,* has changed very little from its Mesozoic progenitor. It is a fair-sized fish with a rather pointed head. The body is covered with large, rounded scales. There is a single, pointed posterior fin running from the dorsal surface around the end of the body to the ventral surface, and obviously formed by a fusion of the original dorsal fins, the caudal fin, and the anal fin. This secondarily simplified, symmetrical tail is known as a gephyrocercal fin. The paired fins are rather elongated and leaf shaped, and in each fin the fleshy portion is covered with scales. Internally the skeleton is greatly reduced; there are no vertebrae but rather an unrestricted notochord, and the bones of the skull are reduced.

The South American and African lungfishes have evolved as side branches from the central stem of dipnoan evolution, as have various fossil forms. Both these modern genera are characterized by gephyrocercal tails, showing evolutionary trends similar to that for *Epiceratodus.* In *Protopterus* of Africa the paired fins are reduced to long, slender whip-like appendages, and in *Lepidosiren* of South America reduction of these fins has progressed to an even more extreme state, so that they are comparatively small.

The distribution of the modern lungfishes on southern continents has been accorded considerable significance by certain students of earth history, who have made the claim that such a pattern of distribution indicates former close connections between the land areas of the southern hemisphere. It is well to keep in mind the fact that various fossil lungfishes were widely distributed over the earth, as indicated above for the genus *Ceratodus,* so that the distribution of the modern genera may very well represent the remnants of areas of habitation that were once of broad extent. However that may be, it is fortunate for us that lungfishes have survived to modern times on several continents because they give us an oblique glimpse of the important vertebrates that formed the link between fishes and the first land-living vertebrates. In the dipnoans we see the collateral uncles of the amphibians.

THE CROSSOPTERYGIAN FISHES OR LOBE FINS

To trace the direct line of evolution from fishes to land-living vertebrates it is necessary to consider the other group of choanate fishes, the crossopterygians. These fishes, like the dipnoans, appeared in middle Devonian times, and, like the first dipnoans, they possessed certain generalized choanate characters. For instance, the early crossopterygians, as exemplified by the Devonian genus, *Osteolepis*, were fusiform fish with a strong, heterocercal tail, with lobate, archipterygial paired fins, with two dorsal fins, and with heavy, rhombic scales of the cosmoid type. From this point on, however, striking differences can be seen between the first crossopterygians and their dipnoan cousins.

In the crossopterygians there was no trend toward reduction of the endoskeleton as there was in the dipnoans. *Osteolepis* was characterized by a strong notochord, as were other Devonian crossopterygians, but in this line of evolutionary development the bony elements of the vertebral column were prominent and on their way toward a high degree of functional perfection, as we shall see. The skull and the jaws were completely bony, and the bony pattern was well defined and comparable to that seen in other bony fishes, as *well as that in the early land-living vertebrates*. This is a point of the utmost importance, for it (together with other evidence) indicates the position of the crossopterygians on the direct line of descent between fishes and amphibians.

In *Osteolepis*, on top of the skull between the eyes, there were two large bones that can be homologized as the parietal bones of other vertebrates. On the suture between them there was a pineal opening. In front of the parietals were the frontals and, in addition, a series of small bones covering the rostral portion of the head. Around the eyes were the various circumorbital bones that are seen in the higher bony fishes and the early amphibians, and on the sides of the head were the several temporal bones. Behind the parietal bones and cutting across the skull transversely was a prominent joint, separating the front part of the skull from the postparietal region. It is obvious that there was a certain amount of movement on this joint; the front of the skull could be raised or lowered somewhat in relation to its back portion.

The brain case was highly ossified in *Osteolepis* and other Devonian crossopterygians, and this structure, too, was jointed immediately below the joint in the skull roof. It is possible that the joints in the skull and the brain case of the crossopterygians gave enough flexibility to the head to ease the shock of biting when the jaws were snapped shut.

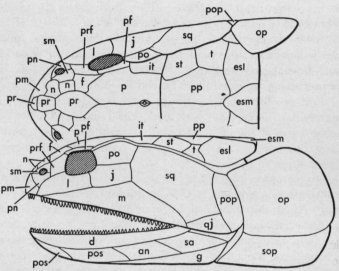

FIGURE 23. The skull of *Eusthenopteron*, a crossopterygian or lobe-finned fish, in dorsal and lateral views. Here we see the basic pattern of skull and jaw bones that was inherited by the early land-living vertebrates, the ancestral tetrapods. For abbreviations, see page 449.

Although there were teeth on the palate in the early crossopterygians, the largest and most important teeth were around the margins of the jaws, both above and below. These teeth were sharp and pointed and well adapted to grasping prey, and it seems obvious that the early crossopterygians were carnivorous fishes. When the teeth of these ancient crossopterygians are cut across and examined under the microscope it can be seen that the enamel is highly infolded to form an exceedingly complex labyrinthine pattern. For this reason the teeth of the crossopterygians are designated as labyrinthodont teeth, and it is an important fact that in the early land-living amphibians the teeth were likewise labyrinthodont in structure.

The crossopterygian fishes had well-developed internal nares or nostrils on the palatal surface of the skull between the vomer and palatine bones, which probably increased the effectiveness of the nose as a sensory organ. Their nasal passages, as in the higher land-living vertebrates, went direct from the external nares or outer nostrils through the internal nares into the mouth or pharynx.

Of particular interest is the internal structure of the paired fins of the early crossopterygian fishes, which are in decided contrast to the paired fins of the dipnoans. In the early crossopterygians there was a single proximal bone in the fin that articulated with the girdle. This is best seen in the pectoral fin, the structure of which is especially well known. Below the single upper fin bone were two bones articulating with it, and beyond these were still other bones radiating toward the distal edges of the fin. Such a scheme of bone arrangement in the fins could very well have formed the starting point for the evolution of the limb bones in land-living animals. There is every reason to believe that the single proximal bone in the paired fins of the crossopterygian fishes is to be equated with the upper bone of the tetrapod or land-living vertebrate limb, namely, the humerus in the front leg and the femur in the hind leg. Likewise, the next two bones of the fish fin can be homologized with the radius and ulna of the front leg and the tibia and fibula of the hind leg in the land-living vertebrates. Beyond this point homologies are not easy, but it seems probable that the various bones of the wrist and ankle and of the hand and foot evolved from the complex of distal bones seen in the crossopterygian fin.

In many respects, therefore, the early crossopterygian fishes have the characters that we might expect in ancestors of land-living animals, and that is why we can consider these fishes as direct progenitors of the first amphibians. The crossopterygians are to us perhaps the most important of fishes; they were our far-distant but direct forebears.

So far we have been concerned with the first Devonian crossopterygians as typified particularly by the genus *Osteolepis*. From this basal stock the crossopterygians evolved in two general lines, one being represented by the suborder Rhipidistia, the other by the suborder Coelacanthini. The osteolepids were rhipidistians.

The rhipidistians were primarily fresh-water fishes. Beginning with the osteolepids in middle Devonian times they followed a dichotomous pattern of evolution through the remainder of the Paleozoic era, after which they became extinct. One line of the rhipidistians was that of the holoptychians, characterized by the genus *Holoptychius* of late Devonian times, an evolutionary side branch which paralleled in an interesting way some of the lungfishes. Thus in the

advanced holoptychians like *Holoptychius*, the body became robust
and the scales large and rounded somewhat like those of the
Australian lungfish. Also the paired fins were elongated in a manner
similar to that seen in the lungfishes, and the median fins, though
not fused with the caudal fins, were nevertheless set far back so that
they were in close proximity to the tail.

Of more interest to us is the group of rhipidistians known as
rhizodonts, of which the Devonian genus *Eusthenopteron* is of particular importance. These fishes were obviously on the direct line
toward the early amphibians, and they showed various advances over

Eusthenopteron

Figure 24. A progressive crossopterygian or lobe-finned fish that had evolved
in the direction of the early land-living amphibians. About one-sixth natural
size.

their osteolepid ancestors. *Eusthenopteron* was an elongated, carnivorous fish, with a skull pattern remarkably prophetic of the skull
pattern seen in the early amphibians. It was characterized by the
advanced nature of the vertebrae. The notochord was strong, but
around it at regular close intervals was a series of rings. Above
each ring a spine projected up and back, and on the dorsal side of
the notochord between the rings were small nubbins of bone. The
dorsal spines are to be homologized with the spines of the early
amphibian vertebra, whereas the rings may be compared with the
intercentra, and the small intermediate bony nubbins with the centra
of the tetrapod vertebra. The tail in *Eusthenopteron* was symmetrical, with the vertebral column extending straight back (not up as
in a heterocercal tail) to the tip. The reduction or suppression of a
caudal fin of this type would have been a relatively simple matter.
In addition to the progressive characters already cited for *Eusthenopteron*, the paired fins were of the structure already described as
directly antecedent to the tetrapod limb. It was indeed but a short
step from *Eusthenopteron* to a land-living vertebrate.

The other group of crossopterygians, the coelacanths, was far removed from the "main line" of evolution toward the early land

vertebrates. These were predominantly marine fishes, often rather deep bodied, with lobate paired fins. There was a reduction of the internal elements of the lobed portion of these fins, while the thin fin supported by the fin rays increased in relative size. The tail, which was symmetrical and of the diphycercal type, possessed an additional small lobe, in line with the body axis and between its main upper and lower lobes. The skull was short and deep with considerable reduction of the skull bones, and of the marginal teeth except for the teeth on the premaxillary bones and on the tips of the dentaries of the lower jaws. The lung or swim bladder was commonly calcified and thus preserved in the fossil materials.

The coelacanths, though beginning in Devonian times, were especially characteristic of the Mesozoic era, and they are found in a number of marine deposits belonging to this phase of earth history. The general description for a coelacanth, given above, can be applied most aptly to the Cretaceous genus *Macropoma*, a typical member of the suborder.

Until a few years ago it was thought that the coelacanths became extinct at the close of the Cretaceous period, since no post-Cretaceous fossils have ever been found. In the winter of 1938–1939 a trawler off the coast of South Africa dredged up a large fish that proved to be a living coelacanth. Owing to a series of unfortunate events little more than the skin of this fish was saved. The fish, named *Latimeria,* is rather large, being about five or six feet in length. In form it is extraordinarily similar to *Macropoma* of the Cretaceous period. It has brilliant blue scales, rounded and of large size, and the lobed paired fins are long and strong.

For fourteen years after its discovery, this single specimen was the only known example of *Latimeria.* Then in December, 1952, a second specimen was caught off the coast of Madagascar, an event that set off a train of excited newspaper and magazine articles. This fish was flown to South Africa in a special airplane, and elaborate plans were made for a detailed study of it. But hardly had the excitement died down when several more specimens of *Latimeria* were caught, also near Madagascar. The chances look good for more coelacanths to be hooked in the future, so that in time we shall obtain a detailed knowledge of the anatomy of *Latimeria,* last of the coelacanths and the one persisting crossopterygian genus. Here we have a valuable link with the past that gives us a glimpse of an important group of vertebrates, hitherto known only from the fossils.

APPEARANCE OF THE AMPHIBIANS

At some time during the Devonian period, possibly during the later phases of Devonian history, some of the crossopterygian fishes came out on the land. Very likely these were rhizodonts, of the type represented by the genus *Eusthenopteron*. It was a bold step, a venturing of early vertebrates into a completely new environment to which they were only partially adapted. Once having made the step, however, the advanced air-breathing fish soon became transformed into a primitive amphibian. With this change vast new possibilities were opened for the evolutionary development of the vertebrates.

What were the factors that led the crossopterygians out of the water and on to the land? Professor A. S. Romer has suggested that it was paradoxically a desire for more water that brought about the first excursions of crossopterygians away from their river and lake environments. According to this idea some of the late Devonian crossopterygians may have been forced by excessive drought to seek new fresh-water pools or streams in which they could continue to live, and thus they struggled out on the dry ground in an effort to reach the water that was so necessary for their survival. This is certainly a logical explanation of the first stages in the change from an aquatic to a terrestrial mode of life, but there may have been other factors that also contributed to the initial break from life in the water. Perhaps there was a gradual series of changes through time that resulted in increasingly wider excursions away from the water. Perhaps the search for food upon the land may have been as much of a motivating force in this change as the search for fresh bodies of water.

We can only speculate about this. What we do know is that the first amphibians actually appeared at the end of Devonian times, during the transition from the Devonian to the Mississippian period. In upper Devonian sediments in east Greenland fossils of primitive amphibians that are essentially intermediate between the advanced crossopterygians and characteristic early amphibians have been discovered in recent years. These annectant amphibians are known as *ichthyostegids*, of which the genera *Ichthyostega* and *Ichthyostegopsis* are typical.

THE ICHTHYOSTEGIDS

Ichthyostega had a skull about six inches in length. The skull was solidly constructed. Its pattern of roofing bones was closely com-

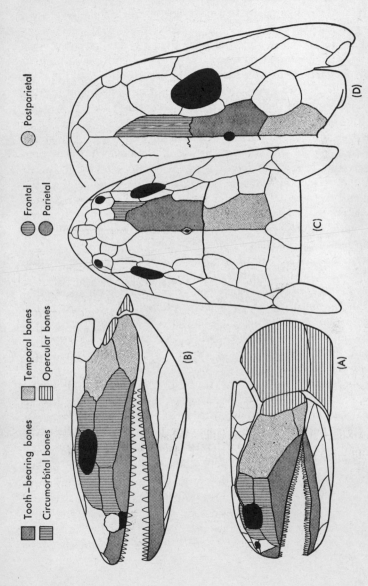

FIGURE 25. (A and C), lateral and dorsal views of the skull and lower jaw of the Devonian crossopterygian fish, *Eusthenopteron*. (B and D), similar views of the skull and lower jaw of the Devonian amphibian, *Ichthyostega*. This comparison shows the similarity in the arrangement of the bones in fish and amphibian, but the differences in proportions.

parable to the pattern seen in the advanced crossopterygian fishes, yet there were some differences. In the ichthyostegid certain fish bones, such as the operculars that covered the gill region, were lost; but some of the fish bones, like the preoperculars, were retained as reduced elements. Of more importance than any loss of bones were the changes in proportion between the fish skull and the amphibian skull. In *Eusthenopteron,* for example, the rostral portion of the skull in front of the eyes was very short, whereas the postparietal portion of the skull was very long. In *Ichthyostega* this situation was reversed; the skull in front of the eyes had become greatly enlarged, whereas the postparietal portion of the skull had been much shortened, with a consequent reduction in size of the bones in this region. It is interesting to see that *Ichthyostega* was only slightly advanced beyond the crossopterygians in location and development of the internal and the external nares, for the external nasal openings were far down on the side of the skull, and were separated from the internal nares, which were in the front of the palatal region, only by a thin bar of the maxillary bone.

In the postcranial skeleton *Ichthyostega* showed a strange mixture of fish and amphibian characters. The vertebrae had progressed but little beyond the crossopterygian condition, whereas in the caudal region the *fin rays of the fish tail were retained.* In contrast to the primitive vertebrae and the persistent fish tail, there were strong pectoral and pelvic girdles, with which were articulated completely developed limbs and feet, quite capable of carrying the animal around on the ground.

Ichthyostega was well on the way toward being a full-fledged amphibian, in spite of the retention of certain fish characters. Consequently it can be placed among the early amphibians, of which it is a primitive representative. From this point we can follow the evolution of the amphibians as they developed along various lines, one of which led toward still higher types of vertebrates.

Devonian Scene

6 · Early Vertebrate Faunas

ENVIRONMENTS OF THE EARLY VERTEBRATES

In a reading of the geological record we see that four classes of backboned animals—the jawless vertebrates, the placoderms, the Chondrichthyes or sharks, and the Osteichthyes or bony fishes—appeared in late Silurian and Devonian times. A fifth class, the amphibians, came into being at the very end of the Devonian period. Moreover, for all the fishes, using that term in a very broad sense of the word, the Devonian was a period of evolutionary advancement during which time they established themselves as dominant aquatic animals throughout the world. Therefore the Devonian period was without doubt one of the most crucial times in the history of life upon the earth, when new lines of evolution were being explored, and when the backboned animals were firmly started on the long and complex evolutionary development that was to terminate in the highly specialized vertebrates of the present day. We might think of a great "evolutionary explosion" as having occurred during the Devonian period, with consequences of the utmost importance to the subsequent history of life on the earth.

The history of the vertebrates during late Silurian and Devonian times was, as we have seen, largely a history of animals that lived in continental fresh waters, in rivers and streams and lakes. Therefore it is reasonable to think that the shallow waters of continental drainage systems were the environments in which the primitive pre-Devonian vertebrates enjoyed their evolutionary successes, even though it is quite probable that the ultimate ancestors of the backboned animals, the forms that connected the vertebrates with their invertebrate progenitors, were inhabitants of the seas and the oceans. It is certainly evident that once having begun their several lines of adaptive radiation in fresh waters, the early vertebrates continued in these environments and did not expand into the seas to any appreciable extent until after the Devonian period.

Many of the upper Silurian and Devonian vertebrates are found in rocks consisting to a large proportion of sandstones and black shales, which would indicate that these animals were living in waters that received great amounts of detritus eroded from near-by lands. In this connection it might be said that the Devonian period was the time when plants were first making a successful conquest of the land, and, although Devonian plants were probably numerous, they possibly did not form heavy soil covers as did the plants of later geologic ages. Therefore the land surfaces in Devonian times may have been comparatively bare, so that erosion was very active. Under such conditions, large amounts of sands and muds would have been deposited in the rivers and lakes of those days, and even in the shallow waters along the margins of the continents. These ecological conditions must be kept in mind in making interpretations of Devonian faunas and in drawing comparisons between them.

The early vertebrates of late Silurian and Devonian times were generally protected by heavy armor, as we have seen. This armor may have been in part a defense against attacks from some of the large voracious invertebrates that lived in those days, especially in the estuarine and offshore waters of the coasts. But since many of the early agnathans, placoderms, and fishes were obviously inhabitants of environments where large, predaceous invertebrates were not particularly numerous, and sometimes not even present, it must be supposed that the heavy armor that was so universally present in the ancient backboned animals served largely to protect them from each other. Competition must have been intense, and at an early stage in vertebrate history there were aggressive types that fed upon other backboned animals.

Thus the picture that we get of life during late Silurian and Devonian times is one of considerable diversity and active competition between the early vertebrates. There were numerous armored ostracoderms, generally living on the bottom and feeding there, though some of the anaspids were obvious surface-living plankton feeders. There was a great variety of placoderms adapted to many different modes of life. Some of them, like the acanthodians, were rather generalized animals of very fish-like form and habits. Some, like the antiarchs, were remarkable animals in that they paralleled the ostracoderms to some extent, whereas in certain respects, such as the development of their jointed, paired appendages, they even came to resemble marine arthropods like lobsters. Still other placoderms, like the late Devonian arthrodires, were highly predaceous, and were the first of the vertebrates to evolve into giants. These huge placoderms, unlike the other early vertebrates that have been enumerated, inhabited the oceans, for they were too large to find a living in the restricted waters of rivers and small lakes. Then at this stage of earth history there were the early sharks exploring the possibilities of life in the sea, some of them sharing the environment with the giant arthrodires. Finally there were the primitive bony fishes, including the first actinopterygians such as *Cheirolepis,* the early lungfishes, and the ancestral crossopterygians. These were for the most part fresh-water fishes.

These Silurian and Devonian vertebrates are widely spread in the sedimentary deposits of several continental regions, and it is probable that if the geologic record were more complete a world-wide distribution of the early backboned animals would be indicated. As the record is preserved, it shows that the early vertebrates lived at many localities in Europe, as far north as Spitsbergen and Greenland, in North America, and in certain parts of Asia and Australia. It is probable that the climates of the earth were much more uniform then than they are now, and that as a result in part of such climatic uniformity environments were correspondingly uniform, as compared with the varied environments in which modern vertebrates live. Certainly the fresh-water vertebrates of those days indicate essentially similar conditions at widely separated points on several continents, whereas the marine types, such as they are, point to general uniformity in the oceans of the earth.

It is significant that some of our best-known Silurian and Devonian faunas are found in northerly regions. The presence of various ostracoderms and fishes in Spitsbergen and Greenland and the occurrence of primitive amphibians in Greenland in sediments representing the final stages of Devonian history show that environments must have been favorable to these cold-blooded vertebrates in what are now boreal zones. Some students would regard such occurrences as evidence (to be combined with other criteria) that continents have not always been in the positions they now occupy, that there was a drifting of land masses during past geologic ages so that some parts of the earth now occupy environments rather different from those in which they were formerly situated. Other students maintain that

continents have always been in essentially the positions they now
occupy, and that geologic evidence of past climates and environments
different from those of today for any particular portion of the earth's
surface are an indication of world-wide changes in climate through
time. The question is too involved and too much of a side issue
to be argued at this place. The fact remains that late Silurian and
Devonian faunas of similar type are found in different continental
areas, separated from each other by wide ranges of latitude.

THE DISTRIBUTION OF EARLY VERTEBRATE-
BEARING SEDIMENTS

The first well-known vertebrate faunas are found in rocks that are
assigned to the Ludlovian and the subsequent Downtonian stages
of late Silurian history. The most abundant fossils occur in northern
Europe, especially in England, the Scandinavian region, and Spitsbergen, although some fossils have been found at scattered localities
in North America. Vertebrate faunas of this age are unknown in
other parts of the world.

In the Ludlow stage of Silurian history we can see in England a
passage from older marine sediments to younger estuarine and continental deposits, and it is in these latter beds that the vertebrates
make their first well-documented appearance. The succession from
the marine to the continental type of deposits was the result of broad
uplifts through northern Europe from England to Scandinavia, known
as the Caledonian Revolution, that raised great masses of land above
the sea and initiated new environmental conditions throughout this
region. The development of continental environments for fresh-water
vertebrates by this uplift is recorded in the Ludlow rocks of western
England by the Ludlow bone bed, a thin stratum of wide extent,
filled with the plates and spines of small ostracoderms.

By the subsequent stage of earth history, the Downtonian, the
continental uplift was far advanced. Great areas of fresh-water
deposits were laid down, many of them containing the remains of
ostracoderms. These are the so-called Passage Beds of the Downtonian, immediately antecedent to the beginning of Devonian sedi-
mentation, and so intimately linked with Devonian strata in some
regions that many authorities have included them in the Devonian
sequence. The vertebrates of the Downtonian are much more widely
distributed than those of the preceding Ludlovian stage of earth
history, and indicate, among other things, the spread of continental
conditions favorable to the evolution and geographic expansion of

the ostracoderms. Downtonian faunas are found not only in England and Scotland but also in the Ukraine, in various parts of Scandinavia, and in Spitsbergen. At the famous locality of Oesel, an island in the Baltic Sea, vertebrate remains are found in limestones that indicate possible estuarine conditions.

The most famous sequence of Devonian vertebrate-bearing sediments is the classic Old Red Sandstone of England, Scotland, and Wales, first studied and described by Hugh Miller, more than a century ago. The Old Red Sandstone is divisible into three consecutive portions, lower, middle, and upper, representing respectively the three broad stages of Devonian history. Portions of this sequence are exposed at various localities throughout Great Britain, especially along the Welsh border, in the southeastern highlands of Scotland along Moray firth, in northern Scotland, and in the Orkney Islands. The physical expression of the Old Red Sandstone varies, ranging from heavy, red sandstones, as indicated by the name, to coarse conglomerates on the one hand, to gray and black shales and siltstones and even to limestones on the other. In these rocks are contained numerous fossils, not only of ostracoderms, as in the preceding Ludlovian and Downtonian sediments, but also of placoderms and fishes, appearing here for the first time. Indeed, it is from the Old Red Sandstone that we have obtained much of our knowledge of the evolution of early vertebrates and the development of Devonian faunas.

Sediments comparable to various parts of the Old Red Sandstone are found in other parts of the world, and they have yielded many fossils to add to our knowledge of vertebrate evolution during the Devonian period. Rocks of lower Devonian age, comparable in a general way to the lower Old Red Sandstone, are found in the Ukraine, in Spitsbergen, and in central Germany, this last being a marine deposit. In North America lower Devonian vertebrates are found near Campbellton, New Brunswick, and at Beartooth Butte, Wyoming. Middle Devonian sediments containing vertebrates are found in the European localities already listed; in North America fossil vertebrates of this age are found in several eastern states. Of particular interest are the middle Devonian vertebrates of Ellesmere Land and eastern Greenland, since they commence a record for the evolution of vertebrate faunas in an area that was to be of great importance during middle and late Devonian times. Middle Devonian vertebrates are found also in New South Wales, Australia.

As might be expected, the record of Devonian vertebrate faunas continues in rocks of late Devonian age in Europe, especially in the

CORRELATION OF LOWER AND MIDDLE PALEOZOIC VERTEBRATE-BEARING SEDIMENTS

		England	North and Central Europe			Spitsbergen	North America			Other Continents		
		Old Red Sandstone	Baltic States	Rhineland—Wil-dun-gen	Russia		Ellesmere Land E. Green-land	Cleve-land shales	Scau-menac	New South Wales	Antarc-tica	Central Asia
Devo-nian	Upper	Upper					Ellesmere Land E. Greenland	Cleveland shales	Scaumenac			
	Mid-dle	Mid-dle		Rhine-land—Wil-dum-gen	Russia	Wijhe Bay Series						
	Lower	Lower	Podolia, Ukraine			Wood Bay and Gray Hoek Series		Camp-bell-ton	Bear-tooth Butte	New South Wales	Antarc-tica	Central Asia
Silurian		Downton sand-stone Temeside shales	Oesel Gotland			Red Bay Series						
		Ludlow Bone Bed										

British Isles, the Baltic States, and at the locality of Wildungen in Germany. In Ellesmere Land and East Greenland upper Devonian faunas continue the history of vertebrate evolution in that area, and at the top of the sequence are found the first amphibians, the ichthyostegids. Various important upper Devonian faunas are known from North America, especially the fauna of Scaumenac Bay, Quebec, which has yielded fine fossils of *Bothriolepis* and of lungfishes and crossopterygians, and the fauna of the Cleveland shales in Ohio, in which are found giant arthrodires like *Dinichthys* and the early shark, *Cladoselache*. Upper Devonian faunas are also found in the southern hemisphere in Australia, and in the Antarctic.

The sequence of these various upper Silurian and Devonian faunas and their correlative relationships are shown in the accompanying chart.

THE SEQUENCE OF EARLY VERTEBRATE FAUNAS

It would appear that the upper Silurian vertebrate faunas were dominated by ostracoderms, for at this stage of earth history the jawed vertebrates probably were not very numerous. But ostracoderm supremacy did not last for long, because by the beginning of the Devonian period the jawed vertebrates had become well established. The ostracoderms continued, but their place in nature was being challenged by the early acanthodian placoderms. At this time, too, the early arthrodires were prominent in the faunas. Missing from the early Devonian faunas were the sharks and all but scattered and primitive representatives of the bony fishes.

In the transition from early to middle and late Devonian history there were great changes in the nature of the vertebrate faunas. The ostracoderms, which had been rather abundant in early Devonian times, were greatly reduced, and continued to the end of the period only as remnants of a once numerous group of vertebrates. The acanthodians also were cut down to a fraction of their former abundant expression, although these placoderms continued to the end of the Paleozoic era, the only placoderms to survive the close of Devonian times. On the other hand, the arthrodires expanded through middle and late Devonian times, but with a shift of emphasis from fresh-water to estuarine and marine types. It was in the final stages of Devonian history that the arthrodires reached the culmination of their evolution as the giant predators of the Cleveland shales. In addition, some new placoderms, the antiarchs, appeared in middle and late Devonian times.

The most important event in the history of the vertebrates during middle Devonian times was the appearance of the Osteichthyes, and it is probable that the sudden influx of the new and comparatively advanced bony fishes was instrumental in leading to the decline and final disappearance of the more primitive vertebrates such as the ostracoderms and most of the placoderms. From middle Devonian times on, the bony fishes evolved with great rapidity and variety, first as fresh-water types and in subsequent ages as marine fishes. Even in the first stages of their evolutionary development in middle Devonian times, the Osteichthyes had differentiated into actinopterygians on the one hand and into lungfishes and crossopterygians on the other. Evidently the initial phases of osteichthyan history, during which the separation of these primary lines took place, were consummated with great evolutionary dispatch, so that almost from the beginning the main lines for the development of the bony fishes had been delineated. Among the fishes the sharks were the last to appear. There are indications of them in middle Devonian faunas, but it is not until we reach upper Devonian sediments that we find well-documented records showing the beginnings of shark evolution.

The climax of vertebrate evolution during Devonian times was reached with the appearance of the first amphibians at the close of the period. This event ushered in a new phase of vertebrate evolution —the beginning of tetrapod history. The story of the rise and the differentiation of the land-living vertebrates concerns the Carboniferous and later periods of geologic history, and will be the subject of the subsequent chapters of this book.

Ichthyostega

7 · Amphibians

THE SPECIAL PROBLEMS OF LIVING ON LAND

When the descendants of certain crossopterygian fishes ventured out of the water on to the land at the end of the Devonian period and jumped the gap, so to speak, from one vertebrate class to another to become the first amphibians, the backboned animals entered upon a completely new course of evolutionary development, ·quite different from anything in their previous history. For the first time the vertebrates were invading a new environment, very different from the one in which they had lived for millions of years. This was, needless to say, a profound step that opened broad avenues for evolution over a tremendous range of adaptations. It was an unprecedented step, involving great transitions in vertebrate structure and a change in the emphasis of evolutionary trends. From this point on, the evolution of the vertebrates other than fishes was directed primarily along lines of adaptation for life on the land (and in the air), although there were secondary reversions to life in the water among various land-living animals.

The first amphibians, the ichthyostegids as we know them in the geologic record, evolved in directions quite different from those followed by their immediate fish ancestors. Even though there are many common characters that connect the higher crossopterygian fishes with the primitive amphibians, there are at the same time great differences between the two groups of vertebrates that result from the specializations of the one group to life in the water and the other to life out of the water. Let us consider these differences, especially in light of the new problems facing the first land-living vertebrates.

One of the important problems with which the early amphibians had to contend was breathing or respiration. The fish ordinarily obtains its oxygen from the water by means of gills, whereas the land-living vertebrate secures oxygen from the air by means of lungs. As we have seen, the problem of respiration out of the water had been solved for the amphibians by their fish ancestors, the crossopterygians, in which lungs were well developed and probably frequently used. We may say, therefore, that the amphibians had a "head start" on the problem of breathing in the air, so that it was actually not much of a problem for them; they had merely to go on using the lungs that they had inherited from the crossopterygians. The main point of difference between the fishes and amphibians in this respect was that in most of the fishes that had lungs the gills were still the primary method for respiration and the lungs generally formed an accessory breathing mechanism, whereas in most of the amphibians the situation was reversed. These first land-living vertebrates were primarily air-breathing animals, using their lungs for this function, although in their young or larval stages they continued to breathe by means of gills, as we know not only from the evidence of living amphibians but also from fossil evidence.

Another problem to confront the first land-living vertebrates was desiccation or drying-up. This is no problem to the fish, which is continually bathed by the liquid in which it lives, but to the land-living animal it is a crucial and frequently a severe problem. The first amphibians, therefore, were faced with the necessity of retaining their body fluids when they were no longer immersed in the water. It is probable that the earliest amphibians such as the ichthyostegids never ventured very far away from the water and returned frequently to streams and lakes, as indeed do many modern amphibians. Even though such habits would have limited the excursions of ancient amphibians away from water, it is nevertheless probable that these animals at an early stage in their history evolved integuments or body coverings that would protect them against the drying effects of the air. There is now evidence to indicate that some of the first amphibians retained the scales that had covered the body in their fish ancestors, which may mean that these tetrapods did not venture far from the ancestral habitat. There is also evidence to show that as the amphibians evolved, especially during the Permian period, they

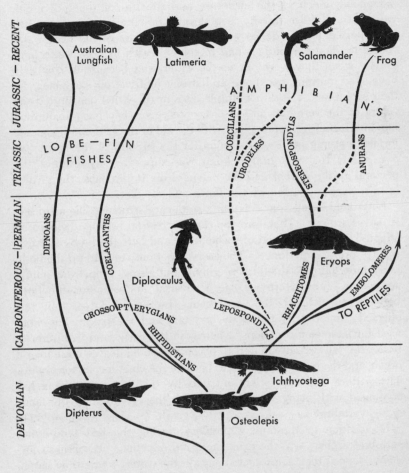

FIGURE 26. Evolution of the lobe-fin fishes and the amphibians.

developed tough skins, frequently underlain by ossicles or bony plates. As the outer covering became increasingly efficient for preventing evaporation of body fluids, and served as a tough coat that shielded the animal from its environment, the amphibians became increasingly independent of the water and more able to spend much of their time on the land. This was an important factor in the evolutionary history of these animals, and more particularly of those higher vertebrates, the reptiles, that arose from the amphibians.

To an animal living on the land gravity is a powerful factor, influencing much of the structure and the life of the individual, whereas to the fish gravity is of lesser consequence, since the fish is supported by the dense water in which it makes its home. Of course the first amphibians had to contend with increased effects of gravity when they were out of the water, and because of this they developed a strong backbone and strong limbs at an early stage in their evolution. The rather simple discs or rings that constituted the centra of the vertebrae in the crossopterygians became transformed into interlocking structures that with the aid of muscles and ligaments formed a strong horizontal column for the support of the body. At two points this vertebral column was supported by girdles, the pectoral girdle in front and the pelvic girdle in the back; the girdles in turn were supported by the limbs and the feet.

But a land-living animal is not a stationary structure like a bridge. It moves around. Therefore the early terrestrial vertebrates became adapted to a new method of locomotion, and here the limbs and feet were of prime importance. They served not only to hold up the body in counter-action to the force of gravity but also to propel the animal across the land. Here we see a reversal in locomotor functions between the fish and the amphibian. In the fish locomotion was effected primarily by the body and tail, and the paired fins were used for balancing functions, whereas in the early land-living vertebrates the tail was attenuated to become in some degree a balancing organ, and the paired appendages became the chief locomotor organs. The pattern for locomotion initiated by the first amphibians has continued with many variations through the evolution of the land-living vertebrates.

In addition to these new problems facing the first land-living vertebrates, there was the problem of reproduction. The fishes commonly deposit their unprotected eggs in the water, where they hatch. Land-living animals must either go back to the water to reproduce, or they must develop methods for protecting the eggs on the land. The amphibians made several great advances in their adaptations to life on the land, but they never solved the problem of reproducing themselves away from moisture. Consequently these animals throughout their history have been forced to return to the water, or among some specialized forms to moist places, to lay their eggs.

THE BASIC DESIGN FOR LIFE ON THE LAND

How did the early amphibians respond in their evolutionary development to the new requirements imposed upon them as a result of the change from an aquatic to a land-living mode of life? As has been mentioned above, the ichthyostegids that appeared at the end of the Devonian period took the first steps to meet the basic requirements for life on the land. Among the immediate successors of the ichthyostegids, the amphibians of Mississippian and Pennsylvanian times, adaptations for land life reached a point of stabilization, so that the primary characters of the tetrapods or four-legged vertebrates were established. These ancient tetrapods and many of their descendants are known as labyrinthodont amphibians (from the structure of the teeth) or stegocephalian amphibians (from the solidly roofed skull), and much of amphibian history is concerned with the evolution of the labyrinthodonts.

In the amphibians of Carboniferous times the adaptations for breathing air were advanced beyond those of their ichthyostegid forebears. For example, in the ichthyostegids the external nostrils were far down on the margins of the skull and separated from the internal narial openings only by a thin bar of bone; in the later amphibians the external nostrils were located on the dorsal surface of the skull, and the internal nares, now in the front part of the palatal region, were quite separated from them. Consequently there was a well-defined nasal passage in these amphibians, leading from the external nostrils into the throat, and this was the basic plan for air intake that was to be followed during the evolutionary development of all the higher vertebrates.

In the ichthyostegids, as we have seen, the vertebrae were but little advanced beyond the crossopterygian condition, which means that the spinal column was not efficiently designed for supporting the body of the animal out of the water. However, the successors of the ichthyostegids had apsidospondylous vertebrae, of which the bony elements, preformed in cartilage, had progressed to such a degree as to have interlocking joints. These vertebrae constituted in series a strong column, quite capable of holding up the body against the downward pull of gravity. This was an important advance in the evolution of land-living vertebrates; it provided the mechanism whereby these animals could evolve to considerable size.

In these early vertebrates the girdles became comparatively strong,

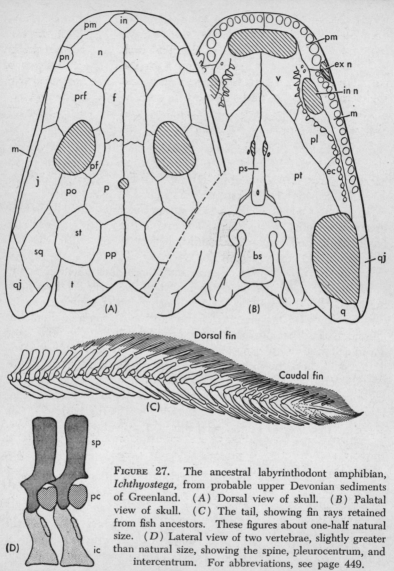

FIGURE 27. The ancestral labyrinthodont amphibian, *Ichthyostega*, from probable upper Devonian sediments of Greenland. (*A*) Dorsal view of skull. (*B*) Palatal view of skull. (*C*) The tail, showing fin rays retained from fish ancestors. These figures about one-half natural size. (*D*) Lateral view of two vertebrae, slightly greater than natural size, showing the spine, pleurocentrum, and intercentrum. For abbreviations, see page 449.

the pectoral girdle (when seen from in front) taking the form of a broad U in which the fore part of the body was slung by strong muscular attachments, the pelvic girdle being a heavy V, attached by a single vertebra to the backbone. The limb bones, characteristically broad and heavy, were composed in each leg of a strong proximal bone, the humerus of the fore limb and the femur of the hind limb, and two distal bones, the radius and ulna of the fore limb and the tibia and fibula of the hind limb. There were hands and feet with five toes, articulating with the limbs by means of carpal or wrist bones, and tarsal or ankle bones. In conjunction with the perfection of the limbs, the tail became variously reduced.

The skull in the early Carboniferous amphibians was heavy, and was solidly roofed by skull bones that had been inherited in a direct line through the ichthyostegids from crossopterygian ancestors. Only five openings pierced the skull roof, the two nostrils, the two eyes, and behind the eyes the pineal foramen, an opening that during life contained a median light receptor. At the back of the skull there was a prominent notch on either side, bounded above by the tabular bone of the skull roof and below by the squamosal bone of the temporal region of the skull. This tympanic notch was for the accommodation of the eardrum, a new character in the amphibians. From the eardrum, a tight membrane that stretched across the tympanic notch, a single bone, the stapes, bridged the gap between the outer portion of the skull and the wall of the brain case. One end of the stapes was attached to the tympanic membrane, and the other end was inserted into a hole in the side of the brain case, and by means of this arrangement sound waves that impinged upon the eardrum were transmitted by the stapes to the inner ear. The stapes was the old fish hyomandibular, transformed from a bone originally part of a gill arch, subsequently a prop to hold the jaws and the brain case together, into its new use as part of a hearing device. This is an interesting example of transformation through evolution of a structure from one function to an entirely new function—a process that has occurred time and again during the history of life.

Numerous sharp teeth bordered the edges of the jaws in the early amphibians, and in addition there were other teeth located on the horizontal surfaces of the bones in the front part of the palate. These teeth had the complex labyrinthine structure of the enamel that was so characteristic among many crossopterygian fishes. The palate in the early amphibians was commonly solid or but slightly fenestrated, and there was generally a joint between the pterygoid bones of the palate and the brain case, allowing some movement between the brain case and the skull. On the other hand, there was no joint in the skull itself, as was characteristic of many crossopterygian fishes.

Such was the general plan of the early land-living vertebrate, as shown by the fossil evidence.

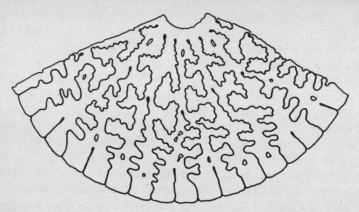

FIGURE 28. Diagrammatic cross-section of a portion of a labyrinthodont tooth, greatly enlarged. The sinuous lines indicate the complex infolding of the enamel surface of the tooth.

THE LABYRINTHODONT AMPHIBIANS— EMBOLOMERES

Among the early descendants of the ancestral ichthyostegids were the amphibians known as embolomeres, appearing during Mississippian times. In these amphibians each vertebra was composed of two discs, one behind the other, known respectively as the intercentrum and the pleurocentrum. The neural arch and spine rested upon the two vertebral discs, and the three elements together—intercentrum, pleurocentrum, and neural arch—composed the embolomerous type of vertebra. There were strong facets or zygapophyses on the front and the back of each neural arch, forming articular surfaces that locked the vertebrae together with strong but movable joints. All in all, the embolomerous vertebral structure was well adapted for supporting a land-living animal.

In many respects the embolomeres retained the generalized features that have already been listed as characteristic of the primitive amphibians. In *Eogyrinus,* a typical genus from the Carboniferous of Europe, the skull was rather deep, with a primitive type of skull-roof pattern, and on each side of the skull there was a large otic notch for the accommodation of the tympanic membrane. The palate was primitive, almost solid, and pierced only by small openings or vacuities; it articulated with the brain case by means of a movable joint.

The shoulder girdle, so close behind the skull that this animal can be said to have very little neck, was a rather complex structure, composed on either side of several bones. The front of the girdle consisted of clavicle and cleithrum, and back of these bones was the scapulocoracoid, with which the upper arm bone, the humerus, articulated. Ventrally the two halves of the shoulder girdle were joined together by the median interclavicle.

The pelvis was a fairly strong, plate-like structure, composed on either side of three bones, the ilium, ischium, and pubis. The ilium consisted of a narrow upper blade which attached to one vertebra, and a broad lower portion. The posterior ischium and anterior pubis were expanded, heavy bones, joining each other and the ilium firmly, and in the region where these three bones met there was a rounded depression, the acetabulum, forming a socket for the articulation of the femur, the upper bone of the hind limb. The two halves of the pelvis were joined along the bottom edges of the pubis and ischium by a heavy symphysis that held the entire structure together in a strong V-shaped support.

There were rather weak limbs attached to the pectoral and pelvic girdles, an indication that *Eogyrinus*, like many of the embolomeres, was to a large degree a water-living amphibian, as might be expected in a very primitive tetrapod that was drifting away from the life lived by its fish ancestors.

THE LABYRINTHODONT AMPHIBIANS—
RHACHITOMES

Early in the history of the amphibians the important group of labyrinthodonts known as rhachitomes arose. They originated in the Mississippian period, but most characteristically they developed in the subsequent Pennsylvanian and Permian periods. In these amphibians the intercentra and pleurocentra of the vertebrae were not equal discs, as in the embolomeres; rather the intercentra were large wedge-shaped elements, and the pleurocentra were comparatively small blocks that fitted in between the intercentra. In each vertebra the neural arch was supported by both the intercentrum and the pleurocentrum. Taken together, this association of bones formed the rhachitomous vertebra, probably the basic, central type of vertebral structure among the labyrinthodonts, since its initial stages are indicated in the ichthyostegids. As in the embolomeres, the neural arch in the rhachitomes carried well-formed zygapophyses for strong articulations between vertebrae.

The rhachitomes became the dominant amphibians of Permian times, and of these the genus *Eryops* from the lower Permian sediments of Texas can be described as a typical example of the group.

Eryops, six feet or more in length, was a heavily built animal. It had a very large, broad, and rather flat skull in which the roofing bones had become thick and rugose. There was a deep otic notch

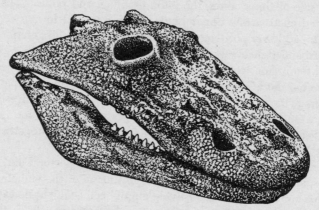

FIGURE 29. The skull and lower jaw of the Permian labyrinthodont amphibian, *Eryops*, about one-sixth natural size. This illustrates the heavy, solid skull of a typical labyrinthodont.

for the ear. In contrast to the embolomeres, the palate in *Eryops* was rather open, with a large fenestra or vacuity on either side. This opening of the palate seemed to go along with the flattening of the skull in *Eryops* and other rhachitomes, and it was probably developed to make room for the large eye and the eye muscles. Another contrast with the embolomeres was the solid joint between the palate and the brain case in *Eryops*. There were strong labyrinthodont teeth around the margin of the jaws and some very large teeth in the palate.

The vertebral column was extraordinarily strong, an indication that *Eryops* was well adapted for life on the land. Moreover, the other parts of the skeleton behind the head were very strong. The ribs were greatly expanded. The shoulder girdle was heavy, with the scapula and coracoid dominant. The cleithrum and the clavicle were in *Eryops* reduced to mere splints along the front edges of the scapula and coracoid. The pelvis was also heavy. The limbs, though short, were very stout. This characteristic is particularly apparent in the humerus, which was almost as broad at either end as it was long, and in the femur, a very thick bone. The lower limb bones and the hands and feet were likewise strongly constructed. There were bony nodules in the skin that formed a heavy armor, to protect *Eryops* from some of its vicious contemporaries.

It is quite apparent that *Eryops* was a thorough-going land animal, even though it probably whiled away many languorous hours in the water. One can think of this amphibian as living a life somewhat similar to the life of a modern alligator, in and out of the water along streams, rivers, and lakes. *Eryops* was probably a fish-eating amphibian, but it must have been rather aggressive, and it may have

FIGURE 30. The skeleton of *Eryops,* a Permian rhachitome about five feet in length.

supplemented its diet by preying upon land-living animals. Certainly there is reason to believe that this big rhachitome was able to compete actively with many of the reptiles of Permian times. In many respects *Eryops* represents the high spot in the evolution of the amphibians.

Although *Eryops* is cited as a typical member of the Rhachitomi, it must not be thought that all these amphibians were large, aggressive carnivores, well suited for life out of the water. The rhachitomes evolved along various lines of adaptive radiation during the Pennsylvanian and Permian periods, and although there were numerous large semi-aquatic and land-living types like *Eryops,* there were others that became specialized for quite different modes of life. For instance, in one group of the rhachitomes there were animals of medium size, characterized especially by elongated rather pointed skulls, the jaws of which were provided with numerous sharp teeth. These were the archegosaurs, and it seems obvious that they were primarily water-living, fish-eating animals. Still other rhachitomes were small, and were adapted for ecological niches unavailable to the big predatory forms.

Of these, the genus *Trimerorhachis* from the Permian beds of Texas is especially well known. It was a rhachitome no more than a foot or two in length, with a much flattened skull, in which there was some reduction of bone and a corresponding increase of cartilage. The body of *Trimerorhachis* was covered with an armor of over-lapping scales that appear to be homologous with fish scales. It is reasonable to think, in the light of these features and because of the types of sediments in which *Trimerorhachis* is found, that this

Eryops

FIGURE 31. *Eryops* represents a high point in the evolution of the amphibians. This big Permian rhachitome was as large as many of the reptiles of the time, and probably was able to compete actively with them.

was a water-living amphibian, inhabiting shallow streams and ponds and feeding upon small animals in such a habitat. Another small rhachitome from the Permian beds of Texas that may be contrasted with *Trimerorhachis* is the genus *Cacops*, characterized by a heavy skull, with an enormous otic notch closed behind by a bar of bone, by a relatively short body and strong legs, by a reduced tail, and by a covering of heavy, bony armor over the back. Evidently *Cacops* was a land-living amphibian, strongly protected by its armor against the depredations of predators. This amphibian must have had an enormous eardrum; perhaps it was a nocturnal animal like many of the modern frogs.

In certain late Pennsylvanian and early Permian deposits in Europe the skeletons of very small labyrinthodonts, commonly known as "branchiosaurs," have been found. It has been argued by some paleontologists that these little amphibians constitute a separate group, which has been called the Phyllosopondyli. In recent years, however, Professor Romer of Harvard University has shown that the branchiosaurs were probably the larval forms of some of the larger rhachitomes contemporaneous with them, and there is good reason to think that this interpretation is correct. For instance, the branchiosaurs frequently show indications of fossilized gill arches, as might be expected in larval types. Moreover, Romer has shown that in a series of branchiosaurs graded according to size, the eye decreases in relative size from the smallest to the largest members of the series, which is what we might expect in a sequence of developing larval amphibians. For these and other reasons it seems likely that the group of phyllospondyls has no reality in the history of the amphibians.

The rhachitomous amphibians enjoyed a long and successful sojourn over much of the earth's land areas during Permian times, but with the close of this phase of earth history their period of dominance came almost to an end. A few rhachitomous types known as trematosaurs, which persisted into the early portion of the Triassic period, were remarkable in that the vertebrae showed the rhachitomous structure, whereas the skull was advanced far toward the stereospondyl condition so typical of the Triassic labyrinthodonts. These amphibians may have been marine, fish-eating animals, anticipating in a way the plesiosaurs and other marine reptiles that were so abundant in later Mesozoic times. This seeming incursion of the amphibians into the sea was not, however, very successful, for the trematosaurs soon died out, leaving the stereospondyls as the dominant Triassic amphibians.

THE LABYRINTHODONT AMPHIBIANS— STEREOSPONDYLS

The stereospondyls, so characteristic of the Triassic period throughout the world, followed lines of adaptive radiation quite different from those that typified the rhachitomes, from which they were derived. Whereas the rhachitomes were commonly specialized for life on the land (although these amphibians must have spent a great deal of time in the water, as have most amphibians during the long evolutionary history of the class), the stereospondyls were highly specialized aquatic types that probably seldom ventured on to the land. It might be said that the stereospondyls reversed the general trend of evolution that had been followed by the labyrinthodont amphibians from the beginning of the Mississippian period to the end of the Permian period, by returning to the environment of

their ultimate ancestors. The stereospondyl pattern of evolution was
certainly a successful one for the Triassic period, and these animals
became the most common and widely distributed of continental
vertebrates. They continued their evolution right up to the end of
the Triassic period, and then became completely extinct. We can
think of stereospondyl evolution as representing a final vigorous
flowering of the labyrinthodonts before their extinction.

Since these animals had largely abandoned the land, they no
longer needed the strong vertebral column that was so well developed
in the rhachitomes; and, as so often happens among vertebrates that
have returned from life on the land to life in the water, there was
a secondary simplification of the vertebral column. Instead of the
interlocking elements characteristic of the rhachitomes, the vertebral
centra in the stereospondyls were reduced to simple discs composed
of the intercentra alone, above which were the neural arches and
spines. The pleurocentra were lost. This is the stereospondylous
type of vertebral structure, from which the name of these Triassic
amphibians is derived.

The stereospondyls, having returned to an aquatic mode of life,
were not bothered by problems of gravity as were their rhachitomous
ancestors. Consequently there was a common trend among these
amphibians toward an increase in size, with the result that some
stereospondyls surpassed their large Permian ancestors, to become
the largest amphibians ever to live. Not all stereospondyls were
large, but the general trend was in this direction.

The genus *Buettneria,* found in upper Triassic sediments of the
southwestern United States, exemplifies the results of the evolutionary
trends in these last of the labyrinthodonts. In this large stereospondyl, as in so many of the later genera belonging to the group, the
skull was inordinately large as compared with the body. Growth
factors during evolution were such that as the animals increased in
size during time, the skull increased at a greater rate than the body,
so that the late Triassic stereospondyls were almost grotesque because
of their immense heads. Not only was the skull large in these
amphibians, it was about as flat as the proverbial pancake. As might
be expected, flatness in the skull was accompanied by flatness in the
body.

Along with these changes in proportion there was a general trend
among the stereospondyls toward increase of cartilage and reduction
of bone in some parts of the skeleton. Thus the palatal region of
the skull became very open by reduction of bone, and the brain case
became cartilaginous. The elements in the wrist and the ankle were

completely reduced to cartilage, so that they are seldom preserved in the fossils.

Yet strangely enough the reduction of bone in these amphibians was differential. Although the palate became open and the brain case and wrist and ankle components were reduced to cartilage, bone in some other parts of the skeleton was increased, so that the top of the skull became extraordinarily heavy and thick, as did the clavicles and interclavicle, the ventral bones of the pectoral girdle. In surprising contrast, the upper bones of the pectoral girdle were small and weak. So was the pelvis. And as a corollary of these small upper segments in the girdles, the limbs and feet in the later stereospondyls such as *Buettneria* were astonishingly small.

Thus evolution in the stereospondyls led finally to the production of what we might regard as bizarre animals, peopling the streams and ponds of late Triassic times with queerly proportioned beasts such as we might encounter in some mediaeval manuscripts. These amphibians showed a strange combination of characters, yet in spite of this the stereospondyls were remarkably successful animals. It was only at the close of the Triassic period, when many varied land-living vertebrates became extinct, that their history and concomitantly the history of the labyrinthodonts came to a close.

TRENDS IN LABYRINTHODONT EVOLUTION

It may be useful at this point to summarize the varied courses of labyrinthodont evolution by a chart or a table, in order to show at a glance the trends of development in these amphibians. Of course it is not possible to include all the numerous characters involved during the evolution of the labyrinthodonts, but at least some of the more striking ones are considered. Briefly, the evolutionary trends in the labyrinthodonts may be expressed as follows.

	Embolomeres	*Ichthyostegids*	*Rhachitomes*	*Stereospondyls*
Habitat	Primarily aquatic		→ Terrestrial	→ Secondarily aquatic
Backbone	Strong	← Weak	→ Strong	→ Secondarily weak
Vertebrae	Embolomerous	← Prerhachitomous	→ Rhachitomous	→ Stereospondylous
Skull	Deep	← Deep	→ Flattened	→ Extremely flat
Palate	Closed	← Closed	→ Open	→ Widely open
Brain case	Ossified	←	→ Ossified	→ Cartilaginous
Occipital condyle	Single	← Single	→ Double	→ Double
Limbs	Weak	← Strong	→ Very strong	→ Secondarily very weak

This table indicates that evolution in the labyrinthodonts was directional, that it proceeded along certain definite courses from the end of the Devonian to the end of the Triassic periods. In general,

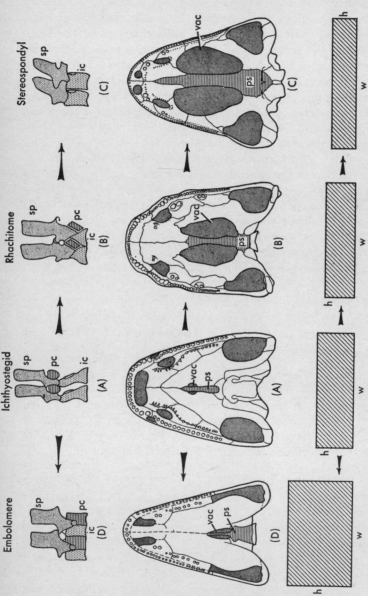

FIGURE 32. This figure illustrates some of the trends in labyrinthodont evolution, as outlined on the preceding page. At the top, two vertebrae of each type in lateral view; in the middle, the skull in palatal view; at the bottom, the proportions of height to width in each skull. Not to scale; the skulls are drawn to the same length. (A) *Ichthyostega*, (B) *Eryops*, (C) *Buettneria*, (D) *Pholidogaster*.

it is possible to trace the rise and the development of these amphibians along two evolutionary trends. From fish ancestors through the primitive ichthyostegids, the labyrinthodonts continued to evolve on the one hand to a high point exemplified by the strongly terrestrial rhachitomes of the Permian, after which there was a secondary return to the water, as seen in the large Triassic stereospondyls. On the other hand, the labyrinthodonts would seem to have evolved from primitive types toward a permanently aquatic mode of life, as shown by the embolomeres. This line was destined eventually to lead to the reptiles, as we shall see.

FROGS AND TOADS

In the strict sense of the word the labyrinthodont amphibians became extinct at the end of the Triassic period, when the last of the stereospondyls disappeared. But in another sense it can be said that certain developmental trends seen in labyrinthodont evolution were continued far beyond the Triassic period by descendants of the labyrinthodonts. Two groups of animals were derived from the labyrinthodonts, the toads and frogs or anurans, and the reptiles.

In branching off from the characteristic labyrinthodont pattern of development, the anurans became what they were and are, first, by a great reduction of bone throughout the body and, second, by extreme specializations for a very particular mode of life. The first indications of such an evolutionary trend are seen among some amphibians of Pennsylvanian age. In the North American genus *Amphibamus* (or "*Miobatrachus*") there was apparently a reduction in the skull of some elements that are missing in the skull of the anurans. Moreover, the vertebrae in *Amphibamus* were modified by a downward expansion of the neural arches and a reduction of the intercentra and pleurocentra. This development is what might be expected in an animal antecedent to the true anurans. In other respects, however, the skeleton of *Amphibamus* was primitive, and in many ways similar to the skeleton in other small labyrinthodonts.

By Triassic times the trend that had begun in *Amphibamus* had been carried farther, as can be seen in the genus *Protobatrachus* from Madagascar. In this amphibian the skull bones were greatly reduced in number and area, to a point approaching closely the condition typical of modern frogs and toads. In addition, the ilium in the pelvic girdle was elongated. Yet in other respects the skeleton in this amphibian was not highly specialized, so one might say that

Protobatrachus had a frog skull on an elongated body with a long tail.

With the advent of the Jurassic period there was a rather sudden and complete change from *Protobatrachus* to the modern type of anuran, a development involving some very great changes in the skeleton. The frogs and toads, from Jurassic times on, have been characterized by an open flat skull, with the bones greatly reduced in area, by a short back, by a complete suppression of the tail in the adult, and by greatly elongated hind legs and short front legs. In line with these developments the vertebrae in the back have been reduced from the primitive number to about eight, and each vertebra is made up of a large neural arch that grows down into the region of the centra. The true centra have been suppressed. This development, it will be remembered, had already begun far back in Carboniferous times in *Amphibamus*. Such vertebrae as have remained behind the pelvis are fused into a single, spike-like bone known as the urostyle. The ribs are completely suppressed. In the ankle there is an elongation of certain bones and the development of an extra joint, to give greater power to the leg for leaping. The shoulder girdle is specialized and strengthened to take up the shock of landing, and the fore limbs, though small, are strongly modified as landing gear.

In this way the frogs and the toads have become adapted to a life by the edge of the water, or even out on land away from the water. The skull with its very large mouth is an efficient insect trap. The hind legs give the animal power to make enormous leaps, either on the land or from the land into the water. We are all familiar with the efficiency of these adaptations in the frogs and toads, which all in all have through the years been very successful, even though very noisy, amphibians. They have lived from the Jurassic period to the present, a span of more than two hundred million years, and today they are distributed far and wide over the earth, in a great variety of habitats.

THE LEPOSPONDYLS

So far in this chapter we have been concerned with the labyrinthodont amphibians and their descendants, the frogs and the toads. As has been indicated, these were the amphibians in which the bony elements of the vertebrae were preformed in cartilage, the aspidospondylous vertebrae. We have seen how the amphibians with this type of vertebrae were the first of the land-living vertebrates and how they became dominant and very numerous during late Paleozoic and Triassic times.

But they were by no means the only amphibians that lived in those distant days. They shared the land and the streams and the ponds with other amphibians, which can be called lepospondyls. In the lepospondyls the vertebrae were not preformed in cartilage, but rather were formed directly as spool-like, bony cylinders around the notochord, and generally united with the neural arch. The lepospondyls have been a highly varied group that appeared as early as the Mississippian period, reached the height of their evolutionary development in the Pennsylvanian and Permian periods, and persist today as the salamanders and the coecilians.

The lepospondyls have never been large, and through most of their history probably never very numerous. It is obvious that during the golden age of the amphibians, the late Paleozoic, the lepospondyls were not direct competitors with their large and multitudinous cousins, the labyrinthodonts; instead they were adapted to certain ecological niches that were not exploited by the labyrinthodonts. For instance, many of the lepospondyls remained as small, generally primitive amphibians, suited for life in the undergrowth at the edge of the water, or to life in the swamps. Such were many of the genera composing the order Microsauria, of which a typical form was the Pennsylvanian genus, *Microbrachis*.

Still other lepospondyls of the late Paleozoic were small, elongated snake-like amphibians in which the legs were suppressed. The genus *Ophiderpeton* of Pennsylvanian age was a characteristic member of this amphibian order, known as the Aistopoda, represented in the fossil record by only a few genera.

The most numerous and varied of the late Paleozoic lepospondyls were the amphibians belonging to the order known as the Nectridia. The Nectridia followed two lines of evolutionary development in Pennsylvanian times, characterized on the one hand by an elongation of the body to an eel-like or snake-like form (paralleling the aistopods) and on the other by a flattening and broadening of the body and the skull. The first of these two evolutionary trends is exemplified by the genus *Sauropleura*, in which the body was long, but not so long relatively as in the aistopods, the limbs were absent, and the skull was very pointed in front. Evidently animals such as this lived a snake-like type of life in the Carboniferous swamps.

Diplocaulus, from the Permian beds of Texas, is a well-known genus that probably represents the culmination of evolutionary development among those nectridians in which the trend was toward

flattening of the skull and body. In this amphibian the bones forming
the sides of the skull and the skull roof grew laterally to such an
extent that they formed broad "horns" or lateral projections that in
the adult caused the skull to be considerably wider than it was long.
This factor of lateral growth became established not only in the

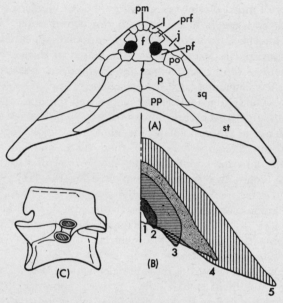

FIGURE 33. The lower Permian nectridian, *Diplocaulus*. (A) The skull in dorsal
view, one-fourth natural size. (B) Growth stages in the skull of *Diplocaulus*
(here shown by the right halves in dorsal view) from a very young individual,
1, to a large adult, 5. (C) Right lateral view of a vertebra, natural size. This
is a characteristic lepospondyl vertebra. For abbreviations, see page 449.

phylogeny or life history of the genus *Diplocaulus* but also in the
ontogeny or life history of the individual. Young individuals of
Diplocaulus had a rather "normal" skull shape, but as growth proceeded the skull grew laterally at a much faster rate than it grew
longitudinally. Consequently the skull in the adult *Diplocaulus* was
shaped something like a very broad arrowhead. The jaws, which
were not involved in this growth, remained small.

The body in *Diplocaulus* was also flat, and the legs were very small
and weak. Evidently this animal was a water-living amphibian,
probably spending most of its time on the bottoms of streams and
ponds. But why did the skull evolve to such a grotesque shape?

The salamanders or urodeles are modern lepospondyls that probably arose from microsaurian ancestors. In the salamanders the body has remained generalized, and evolution has been characterized by a secondary loss of bone and its substitution by cartilage in the skeleton. Salamanders are predominantly water-living amphibians, and some modern forms, like the axolotl of Mexico, retain their larval condition and their gills throughout life. The first urodeles are known from Cretaceous sediments.

There is no fossil record for the coecilians, modern limbless, burrowing amphibians that live in the tropics. It is quite possible, however, that the microsaurian genus *Lysorophus*, found in lower Permian sediments in North America, a small, legless form with a skull peculiarly adapted to burrowing, represents an ancestral stage in the history of the coecilians.

First
Land Eggs

8 · Advent of the Reptiles

THE AMNIOTE EGG

During Carboniferous times a great forward step occurred in the evolution of the vertebrates; the amniote egg appeared. This was a major innovation in vertebrate history, to be compared with the appearance of the lower jaw, or the migration of the backboned animals from the water on to the land, and like these preceding evolutionary events of great moment, the perfection of the amniote egg opened new areas for the development of animals with backbones. The transformation of gill arches into jaws raised the early vertebrates from comparatively small, bottom-living animals to active and aggressive fishes that ranged the waters of the earth. The transition from water to land made available to the amphibians an entirely new environment. And the appearance of the amniote egg liberated the land-living vertebrates completely from any dependence upon the water during the life history of the individual.

In those animals reproducing by the amniote egg development is direct from embryo to adult. The egg is internally fertilized, after which it is deposited on the ground or in some suitable place, or sometimes retained within the oviduct of the female until the young animal hatches. The egg contains a large yolk that furnishes nourishment for the developing embryo. It also contains two sacs, one being the amnion, which is filled with a liquid and contains the embryo, the other the allantois, which receives the waste products produced by the embryonic animal during its sojourn in the egg. Finally, the entire structure is enclosed by a shell that is tough enough to protect the contents of the egg, yet porous enough to allow the passage of oxygen into the egg and the passage of carbon dioxide out. This egg provides a protected environment for the development of the embryo; in effect it furnishes a little private pool, the amnion, in which the embryo can grow, safely screened from the outside world by the tough shell of the egg.

Animals with an egg such as this can wander freely over the land, without having to return to the water to reproduce, as has been

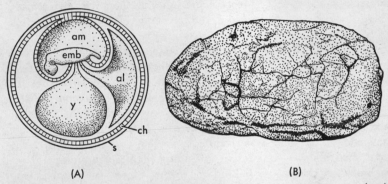

(A)   (B)

FIGURE 34. (A) Diagram of the amniote egg, showing the amnion cavity (am) containing the embryo (emb), the allantois (al), the yolk sac (y), the chorion (ch), and the outer shell (s). (B) The oldest known reptile egg, from the lower Permian of Texas. Natural size.

necessary for the amphibians through the millions of years of their history. The first animals to have the amniote egg were the reptiles.

The reptiles were derived from the amphibians, specifically from certain labyrinthodonts, and the transition from amphibian to reptile took place during the Carboniferous period of earth history. Of course the final crossing of the threshold from the amphibians to the reptiles occurred with the perfection of the amniote egg, but of this there is no fossil evidence. The oldest known amniote egg, which is from lower Permian sediments in North America, represents a time long after the reptiles had become well established on the land. However, among the fossils we can see amphibians trending toward reptiles, and we can point to certain intermediate forms combining characters of advanced labyrinthodonts with those of primitive reptiles. It is particularly important to attempt an evaluation of the position of these intermediate forms in the history of vertebrate life, for they represent the approximate evolutionary stage at which the amniote egg appeared.

THE SEYMOURIAMORPHS

Seymouria is a small tetrapod found in the upper portion of the lower Permian sediments exposed to the north of the town of Seymour, Texas. This vertebrate is much too high in the geologic column to have been an ancestor of the reptiles, yet in its structure it is almost exactly intermediate between the amphibians and the reptiles. Thus *Seymouria* is a good example of a persistent structural ancestor; it shows how paleontological grandfathers may live on with their descendants. It is also a good example of a "connecting link" of which there are many in the fossil record.

In many respects *Seymouria* can be compared with the embolomeres. It seems evident also that this animal and its relatives, known under the collective name of seymouriamorphs, had ancestors in common with the embolomerous amphibians. *Seymouria* had a rather deep skull, with a prominent otic notch at the back for the accommodation of the eardrum, as was characteristic of the embolomeres. The skull was completely roofed, and all the labyrinthodont skull bones were present, including both a supratemporal and an intertemporal bone, behind the eye. There were sharp, labyrinthodont teeth around the margins of the jaws, and in addition there were some large teeth on the palatine bones, as is typical of the labyrinthodonts. The occipital condyle was single, as it was in the embolomeres. Indeed the skull showed many features in common with certain labyrinthodonts.

The postcranial skeleton, on the other hand, displays various progressive characters that link *Seymouria* with the early reptiles. For instance the neural arches of the vertebrae were broadly expanded from side to side and swollen, which is just what we find in the earliest reptiles. Moreover, the dominant vertebral element was the pleurocentrum, whereas the intercentrum was reduced to a small, wedge-shaped bone, again a reptilian character. In the shoulder girdle the interclavicle had a long, median stem, typical of the early reptiles and in decided contrast to the labyrinthodonts. The ilium was expanded much beyond the amphibian condition, and a second vertebra was being incorporated into the sacrum. Primitive reptiles had two sacral vertebrae as contrasted with the single vertebra of the amphibians. The humerus was generally similar to that of early reptiles. Finally, *Seymouria* had an arrangement of toe bones similar to that of the early reptiles, with two phalanges in the thumb and great toe, three in the second digit, four in the third, five in the fourth, and

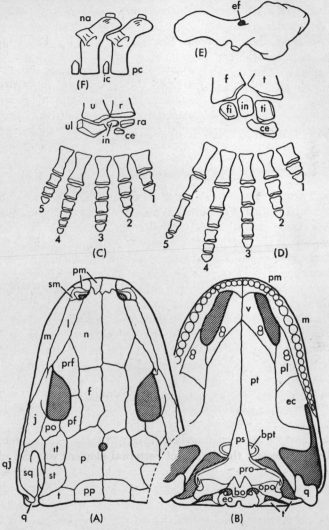

FIGURE 35. The ancestral reptile, *Seymouria*, from lower Permian sediments of
Texas. (A) Dorsal view of skull. (B) Palatal view of skull. (C) Fore foot.
(D) Hind foot. (E) Humerus. (F) Two dorsal vertebrae in lateral view.
All about one-half natural size. For abbreviations, see page 449. Note here the
general labyrinthodont-like arrangement of bones in the skull roof and the three
separate proximal bones of the ankle: the reptile-like phalangeal formula, the
foramen in the humerus, and the swollen arches of the vertebrae.

three in the little finger, four in the little toe. This is the primitive reptilian phalangeal formula, usually expressed as 2–3–4–5–3(4).

Was *Seymouria* an amphibian or a reptile? The answer to this question is whether *Seymouria,* like the reptiles, laid an amniote egg on the land, or whether, like the frogs, it returned to the water to lay its eggs. Unfortunately there is no paleontological evidence at the present time that gives us the answer. In the meantime, therefore, we may place the seymouriamorphs between the two classes of vertebrates, and relate them to either the one or the other. It is here proposed to consider them as stem reptiles.

REPTILE CHARACTERS

The mixture of amphibian and reptilian characters seen in *Seymouria* is indicative of the gradual transition that took place between the two classes during the evolution of the vertebrates. Because the change was gradual rather than abrupt it is difficult to draw clear-cut distinctions between amphibians and reptiles when all the fossil materials are taken into consideration. There are, however, certain characters typical of reptiles and others generally typical that may be outlined at this place.

Of course the reptiles are characterized by direct development from an amniote egg, as contrasted with the metamorphosis during individual development that is seen in the amphibians. Unfortunately, this is a diagnostic character that can only be inferred from the fossil materials.

Structurally the reptiles are generally characterized by a rather deep skull, in contrast to the frequently flattened skull of the labyrinthodont amphibians. The primitive otic notch has been suppressed in the reptile skull, although there are some reptiles that have an otic notch, probably of secondary origin. Another feature typical of the reptiles is the extreme reduction of the postparietal elements in the skull, so that the bones behind the parietals are small, or shifted from the skull roof to the occiput, or even suppressed completely. The pineal foramen, so characteristic of the labyrinthodonts, persists in the early reptiles, but in many advanced forms it disappears. The pterygoid bones of the palate are prominent in the reptiles, and in the primitive forms these bones carry well-developed teeth. In the front of the mouth the reptilian palatine bones may have small teeth, but they lack the large tusk-like palatine teeth, so common in many labyrinthodonts. Finally, the occipital condyle is single in most of the reptiles, a character that is foreshadowed in the embolomeres.

The reptiles are typified by a large pleurocentrum forming the main body of the vertebra, with the intercentrum reduced to a small wedge, or suppressed in the more advanced forms. There are in the primitive reptiles two sacral vertebrae as contrasted with the single amphibian sacral, whereas in many of the advanced reptiles the sacrum includes several vertebrae, sometimes as many as eight. The ilium of course is expanded to form an attachment with the expanded sacrum. In the reptilian shoulder girdle there is an emphasis of the scapula and coracoid, with the cleithrum reduced or suppressed, and with the clavicle and interclavicle often present but much reduced as compared with these same elements in the labyrinthodonts. Among primitive reptiles the ribs form a continuous and generally similar series from the skull to the pelvis, but in the more advanced reptiles there is commonly a differentiation of ribs in the neck, thoracic, and abdominal regions.

The limbs and the feet in the reptiles show certain advances over the appendages in the labyrinthodont amphibians. Even in the primitive reptiles the limb bones are generally more slender than these bones in the labyrinthodonts. In the wrist there are never more than two central bones, as contrasted with the four such elements of the labyrinthodont wrist. In the ankle the proximal bones are reduced to two as contrasted with the three amphibian elements. This reduction has been brought about by a fusion of the inner bone, the tibiale, with the intermedium and also with one central bone, the coalesced element being the equivalent of the astragalus in higher vertebrates. The outer bone, the fibulare, is the equivalent of the calcaneum in the mammals. As mentioned above in the description of *Seymouria* the reptiles have a basic phalangeal formula of 2-3-4-5-3(4), although this number may be modified in many of the specialized reptiles.

Finally the reptiles have a horny epidermis that often takes the form of folded, overlapping scales.

THE COTYLOSAURS

The earliest and most primitive reptiles belong to the order Cotylosauria. *Seymouria* may be considered a basic member of this reptilian order. A more completely reptilian cotylosaur is the genus *Limnoscelis*, found in the lower Permian sediments of New Mexico. This animal embodies many of the characters listed above as typical for the reptiles, and in most respects it makes a very satisfactory primitive reptile.

Limnoscelis was a reptile some five feet or more in length. The skull was solidly roofed, somewhat elongated and rather deep. The eyes were placed laterally. On the skull roof there was a well-developed pineal opening, at the junction between the parietal bones, a character inherited from amphibian ancestors. The postparietal and tabular bones were comparatively small and were pushed back from the top of the skull to the occiput or back surface. There were sharp teeth on the margins of the jaws and small teeth on the pterygoid bones of the palate. The body was elongated and the limbs were strong but rather sprawling. The postcranial skeleton was characteristically reptilian, with reduced intercentra, a large scapula-coracoid complex, a long interclavicle, an expanded ilium, two sacral vertebrae, two proximal bones in the ankle, these being the astragalus and calcaneum, and with the primitive reptilian phalangeal formula.

At an early stage in their history the cotylosaurs, originating in the ancestral seymouriamorphs, split into two evolutionary lines. One was the line of the captorhinomorphs, of which *Limnoscelis* was a primitive member. The other was the line of the diadectomorphs.

The captorhinomorphs were generally small reptiles, even though *Limnoscelis* was an animal of some size. *Captorhinus*, for example, was a Permian genus about a foot or so in length. In this genus, as in all the captorhinomorphs, the skull was truncated at the back, and the quadrate bone for the support of the lower jaw was vertical in position. The jaws were very long, with numerous sharp, pointed teeth. Evidently this little captorhinomorph, like all members of this evolutionary line, was a carnivorous animal, probably preying upon small amphibians and reptiles, perhaps even upon large insects.

In contrast to the generally primitive captorhinomorphs, the diadectomorphs, of which the genus *Diadectes* was a typical member, followed an evolutionary trend leading usually to increase in size and certain specializations of the skull and teeth. *Diadectes*, from the Permian of Texas, was an animal five or six feet in length, and heavily built. Related diadectomorphs, collectively known as pareiasaurs, are found in many parts of the Old World, especially in the Permian deposits of South Africa and northern Russia. The genus *Pareiasaurus*, from the Permian deposits of South Africa, was a massive reptile, eight feet or more in length, standing four or five feet high at the shoulder, and with a broad, expanded body enclosed by a continuous series of long ribs from the neck to the pelvis. In life this ungainly creature may have weighed more than a thousand pounds.

In *Diadectes*, as in other diadectomorphs, the quadrate bone of the skull was pushed forward, and at its upper end, where it joined the

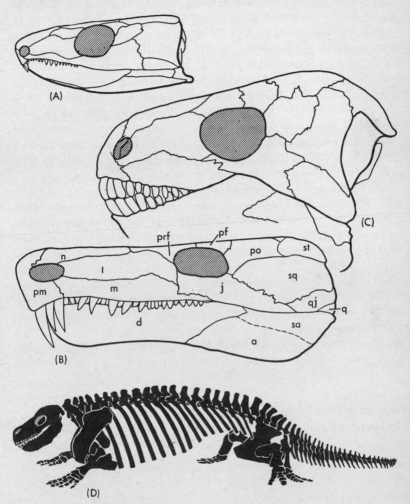

FIGURE 36. Three cotylosaur skulls. (*A*) *Captorhinus,* two-thirds natural size. (*B*) *Limnoscelis,* one-third natural size. (*C*) *Diadectes,* one-half natural size. The skeleton of *Diadectes* (*D*), about six feet long, shows the primitive characters typical of a cotylosaur skeleton. For abbreviations, see page 449.

bones of the skull roof, there was a prominent notch. There is some argument whether this notch is the same as the primitive otic notch in the labyrinthodonts, or whether it is a secondary feature, caused by a specialization in the diadectomorph skull from a more primitive captorhinomorph condition. However that may be, the effect of the forwardly shifted quadrate was to shorten the jaws, which had peg-like teeth in front and transversely broadened teeth in the cheek region. These specializations in the jaws and teeth, together with the capacious nature of the body, suggest that *Diadectes* and its relatives were plant-eating reptiles.

One group of diadectomorphs, the procolophonids, survived into Triassic times, the only cotylosaurs to persist beyond the end of the Permian period. Unlike the other diadectomorphs, the procolophonids were small reptiles, similar to many lizards in size and perhaps in habits as well. It is quite probable that these reptiles fulfilled the rôle in the faunas of Triassic times that the lizards were to take in animal assemblages of later ages.

The procolophonids were widely distributed during the Triassic period. Ancestral forms are known from the upper Permian sediments of Russia, but it was in the Triassic phase of the Karroo series in South Africa that the group became well established. *Procolophon* was the characteristic genus, a small reptile with a rather triangular-shaped, flattened skull, having large orbits and a large pineal opening. During the course of Triassic times the procolophonids spread through central Europe and as far north as northern Scotland, and into North and South America. There was never any notable increase in size among these reptiles, but during the later portions of the Triassic period there was a strong trend among the procolophonids for the eye opening to become enormously large and for spikes to develop on the sides and the back of the skull.

CLASSIFICATION OF THE REPTILES

The dichotomous evolution of the cotylosaurs into the captorhino-morphs on the one hand and the diadectomorphs on the other was an event of prime importance to the subsequent history of the reptiles. It seems probable that all other reptiles were of cotylosaurian ancestry, which means that they were descended from either the one or the other of these cotylosaurian branches. Consequently it appears likely that there has been a basic division among the reptiles, going back to the very beginnings of their evolutionary development. The problem is how the reptiles are to be grouped according to their possible captorhinomorph or diadectomorph derivations, and here the authorities differ. Most students of the reptiles agree that the turtles were probably derived from diadectomorph ancestors, and

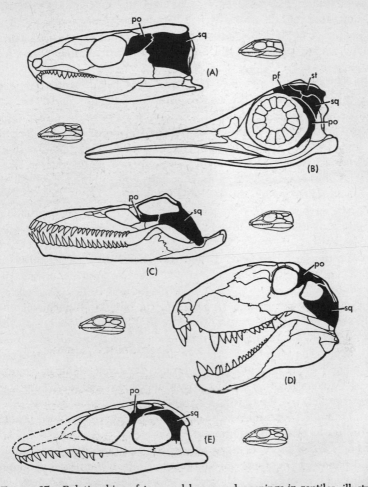

FIGURE 37. Relationships of temporal bones and openings in reptiles, illustrated by the skulls of characteristic genera, and by schematic diagrams. (A) Anapsid skull (*Captorhinus,* a cotylosaur) with no temporal opening. (B) Parapsid skull (*Ichthyosaurus,* an ichthyosaur) with a superior temporal fenestra, bounded below by the postfrontal and supratemporal bones. (C) Euryapsid skull (*Muraenosaurus,* a plesiosaur) with a superior temporal fenestra bounded below by the postorbital and squamosal bones. (D) Synapsid skull (*Dimetrodon,* a pelycosaur) with a lateral temporal fenestra bounded above by the postorbital and squamosal bones. (E) Diapsid skull (*Youngina,* an eosuchian) with superior and lateral temporal openings separated by the postorbital and squamosal bones. Not to scale.

likewise there is general agreement that the pelycosaurs and the mammal-like reptiles arose from a captorhinomorph ancestry. The difference of opinion is concerned with the other reptiles, which in the aggregate constitute the major portion of reptilian evolution through time.

Perhaps the most practical course to take at the present time is to recognize but avoid this controversial problem by classifying the reptiles in an empirical fashion. Generally speaking, a rather satisfactory grouping of the orders of reptiles can be made according to the development of the temporal region in the skull. This system, like any scheme of classification based upon a single character or a set of closely related characters, is not perfect, but it does give a useful arrangement for the study of reptilian orders.

As we have seen, the cotylosaurs resembled their labyrinthodont ancestors in that the skull roof was a solid structure, pierced only by the nostrils, the eyes, and the pineal opening. As the reptiles evolved, the skull roof behind the eyes generally was fenestrated by additional openings, commonly called the temporal fenestrae, the purpose of which was to give room for the bulging of the jaw muscles. In some reptiles there is a single temporal fenestra high up on the skull roof behind the eyes; in others there is a single opening on the side of the skull. In still other reptiles there are two temporal openings, one on the top of the skull roof and one in the side. The upper opening, or superior temporal fenestra, is bounded along its ventral border in some reptiles by the postorbital and squamosal bones, in other reptiles by the postfrontal and supratemporal bones. The lateral temporal fenestra is primarily bounded along its dorsal border by the postorbital and squamosal bones. Finally the two temporal openings, when present, are separated by the postorbital and squamosal bones. Upon these varying relationships of temporal openings (or the lack of openings) the orders of reptiles may be arranged as follows:

Subclass Anapsida
  No temporal openings in the skull behind the eye.
    Order Cotylosauria: the primitive reptiles.
    Order Chelonia: the turtles and eunotosaurs.
Subclass Synapsida
  A single lateral temporal opening, bounded above by the postorbital and squamosal bones.
    Order Pelycosauria: the pelycosaurian reptiles.
    Order Therapsida: the mammal-like reptiles.
    Order Mesosauria: the mesosaurs, which may or may not belong here.

Subclass Parapsida
  A single superior temporal opening, bounded below by the postfrontal
  and supratemporal bones. (This subclass is often designated as the
  Ichthyopterygia.)
  Order Ichthyosauria: the ichthyosaurs or fish-like reptiles.
Subclass Euryapsida
  A single superior temporal opening, bounded below by the postorbital
  and squamosal bones. (This subclass is often designated as the
  Synaptosauria.)
  Order Protorosauria: the protorosaurs.
  Order Sauropterygia: the nothosaurs, plesiosaurs, and placodonts.
Subclass Diapsida
  Two temporal openings, separated by the postorbital and squamosal
  bones.
  Order Eosuchia: the primitive diapsids.
  Order Rhynchocephalia: the rhynchocephalians; *Sphenodon* is the
  survivor.
  Order Squamata: the lizards and snakes.
  Order Thecodontia: the Triassic archosaurs, ancestors of the dominant
  diapsids of Mesozoic times.
  Order Crocodilia: the crocodiles and alligators.
  Order Pterosauria: the flying reptiles.
  Order Saurischia: the saurischian dinosaurs.
  Order Ornithischia: the ornithischian dinosaurs.

PRIMARY RADIATION OF THE REPTILES

Although the cotylosaurs were the first reptiles, grading as they
did back into the labyrinthodont amphibians, it must not be thought
that they stood alone during the early history of the reptiles. Other
reptiles that probably descended from the basic cotylosaur stem
appear at a remarkably early period in the geologic record of these
vertebrates, so that it would seem as if there had been an "explosion"
of various higher categories soon after the reptiles became differentiated as a class. It has already been shown that this is a common
evolutionary phenomenon, repeated time and again through the
history of life.

Among the earliest of the known reptiles were the aquatic mesosaurs, appearing during the Pennsylvanian period at a date fully as
ancient as the time of appearance of the first well-established cotylosaurs. The mesosaurs, typified by the genera *Mesosaurus* and *Stereosternum*, were rather highly specialized in spite of their very early
debut in reptilian history. They were small and elongated reptiles,
with extended jaws at one end of the body, equipped with very long,
sharp teeth, and with a long, deep tail at the other end. The slender,

toothy jaws were obviously adapted for catching fish; the deep tail was plainly a mechanism for swimming. The shoulder and hip girdles were rather small, the limbs were slender, and the feet were enlarged into broad paddles. There can be little doubt but that the mesosaurs spent most of their time in the water, and it is probable

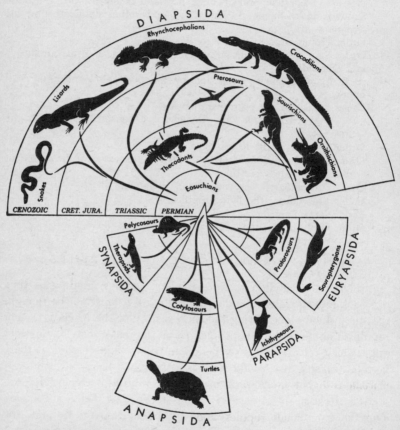

FIGURE 38. Evolution and major classification of the reptiles.

that they seldom if ever ventured on to the land. From the nature of the sediments in which these reptiles are found, it would seem likely that they were inhabitants of fresh-water streams and ponds.

The back of the skull in the mesosaurs is difficult to interpret because it is generally crushed as a result of fossilization. Consequently the precise systematic position of these reptiles has been a matter of debate for many years. At the present time there is considerable sentiment for placing them tentatively among the synapsids, since it appears that there may have been a lateral temporal opening in the skull.

It is a significant fact that the neural arches in the mesosaurs were swollen in much the same fashion as the neural arches of the cotylosaurs, so it would seem likely that these reptiles were of ultimate cotylosaurian ancestry. On the whole it is most probable that the mesosaurs represent a very ancient and independent evolutionary line of reptiles that developed briefly during late Pennsylvanian and early Permian times. They are found in only two localities in the world, *Mesosaurus* in southern Africa and *Stereosternum* in southern

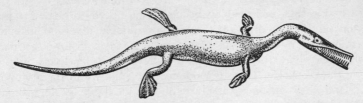

FIGURE 39. *Mesosaurus,* an early aquatic reptile, of small size.

Brazil. This fact (together with other evidence) has led many authorities to believe that there was some sort of a southern continental connection between these two regions during middle and late Paleozoic times. There may have been, but the mere fact that the mesosaurs were aquatic suggests that they may have migrated from the one region to the other without the benefit of complete continental connections.

Whether or not the mesosaurs are placed among the synapsids, these latter reptiles got off to an early start during Pennsylvanian times, as we shall see. The first synapsids were pelycosaurs.

Even the diapsids, in many respects the culminating group of reptiles, had their beginnings in Pennsylvanian times. The first diapsids were small reptiles known as eosuchians. Perhaps the earliest known eosuchian is the genus *Petrolacosaurus* from the Pennsylvanian sediments of Kansas. Another early genus was *Youngina* from the Permian of South Africa.

Petrolacosaurus was a generalized reptile of rather lizard-like form, and probably of lizard-like habits. Of course such a comparison does not imply direct relationship with the lizards. It is a general comparison only, a comparison with something familiar. *Petrolacosaurus* had a slender body and slender limbs, well adapted for scurrying around over the ground.

By Permian times the eosuchians, such as *Youngina*, were small, lightly built animals that were able to run rapidly and thus survive. These were, generally speaking, the founders of a great line—the later diapsid reptiles. The eosuchians themselves were moderately successful, for they lived on along with their numerous diapsid descendants until the opening of Cenozoic times. So it was that these reptiles survived the extinction of the dinosaurs, of which they were the ultimate ancestors.

The ancestry of the parapsids, or ichthyosaurs, is something of a mystery, but it seems probable that these reptiles had their beginning soon after the establishment of the early cotylosaurs. The euryapsids had become well differentiated by early Permian times.

So it was that, once having become established through the perfection of the amniote egg, the reptiles quickly diverged in many directions, to initiate at an early stage in their history the main evolutionary lines that they were to follow. The land was open to them; they were free from dependence upon the water for reproduction, and they quickly made use of the available ecological and evolutionary opportunities. They entered upon a long history, extending from Pennsylvanian times to the present, during much of which, until the end of the Cretaceous period, they were the dominant land animals of the earth. It is our purpose now to follow the various ramifications of reptilian history through more than two hundred million years of geologic time.

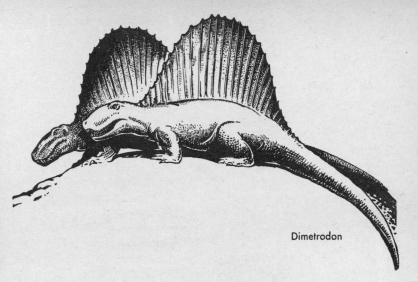

Dimetrodon

9 · Mammal-like Reptiles

DELINEATION OF THE SYNAPSIDA

Among the early reptiles were the synapsids, which first appear in rocks of late Pennsylvanian age. This remarkable and interesting subclass of reptiles bridged the gap between the primitive reptiles and the mammals, for its early members were very close indeed to the ancestral cotylosaurs whereas some of its latest genera approached so closely the mammalian stage that it is a moot question whether these animals should be classified among the reptiles or among the mammals. All this development from primitive reptile to mammal took place between the end of the Pennsylvanian period and the close of the Triassic period.

The synapsids, as we have seen, were those reptiles with a lateral temporal opening behind the eye. In the more primitive genera the opening was bounded above by the postorbital and squamosal bones, but as the synapsids evolved during late Permian and Triassic times the temporal fenestra was enlarged to such an extent that the parietal bone frequently became a part of its upper border. These were constantly quadrupedal reptiles through the extent of their history, and in this respect they differed markedly from various other reptiles, especially many of those that flourished during the Mesozoic era. Furthermore, the synapsids showed few tendencies toward the loss of bones, which is rather remarkable in a group of animals that, at

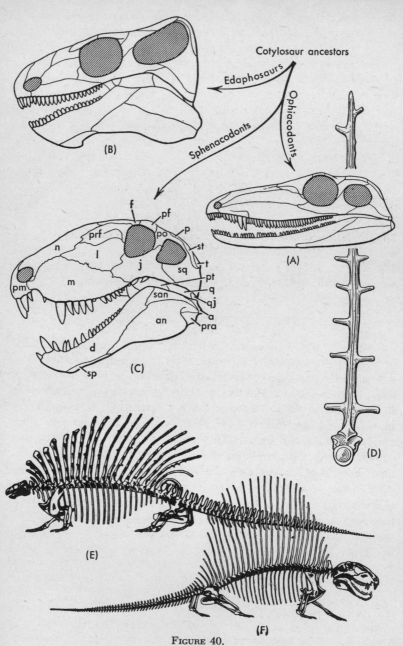

FIGURE 40.

the end of their history, approached so closely the mammalian grade of structural development. Even the primitive pineal opening was retained through much of synapsid history. On the other hand, there was an early trend among the synapsids toward a differentiation of the teeth into anterior incisors, enlarged canines, and laterally placed cheek teeth; and among the later synapsids this development resulted in a rather high stage of dental specialization. In these reptiles the eardrum seems to have had a low position, near the articulation of the jaws.

The vertebrae were primitively amphicoelous, which means that the ends of the centra were rather flat. Among the earlier synapsids there were small, persistent intercentra. In the synapsid shoulder girdle there were two coracoid elements, the primitive coracoid, often called the procoracoid, and a new bone behind it, designated simply as the coracoid. The limbs were in general similar to the limbs in the ancestral cotylosaurs, but they frequently showed evolutionary advances through slenderizing and perfection of the individual bones—an indication that the synapsids were active and rather efficient at getting around over the ground.

THE PELYCOSAURS

The first synapsids were pelycosaurs, of late Pennsylvanian age. These reptiles initiated a line of evolutionary development that is most completely recorded in the upper Pennsylvanian and lower Permian sediments of North America, particularly in Texas, Oklahoma, and New Mexico. Elsewhere the remains of pelycosaurs are fragmentary and scattered.

The early pelycosaurs showed in general the primitive features that have already been listed for the synapsids. Thus the skull had its full complement of bones (lacking the intertemporal bone, which was lost during the transition from labyrinthodonts to early reptiles), there was a pineal opening, there were vertebral intercentra, and the limbs were similar to the limbs of the cotylosaurs, only somewhat more slender. In many respects the skull of some of the early

FIGURE 40. Pelycosaurs. (A) Skull of *Varanosaurus*, one-third natural size. (B) Skull of *Edaphosaurus*, one-fourth natural size. (C) Skull of *Dimetrodon*, one-sixth natural size. (D) Dorsal vertebra of *Edaphosaurus* in posterior view, one-fourth natural size. (E) Skeleton of *Edaphosaurus*. (F) Skeleton of *Dimetrodon*. These reptiles were about six to ten feet in length. For abbreviations, see page 449.

pelycosaurs was very close to the captorhinomorph skull, which is one reason for thinking that these reptiles had a captorhinomorph ancestry.

OPHIACODONTS

The first pelycosaurs can be included in a suborder known as the Ophiacodontia, of which the lower Permian genus *Varanosaurus* was a primitive member. This was a medium-sized reptile about five feet in length, with a slender body, fairly slender limbs, and a long tail. In fact, we might say that *Varanosaurus* was lizard-like in its general aspect, though this characterization must not be taken as an indication of any close relationships with the lizards. In the skull *Varanosaurus* showed certain specializations that were the beginnings of some definite evolutionary trends typical of the pelycosaurs. For instance, the skull was rather narrow, deep, and elongated, with the eyes set far back. The jaws were very long, and the teeth were numerous and sharp. There was no indication of an otic notch, and the ear was located in the vicinity of the jaw articulation.

It was but a short step from *Varanosaurus* to the genus *Ophiacodon*, a large Permian reptile, commonly five to eight feet in length, and in general similar to its predecessor. The skull was very deep, with long jaws, these being provided with many sharp teeth. Evidently *Ophiacodon* was a fish-eating reptile that lived largely along the shores of streams and ponds.

From an ophiacodont stem the pelycosaurs evolved in two directions. One line of pelycosaurian development led to large aggressive, land-living carnivores, the sphenacodonts, the other to large plant-eating forms, the edaphosaurs.

SPHENACODONTS

The sphenacodonts carried forward in Permian times the evolutionary trends that had been initiated among the ophiacodonts, and in the general aspects of the skeleton the two groups show many similarities. In two respects, however, advanced characters developed in the sphenacodonts that went far beyond any of the ophiacodont specializations. In the first place, the sphenacodont dentition was strongly differentiated, a specialization that was correlated with refinements in the skull. There were large, dagger-like teeth in the premaxilla, in the front part of the maxilla, and in the anterior portion of the dentary, whereas the teeth along the lateral borders of the dental arcade were considerably smaller than the anterior teeth. The skull was deep and narrow, which was an adaptation for long, strong jaw muscles that allowed the mouth to be widely opened, and closed with a powerful snap. Such specializations were obviously quite advantageous to very aggressive reptiles that preyed upon other large vertebrates.

The other sphenacodont specialization was the elongation of the vertebral spines, which is not so easy to interpret as the development of the skull and jaws. In the genus *Sphenacodon* the spines were tall, but not unduly so, and it is clear that they might have served for the origin and insertion of strong back and neck muscles. But in another genus, *Dimetrodon,* the spines of the vertebrae from the neck back to the sacrum were tremendously elongated, reaching their greatest height in the middle region of the back. These spines almost certainly supported a web of skin so that there was a longitudinal "sail" down the middle of the back in this remarkable reptile.

What is the meaning of the sail in *Dimetrodon?* This question has been debated for many years, and as yet no conclusive answer has been given. Some have argued that the sail was protective, but it is difficult to see how such a structure would give much protection to the animal. Again it has been suggested that the sail was a sort of "psychological warfare" device; that it made *Dimetrodon* look big and impressive, thereby frightening any potential enemies. This explanation is not very convincing. It has been proposed that the sail was an expression of sexual dimorphism—that *Dimetrodon* with the big sail was the male, and *Sphenacodon* without the sail was the female. But the evidence is against this proposal because the two forms are found in different localities. *Dimetrodon* is found in Texas and *Sphenacodon* in New Mexico, which regions during lower Permian times were separated by a seaway, an obstacle to discourage the most persistently amorous of these reptiles. Perhaps the most logical explanation so far made is that the sail was a temperature-regulating device that added a great area of skin surface for warming up or cooling off the animal. It seems reasonable to think that a structural modification so extreme as this must have been significant in the life of *Dimetrodon,* that it must have had a considerable adaptive value. However that may be, it definitely was not disadvantageous, for *Dimetrodon* was a highly successful reptile over quite a span of geologic time.

EDAPHOSAURS

The second evolutionary line of Permian age springing from an ophiacodont ancestry, that of the edaphosaurs, was quite different from the sphenacodont line. The edaphosaurs were inoffensive plant-eaters, as is shown by the structure of the skull and teeth. In these animals the skull was remarkably small as compared with the size of the body. It was short and rather shallow, as contrasted with

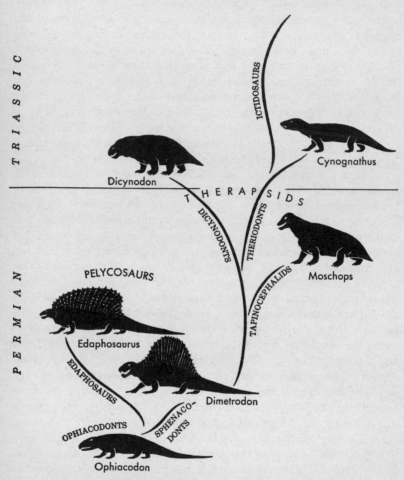

FIGURE 41. Evolution of the synapsid or mammal-like reptiles.

the elongated deep skull of the sphenacodonts. The teeth in the edaphosaurs were not strongly differentiated in size, as were the sphenacodont teeth, but rather were essentially uniform, making an unbroken series around the margins of the jaws. In addition to the marginal teeth, there were in the edaphosaurs extensive clusters of teeth on the palate.

The genus *Edaphosaurus* was characterized by an elongation of the vertebral spines, but the spines were heavier than they were in *Dimetrodon,* and they were ornamented with numerous short lateral spikes or cross-bars arranged irregularly along their length, something like the yardarms on the mast of an old sailing ship. All of which makes *Edaphosaurus* even more of a puzzle than *Dimetrodon.* What could be the meaning of such an adaptation? Surely the growth and nutrition of the sail and the bizarre spines in *Edaphosaurus* must have constituted a serious drain upon the energy of this animal.

Not all the edaphosaurs had sails. *Casea* and the related genus, *Cotylorhynchus,* were massively built edaphosaurs with small heads and barrel-like bodies. *Cotylorhynchus,* the largest of the pelycosaurs, probably played the same rôle among the early Permian reptiles of North America that the pareiasaurs did in South Africa and Russia.

THE THERAPSIDS

Whereas the pelycosaurs were of late Pennsylvanian and early Permian age and are known largely from North America, the therapsids were of middle and late Permian and Triassic age and are known from all the continental regions, but especially from the Karroo sediments of South Africa. It appears likely that the therapsids had a pelycosaurian ancestry, but from the beginning of their history these reptiles followed evolutionary trends that led to the attainment of specializations much different from those reached by any other reptiles. These were the reptiles that took the road leading to the mammals, and some of them approached very closely the mammalian stage of organization.

As indicated above, there was a strong trend among the therapsids for the lateral temporal opening to become enlarged, so that in the advanced forms the upper boundary of the opening was formed by the parietal bone, not by the postorbital and squamosal bones. The quadrate and quadratojugal bones were reduced to very small elements, often loosely connected to the skull, as contrasted with the large quadrate in most reptiles. In the more advanced therapsids there was a secondary palate below the original reptilian palate, this new palate being formed by the premaxillary, maxillary, and palatine bones. It served to separate the nasal passage from the mouth, thereby increasing the efficiency of breathing, especially while the animal was feeding. The pterygoid bones were generally solidly fused to the brain case. .In the lower jaw the dentary bone tended to enlarge at the expense of the other jaw bones. In most therapsids there was a large notch in the angular bone, bordered below by a prominent flange. This character was inherited from the pelycosaurs, in which it was an adaptation for the insertion of strong pterygoid muscles for closing the jaws. The differentiation of the teeth progressed in the therapsids to high levels of development, with the advanced genera showing sharply contrasted incisors, canines, and cheek teeth. In many therapsids the occipital condyle became double, as in the mammals.

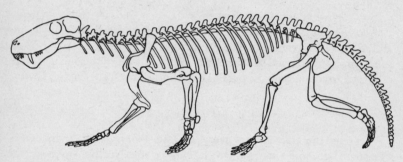

FIGURE 42. Skeleton of the gorgonopsian theriodont, *Lycaenops*, one-fourteenth natural size, illustrating the mammal-like characters and pose in an advanced therapsid skeleton.

In the postcranial skeleton there was frequently a considerable regional differentiation of the ribs and vertebrae, so that the neck was quite distinct from the body. The legs were generally "pulled in" beneath the body, with the elbows pointed more or less backward and the knees forward. The body was thus raised from the ground, so that the efficiency of locomotion was increased. This was a departure from the general sprawling pose so characteristic of the pelycosaurs. The scapula was a large bone in the shoulder girdle, and there were two coracoid elements. The ilium was expanded forward, and there was generally an elongated sacrum, making a strong attachment between the backbone and the pelvis. The feet were well formed and adapted to efficient walking and running over the dry ground.

Within this general plan the therapsids developed during Permian and Triassic times, and in evolving these reptiles followed two general lines of adaptive radiation. One of these therapsid lines was that of the anomodonts, containing the large tapinocephalians, frequently designated as the dinocephalians, and the widely spread dicynodonts; the other was the very mammal-like theriodonts.

TAPINOCEPHALIANS

The Permian tapinocephalians were in many ways the most archaic of the therapsids, and even though these reptiles showed certain therapsid adaptations, such as the expansion of the ilium and the general pose of the limbs, they retained various primitive characters of the pelycosaurs. For instance, they had no secondary palate, and their dentary bone was of moderate size. The particular characters distinctive of the tapinocephalians were their large size and the pachyostosis, or thickening, of the bones in the skull. Often the top of the head was rounded and elevated into a sort of dome or boss, in the middle of which was lodged a large pineal opening. These reptiles were massive animals that must frequently have weighed a thousand pounds or more in life.

In *Moschops,* a typical dinocephalian, the skull was high and short, and the teeth were undifferentiated and rather peg-like. It seems obvious that these teeth, set in comparatively short jaws, were adapted for an herbivorous diet. The shoulders were much higher than the pelvic region in this reptile, so that the back sloped, giraffe-fashion, from neck to tail. The limbs were heavy, and the feet were broad. *Moschops* and its relatives probably wandered over fairly dry uplands during the Permian period, feeding upon the available vegetation.

DICYNODONTS

The dicynodonts, the most successful of the therapsids if phylogenetic longevity, numbers of individuals, and the extent of distribution over continental areas are criteria of success, probably had a dinocephalian ancestry. They appeared in middle Permian times and evolved in a remarkably uniform structural pattern, as seen in *Dicynodon,* through the late Permian and the whole of the Triassic period. During late Permian times they were among the commonest of all reptiles, at least as indicated by the fossil record, and in the Triassic period they spread to all the continents, to enjoy a world-wide distribution.

The dicynodonts ranged in size from reptiles no more than a foot or so in length to large, massive animals, as big as the largest dinocephalians. The body was short and broad, and was supported by strong limbs, so posed that the animal was raised up from the ground in the usual therapsid fashion. The ilium was expanded and strong, and likewise the shoulder girdle was large and strong. The tail was short.

It is in the skull that the dicynodonts show their greatest specializations; certainly it was different from the skull in other therapsids. Although strong, the bones in the temporal region were thinned by an increase of the temporal openings, and by emargination along their lower borders, so that they formed long arches. Indeed the skull in the dicynodonts is noteworthy because of its open construction aı d the presence of long, bony bars rather than broad plate-like

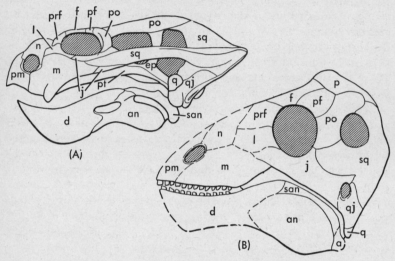

FIGURE 43. Therapsids or mammal-like reptiles from Permian sediments of the Karroo series of South Africa. (A) *Dicynodon,* a dicynodont, one-half natural size or less. (B) *Delphinognathus,* a dinocephalian, one-sixth natural size. For abbreviations, see page 449.

areas behind the eye. The front of the skull and the lower jaw were narrow and beak-like, and except for a pair of large, upper tusks in some of the skulls the teeth were reduced to tiny remnants or were completely absent. There can be little doubt but that the upper and the lower jaws were covered with horny beaks, like the beak in the modern turtles. In many of the dicynodonts the tusks are present in about half of the individuals, which indicates that these tusks were probably sexual characters, presumably present in the males and absent in the females, if our usual concept of the aggressive male and the coy female is valid. All in all this was a rather strange reptilian design, but nevertheless a very successful one. The dicynodonts were very probably herbivorous. One genus, *Lystrosaurus,* of Triassic age, appears to have been aquatic.

THERIODONTS

While the dinocephalians and the dicynodonts were evolving in their own clumsy ways the theriodonts were developing rapidly in a direction that was to lead directly to the mammals. These most mammal-like of the therapsids were small to large carnivorous reptiles, which appeared during middle Permian times and developed through the remainder of the Permian period and into the early and middle phases of the Triassic period. They are found in various parts of the Old World, but are most numerous and best exemplified in the Karroo beds of South Africa.

Some of the early theriodonts were the large titanosuchids, typified by the Permian genus *Jonkeria*. In this reptile the snout of the heavy head was elongated and provided with sharp teeth, including large incisors, behind which, on each side above and below there were long, piercing canines. The cheek teeth were comparatively small. The body in *Jonkeria* was heavy, and the limbs were very stout. Evidently this was a rather lumbering beast that probably preyed upon other large, lumbering Permian reptiles, such as the dinocephalians or the pareiasaurs.

However, most of the theriodonts were small to medium-sized therapsids, well developed for comparatively rapid movement in pursuit of their prey. *Cynognathus* can be described as a genus typical of these theriodonts. This lower Triassic therapsid was at its maximum size about as large as a big dog or a wolf. It had a rather large skull that in general form was vaguely dog-like, hence the name *Cynognathus*. The skull was elongated and rather narrow. Behind the eye there was an enlarged temporal opening, of which the parietal bone formed the upper portion, and within which very powerful muscles were located for closing the jaws. In the skull the maxillary bone was expanded to form a large plate on the side of the face, whereas in the mandible the dentary bone was so large as to form almost the entire body of the lower jaw, with the bones behind the dentary quite small and crowded.

The teeth were highly specialized and differentiated. In the front of the jaws, above and below, were small, peg-like incisors, obviously adapted for nipping. Behind the incisors was a gap, followed in both jaws by a greatly enlarged tooth, the canine. The canines were certainly for piercing and tearing, and they indicate the highly predaceous habits of *Cynognathus*. Behind the enlarged canines and separated from them by another gap were the cheek teeth or post-

canines, which in *Cynognathus* were limited in number to about
nine on each side and were specialized by the development of
accessory cusps on each tooth. These teeth were for chewing and
cutting the food, and they indicate that *Cynognathus* must have cut
its prey into comparatively small pieces before eating it, rather than

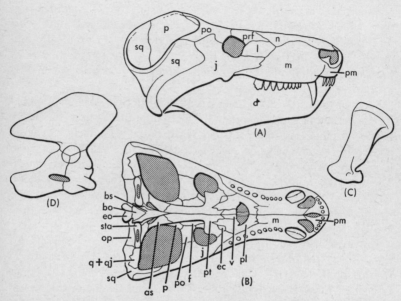

FIGURE 44. The lower Triassic mammal-like reptile, *Cynognathus*. (*A*) Lateral
view of the skull. (*B*) Palatal view of the skull. (*C*) Lateral view of the
scapula. (*D*) Lateral view of the pelvis. All about one-sixth natural size. For
abbreviations, see page 449. This figure shows particularly the enlarged temporal opening of the skull, the differentiated dentition with a large canine and
cusped cheek teeth, the large dentary forming the major portion of the lower
jaw, the spine along the front of the scapula, and the extended ilium of the
pelvis.

swallowing the food whole as do many reptiles. In this reptile there
was a well-developed secondary palate, which separated the nasal
passage from the mouth. The indication that *Cynognathus* com-
minuted its food, together with the evidence that the nasal passage
was separated from the mouth, show that this animal was very active.
Small pieces of meat would be quickly assimilated in the digestive
tract, and would quickly replenish an energy output that in this
animal must have been proportionately much greater than in the
"typical" reptile.

The quadrate bone in the skull and the articular bone in the lower jaw formed the hinge on which the jaws worked, but these bones were very small. The skull articulated to the backbone by a double condyle, formed by the exoccipital bones.

The vertebral column in *Cynognathus* was strongly differentiated into a cervical region with very small ribs, a dorsal region with large ribs, a lumbar region, again with small ribs, a sacrum involving several vertebrae, and a tail. Since the sacrum was elongated, the ilium was enlarged, mainly by a forward growth of the iliac blade, and this gave it a very mammalian appearance. The scapula was

Cynognathus

FIGURE 45. A cynodont, an advanced mammal-like reptile about the size of a large dog, of early Triassic age.

also advanced toward the mammalian condition in that its front border was everted or turned out. Here was the beginning of the scapular spine, so characteristic of the mammals.

The limbs were held beneath the body in *Cynognathus*, with the knee pointing forward and the elbow pointing backward to a considerable degree, a pose that increases the efficiency of locomotion in a four-footed animal. The feet were well formed, and adapted for walking by an equal development of the toes. In this animal there was no loss of the primitive phalangeal bones; rather some of the phalanges were greatly shortened. In some other theriodonts, however, there was commonly a reduction of phalangeal elements to the mammalian number of two in the thumb and great toe and three in all the other toes.

The various specializations that have been described for *Cynognathus* show that it was a very active carnivore. For a reptile it was getting close to the mammalian stage of development in many respects, and we wonder whether it was like the mammals in characters that are not indicated in these fossils. Did *Cynognathus* have a coat of hair? Did it have a fairly constant body temperature?

The theriodonts known as gorgonopsians, of which the Permian genus *Lycaenops* is typical, initiated many of the trends that were to culminate in the later theriodonts. Thus in these earlier theriodonts the dentary bone was large, but not so large as in *Cynognathus,* the teeth were differentiated but not highly specialized, there was as yet no secondary palate, the occipital condyle was single, and so on.

From the Permian gorgonopsians there evolved not only the Triassic cynodonts, like *Cynognathus,* but also, in another direction, the thero-cephalians of Permian and Triassic age. The earlier therocephalians, like the genus *Lycosuchus,* were in many respects as primitive as the gorgonopsians, but they did show certain advances such as the enlargement of the temporal opening and the reduction of the phalanges to the mammalian formula. The later therocephalians, like *Bauria,* carried some characters to a high degree of specialization. For instance, in *Bauria* there was no bar of bone separating the orbit from the temporal opening, which is the condition typical for primitive mammals. There is reason to think that the most highly developed theriodonts, the ictidosaurians, arose from a therocephalian stem.

THE ICTIDOSAURS

During the Triassic period a group of reptiles appeared that bridged the gap between the advanced theriodonts and the primitive mammals. They were the ictidosaurs of Triassic and early to middle Jurassic age, as completely intermediate between the reptiles and the mammals as were the seymouriamorphs between the amphibians and the reptiles.

In the ictidosaurs many of the characters that in the other therapsids had reached such a high state of perfection were carried even farther toward the mammalian condition. The temporal opening was very large indeed, and was confluent with the orbit. There was a great emphasis of certain skull bones, and there was a complete suppression of other bones, notably the prefrontals, the postfrontals, and the post-orbitals. However, the ictidosaurians retained the quadrate bone in the skull and the articular bone in the lower jaw, even though these elements were reduced to such small size that they were almost no longer functional. For this reason and perhaps no other the ictido-saurs are classified as reptiles. In the mammals the quadrate and articular bones have migrated from the articular region to the middle ear, where as we shall see they have been transformed into two of the bones concerned with transmitting vibrations from the eardrum to the inner ear. But since in the ictidosaurs the transformation of the quadrate and articular bones had not taken place, these animals can arbitrarily be placed within the reptiles. All of which indicates how academic is the question of where the reptiles leave off and the mammals begin.

Although the ictidosaurs as a group closed the gap between mammals and reptiles, some of these animals were highly specialized along lines independent of the stem mammals. For instance, the most completely known of the ictidosaurians, the tritylodonts, were

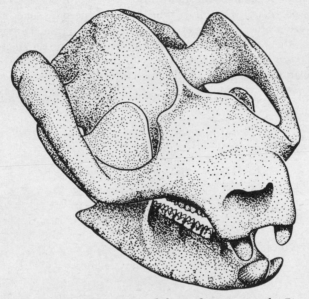

FIGURE 46. The skull and lower jaw of the ictidosaurian reptile, *Bienotherium*, about three-fourths natural size. This illustrates the strongly mammal-like nature of the skull, jaw, and dentition in this advanced mammal-like reptile.

in some ways rather rodent-like. These reptiles, typified by *Tritylodon* from South Africa, *Bienotherium* from western China, and *Oligokyphus* from England, were small animals, in which the skull had a high sagittal crest and huge zygomatic arches for the accommodation of very strong jaw muscles. The dentition was peculiar. There was a pair of enlarged anterior incisor teeth above and below, separated by a long gap or diastema from the cheek teeth. The cheek teeth, of which there were seven on each side, were rather square, and each tooth bore rows of cusps, arranged longitudinally. In the upper teeth there were three such rows to each tooth; in the lower teeth, two. The two rows of cusps in the lower teeth fitted in the grooves between the three rows of upper cusps. Evidently the lower jaw moved forward and backward when the jaws were closed, thus grinding food between the cusped teeth, in somewhat the same fashion as some modern rodents grind their food.

The ictidosaurs were almost across the threshold that separated reptiles from mammals, and in so evolving they had brought about the doom of the synapsids, and eventually of the reptiles, as dominant vertebrates. They established the foundation for the subsequent rise and triumph of the mammals, but this was not to take place for many millions of years. During a time lapse of perhaps one hundred million years after the rise of the first mammals from ictidosaurian ancestors the reptiles were to be supreme. They dominated the Mesozoic era completely, and it is with the long and involved story of reptilian glory that we shall now concern ourselves.

A Coal Forest

10 · Conquest of the Land

EARLY LAND-LIVING VERTEBRATES

To go back a little in our story, we recall that the Devonian period was a crucial time in the evolutionary history of the backboned animals, for it was then that the several classes of Pisces, of fishes in the very broad sense of the word, became well oriented along the lines of evolutionary development that they were to follow during subsequent geologic ages. It was the period of the first flowering of the vertebrates.

The Devonian period was an important time for other forms of life as well as for the vertebrates, for this was the age during which the plants established themselves on the lands of the earth. And although it is probable that invertebrates first ventured on the land in Silurian times, it was not until the Devonian period that animals without backbones became numerous and well adapted for land life. By late Devonian times primitive forests covered the lands, forming havens for various scorpions and spiders and ancient insects that scurried about over the ground or climbed into the green shelter of the plant life. We might say that the stage was set for the egress of vertebrates from their ancestral watery home.

As we have seen, the transition among vertebrates from life in the water to life on the land, the transition from fish to amphibian, took place at the very end of the Devonian period. With the opening of Carboniferous times the early land-living vertebrates were feeling their way into a new environment, where plants and insects and other forms of life offered new food supplies and the opportunities for new ways of living.

During the Mississippian period the amphibians enjoyed an initial dominance on the land that was the natural result of their position as the first and for the time being the only land-living vertebrates. There were no other animals to challenge them. But their complete dominance was short lived, because in Pennsylvanian times the reptiles arose to share the land with the amphibians. Although the reptiles, even in their most primitive manifestations, were generally more efficient and better adapted as land-living animals than the amphibians, they by no means suppressed their primitive but persistent predecessors. For a long time amphibians and reptiles lived side by side, and it is probable that many of the large labyrinthodonts were able to compete on more or less equal terms with their reptilian contemporaries. It was not until well after the beginning of the age of dinosaurs, when reptiles had advanced to comparatively high stages of development, that the large labyrinthodont amphibians finally vanished from the land faunas.

As might be expected, the proportion of amphibians is high in the early faunas of land-living vertebrates, but it decreases through Carboniferous and Permian times, in the progression from earlier to later vertebrate associations. For instance, the Pennsylvanian faunas of Linton, Ohio, of Mazon Creek, Illinois, of Joggins, Nova Scotia, and of Kounová in Czechoslovakia are composed almost entirely of amphibians or of fishes and amphibians, with reptiles constituting insignificant proportions of the assemblages. It is probable that the preponderance of amphibians in these faunas does not reflect a true picture of the times, because these were associations of swamp-dwelling animals, in which amphibians would naturally be predominant. Nevertheless it would appear that amphibians were very abundant in many of the Carboniferous land faunas. In this connection it should be mentioned that the lower Permian faunas of Texas, although rich in amphibians, are even richer in reptiles. In the later Permian faunas, for instance those of Europe, of Russia, and of South Africa, the reptiles are overwhelmingly predominant, whereas amphibians are comparatively scarce. Some of these differences may be the result of differences in environments, but, allowing for this, it is probable that they do reflect to a considerable degree the expansion of the reptiles during late Paleozoic times.

ENVIRONMENTS OF EARLY LAND-LIVING VERTEBRATES

What were the conditions that led to the divergent evolutionary trends among amphibians and reptiles at the end of the Paleozoic era? Why did the amphibians predominate until about the beginning of the Permian period, after which the reptiles became the ruling land vertebrates?

Probably in Mississippian and Pennsylvanian times lands were low all over the earth. These were periods of uniformity in topography and in climates. Dense forests of primitive plants covered the lands, and it would appear that tropical environments extended from the equatorial regions to high latitudes in both the northern and the southern hemispheres. Swamps were abundant. This was the great age of coal formation.

Such environments would have been favorable to the adaptive radiation of amphibians. It is significant that during Carboniferous times the transition from ancestral crossopterygian fishes to land-living amphibians was completed.

With the close of the Pennsylvanian period and the advent of the Permian period a change of environments took place. There were uplifts of the continental areas. The topography of the land became more varied than it had been previously, and with this development there were correlative changes in climate. The uniformity so characteristic of the Carboniferous age gave way to varied climatic conditions and consequently to varied environments. Local environments ranged from streams, ponds, and swamps to dry uplands. There was probably an alternation of wet and dry seasons taking place each year. In these varied environments of the Permian period the reptiles became the dominant land-living vertebrates.

THE DISTRIBUTION OF UPPER PALEOZOIC VERTEBRATE FAUNAS

Although the invasion of the land by vertebrates took place with the transition from Devonian to Mississippian times, there is virtually no record of what happened immediately after this event. The

Mississippian was seemingly a time of extensive marine inundations, and very few continental deposits have survived from that age to give us a record of what life was like on the land. The marine limestones of the Mississippian period preserve an extensive record of invertebrate faunas, with here and there the remains of fishes, but except for a few scattered localities there are no fossils of land-living vertebrates from this portion of the geologic record.

With the advent of the Pennsylvanian period conditions changed, and there were broad continental areas where extensive swamps and dense tropical forests of primitive plants covered the land. Consequently in the continental sediments of the Pennsylvanian period there are various fossil localities at which early land-living vertebrates have been found. Among the earliest of the Pennsylvanian vertebrate faunas are those already mentioned—the faunas of Joggins, Nova Scotia, Linton, Ohio, and Mazon Creek, Illinois, all of middle Pennsylvanian age. At Linton the fossils are found in a cannel coal, at Mazon Creek, in concretionary nodules. The preservation of the fossils at Joggins is particularly interesting. Here are many trunks of ancient trees, standing upright in the sediments, just as they stood in life. It would appear that these trees died and decayed while they were still standing. Mud and sand washed into the hollow tree trunks, and in many of these natural coffins were buried the skeletons of early amphibians, often beautifully and completely preserved.

In some of the English coal fields are also found early fossil amphibians.

In the upper Pennsylvanian sediments the record of early land-living vertebrates becomes even more complete than it was in the earlier sediments. The Pittsburgh faunas of Pennsylvania, West Virginia and Ohio give us a glimpse of varied amphibians and reptiles directly antecedent to the Dunkard faunas that occupied this area during early Permian times. Similar faunas occur at Nýřany and Kounová, Czechoslovakia, and the many resemblances of these faunas to the late Pennsylvanian faunas of North America indicate that there must have been close relationships between the Eurasiatic and North American continents at that time. Certainly it would seem that there was a free interchange of land-living vertebrates between these areas.

The upper Pennsylvanian land faunas, valuable as they are as a record of early terrestrial vertebrates, are restricted as compared with the faunas of the Permian. This was the period in geologic history when land-living vertebrates enjoyed their first great evolutionary expansion, when the varied land surfaces, the diverse climates, and probably the alternation of seasons gave scope for a wide adaptive radiation of the amphibians and the reptiles, especially the latter, into many differing environments. This was the period when the reptiles became the truly dominant land animals, even though the labyrinthodont amphibians remained as important constituents of the faunas. In truth, this was the beginning of the Age of Reptiles.

The finest lower Permian faunas are those of the red beds of northern Texas, Oklahoma, and New Mexico. In Texas a sequence of richly fossiliferous formations extends up from the Pennsylvanian-Permian boundary. The lower part of this sequence is designated as the Wichita series, the upper part as the Clear Fork, and within the successive horizons of these series it is possible to trace the progressive evolution of various lower Permian amphibians and reptiles. It is in this sequence that much of the history of labyrinthodont evolution is revealed. The record of the cotylosaurian reptiles is also extensive, and that of the pelycosaurs outlines virtually the entire evolutionary development of these reptiles. The New Mexico sediments, known as the Abo and the Cutler formations, are generally correlative with the Texas sediments. However, the evidence indicates that there was a seaway between the two regions during Permian times, so that the animals were physically separated from each other during considerable portions of their histories.

The lower Permian faunas of other continents are less well documented than the faunas of Texas, but they give some evidence of what land life was like in other regions. In Autun, France, a fauna is found that is in many ways similar to the fauna of the Texas red beds, and similar lower Permian fossils are found in Germany, especially around Dresden. Some fossils are found in southern Brazil and some in northern India.

With the uppermost horizons of the Clear Fork series of Texas and related sediments in this and adjacent regions, the record of Permian land life in North America virtually comes to an end. Except for some very interesting series of middle Permian footprints found in the Coconino sandstone of the Grand Canyon region, there is nothing that gives us any clues to the history of land-living vertebrates in North America during the later portions of the Permian period. For a continuation of the story it is necessary, therefore, to turn to other continental areas.

In two regions of the Old World middle and upper Permian sediments are exposed in continuous and unparalleled series, from which extensive collections of vertebrates have been made. One of these regions is in northern Russia, where sediments of the Dvina series are exposed, and the other is in the Karroo Desert of South Africa, the locale of the famous Karroo series. The Dvina sediments form a continuous sequence ranging through the middle and upper Permian period and into the lower portion of the Triassic period. The series has been divided into five zones, of which the first three are of middle Permian age, the fourth of upper Permian age, and the fifth of lower Triassic age. The Karroo series, one of the classic stratigraphic sequences of earth history, also ranges through the Permian and Triassic periods, in this case covering the complete extent of both these geologic ages. It begins with the Dwyka and Ecca beds of lower Permian age, passes upward into the Lower Beaufort beds of middle and upper Permian age, and continues in the Upper Beaufort and Stormberg beds of Triassic age. These sediments succeed each other without any appreciable breaks, and show a gradation from the Permian into the Triassic period—one of the few places in the world where such a passage between two major geologic systems can be seen.

The faunas of the Permian of Russia and South Africa show many close similarities that indicate an intimate relationship between these regions during the final stages of Paleozoic history. Evidently there were continuous land connections between the two areas, and similar ecological and climatic conditions, so that land animals could migrate back and forth. The faunas were predominantly of the "upland" type, consisting for the most part of animals that lived on open plains. These are the faunas that show the greatest development of the therapsids, the mammal-like reptiles, particularly in the South African area. In the Karroo there is an almost overwhelming array of therapsids—dinocephalians, dicynodonts, and theriodonts—through thousands of feet of thickness of the Beaufort beds. Although the therapsids make up the bulk of the Karroo and Dvina faunas, there are also other prominent constituents, notably the large cotylosaurs known as pareiasaurs, and labyrinthodont amphibians.

It is from these two regions that much of our knowledge of middle and late Permian vertebrates has been derived. Other upper Permian localities are scattered, and for the most part have yielded but fragmentary faunas. In central Europe are the classic Kupferschiefer and Zechstein of Germany, predominantly marine beds coming above the lower Permian Rothliegende. In southern Scotland is the Cutties Hillock locality, from which a small fauna has been recovered.

Other localities that might be mentioned, all of upper Permian age, are the Ruhuhu and Tanga beds of East Africa, the Chiweta beds

CORRELATION OF UPPER PALEOZOIC VERTEBRATE-BEARING SEDIMENTS

		North America	England and Europe		Russia		S. Africa Karroo	E. Africa, etc.	Other Continents
Permian	Upper		Cutties Hillock	Zechstein	Dvina	IV	Lower Beaufort	Ruhuhu Tanga Chiweta Mangwa	Upper Newcastle coals, Australia Bijori, India
	Middle		Magnesian limestone	Kupferschiefer		III			
						II			
	Lower	Clear Fork / Abo-Cutler	Autun	Rothliegende		I	Ecca		
		Wichita / Dunkard	Branau				Dwyka		
Pennsylvanian	Upper	Pittsburgh Danville	Nýrany, Kounová						
	Middle	Linton Mazon Creek ·Joggins	English coal fields						
	Lower		Scottish coal fields						
Mississippian		Mauch Chunk Albert Mines (N. B.) Mississippi Valley	Edinburgh coal field, Scotland Bristol, England						

of Nyassaland, the Bijori beds of central India, and the upper New-
castle coals of Australia.

The correlative relationships of the Permo-Carboniferous vertebrate-bearing sediments, so briefly described in the foregoing paragraphs, are indicated by the accompanying chart.

VERTEBRATES AT THE CLOSE OF PALEOZOIC TIMES

The broad uplifts of continental land masses in Pennsylvanian and
Permian times resulted in the firm establishment of the vertebrates
upon the land, their differentiation into varied lines of evolution, and
their wide distribution throughout the world. So it was that by the
close of the Permian period the land was dominated by cold-blooded

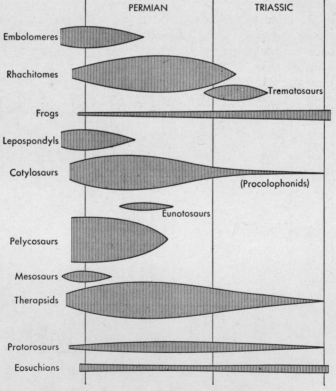

FIGURE 47. Range and relative abundance of tetrapods within and beyond the
Permian period.

tetrapods, by amphibians, and particularly by reptiles. The labyrinthodonts had passed the zenith of their evolutionary history and
were on the decline toward a secondary return to the water. They
were numerous and still successful as land-living animals, but they
were gradually giving way to the more aggressive reptiles. The
primitive reptiles, the cotylosaurs, had virtually completed their
evolutionary development and, except for one small remnant that
was to continue into and through the Triassic period, were at the
point of extinction. The pelycosaurs, too, had gone through their
evolutionary history, but were succeeded by their descendants, the
therapsids. The mammal-like reptiles were, at the close of the
Permian period, in the full flush of their expansion, and they were
destined to continue and to reach great heights of progressive adaptation in the subsequent Triassic period.

Finally there were various other reptiles, of small consequence in
Permian history, but significant as ancestors of reptiles that were to
be very important and numerous in later periods of the earth's story.
These were the protorosaurs, probable ancestors of the Mesozoic
plesiosaurs and their relatives; the eunotosaurs, perhaps the ancestors
of the turtles; and the eosuchians, certainly the ancestors of the
numerous diapsid reptiles—the thecodonts, crocodilians, the flying
reptiles, and the dinosaurs that were to be the rulers of the Mesozoic
era.

Coelophysis

II · Early Ruling Reptiles

THE ADVENT OF A NEW AGE

Up to this point the history of the backboned animals has been outlined from its early stages, in Ordovician, Silurian, and Devonian times, to a climax at the end of the Permian period. Then highly varied fishes inhabited the streams and the ponds of the continents, and the oceans that surrounded the lands, numerous and diverse representatives of the earliest land-living vertebrates, the amphibians, lived in the watery and swampy environments of the land areas, and the reptiles, in those times the most advanced of the terrestrial vertebrates, were establishing the pattern of dominance that was to characterize their history for many millions of years to come. Some excursions have been made into the later history of certain vertebrates during the telling of the story, but on the whole the account has been largely concerned with the animals that lived before the close of the Paleozoic era.

We now come to a new phase in the history of vertebrate life, the development of backboned animals during the Triassic period, the earliest subdivision of the Mesozoic era. The Triassic period was important as a time of transition between the old life of the Paleozoic era and the progressive and highly varied new life of the Mesozoic. Many Triassic fishes, amphibians, and reptiles were developing in the directions of future vertebrate evolution; at the same time certain elements in the Triassic faunas represented the holdovers of persistent forms from Paleozoic times.

Among the land-living vertebrates, the holdovers from the Permian that continued into and through the Triassic period were the labyrinthodont amphibians, certain cotylosaur reptiles, the eosuchians, the therapsids, and the protorosaurs. The labyrinthodonts, in the form of the stereospondyls, enjoyed a final burst of prolific evolution during the Triassic period before they became extinct. The progressive therapsids, particularly the very mammal-like theriodonts, reached advanced stages of structural development before they too disappeared, toward the close of Triassic times. The cotylosaurs of the Triassic, the procolophonids, represent on the other hand an interesting remnant of little evolutionary importance. Finally, the Triassic protorosaurs, to be discussed below, and the eosuchians represent comparatively small groups of reptiles, continuing from equally restricted Permian ancestors.

As contrasted with these holdovers from the Permian period, there was a great array of new land-living vertebrates, many of them the ancestors of flourishing evolutionary lines that were destined to continue through the Mesozoic era, and sometimes on through the remainder of geologic time right up to the present day. Thus ancestors of the frogs appeared during Triassic times, the progenitors of a group of vertebrates that has been and is singularly successful. Likewise, the first representatives of another very successful group, the turtles, made their appearance in the Triassic period. This was a period when various highly specialized marine reptiles were entering upon their long histories. For instance, the first ichthyosaurs are found in rocks of Triassic age. The placodonts and the nothosaurs also lived during Triassic times, and from the nothosaurs, at the very end of the Triassic period, the plesiosaurs arose. Rhynchocephalians were widely distributed over the continental regions of the earth during the Triassic period, and, although seemingly never very numerous, these reptiles have been remarkably persistent, even to the present day.

But of all the new animals that appeared during the Triassic period, perhaps the most important were the thecodonts and the ictidosaurs. The thecodonts were the first reptiles known as archosaurs, and they were the direct ancestors of the reptiles that were to be so completely dominant during the later periods of Mesozoic history, namely, the crocodilians, the flying reptiles, and particularly the numerous dinosaurs. The thecodonts set the archosaurian pattern that was extraordinarily successful for more than one hundred million years.

The ictidosaurs were, as we have seen, the direct ancestors of the mammals. Although the mammalian descendants of ictidosaurs were destined to play a very small evolutionary rôle while the dinosaurs were dominant during the remainder of the Mesozoic era, they came into their own with the advent of Cenozoic times.

INTRODUCING THE THECODONTS

The diapsid reptiles are divisible into two large subclasses, each composed of several orders. One of these, the Lepidosauria, contains the most primitive of the diapsids, the Eosuchia, and in addition the Rhynchocephalia, and the Squamata, or lizards and snakes. The other, the Archosauria, contains the Thecodontia, the Crocodilia or crocodiles, the Pterosauria or flying reptiles, and two dinosaurian orders, the Saurischia and the Ornithischia. Of these two subclasses, the archosaurians are especially important to the student of evolution, and among the archosaurs the thecodonts, the stem archosaurians, are of particular concern to us at this place.

The thecodont reptiles were comparatively limited in their adaptive radiation and in the numbers of their genera and species, and they were very definitely limited in their geologic history. These reptiles appeared at the beginning of the Triassic period and they became extinct at the close of Triassic times, thereby enjoying the distinction of being the only reptilian order limited in its phylogenetic history to one geologic period. Yet brief as was the history of the thecodonts, it was an evolutionary development of great consequence.

THE PSEUDOSUCHIANS

The thecodonts can be divided into two suborders, the Pseudo-suchia and the Phytosauria. Of these two groups the pseudosuchians were the more primitive of the thecodonts, and some of them may be regarded as exemplifying in effect the basic plan for all of the archosaurians. *Euparkeria,* from the lower Triassic of South Africa, represents very nicely the primitive thecodont structure.

Euparkeria was a small reptile, perhaps three feet in length, and was very lightly built. The bones were delicately constructed, and many of them were hollow, like bird bones. This little reptile was bipedal; it walked on comparatively long, strong, bird-like hind legs,

whereas the fore limbs were relatively small and obviously of little
use for locomotion. Rather they were used for grasping, particularly
as an aid to feeding. The animal was pivoted at the hips, and there
was a long tail that served as a sort of counterbalance to the weight
of the body. The pelvis was in many respects of primitive form,
but even in the early pseudosuchians it showed the beginnings of
specializations that were to become increasingly marked in later
archosaurians. Thus the ilium was somewhat expanded, and in the
ischium and the pubis there was a downward growth whereby these

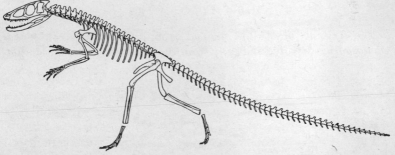

FIGURE 48. Skeleton of a generalized thecodont reptile, *Hesperosuchus*, an
animal about four feet in length.

became transformed from primitive plate-like bones into rather slender, rod-like elements. In the shoulder girdle, the scapula and
coracoid were the dominant bones, whereas the other pectoral elements were greatly reduced.

The skull, like the rest of the skeleton, was lightly constructed.
It was narrow and deep, with a large eye and two large temporal
openings on each side. It was further lightened by the development
of openings in front of the eye, the antorbital openings. Such fenes-
trations were quite typical of almost all the archosaurians. Finally,
there was a large opening in the side of the lower jaw, again a
character that was carried through archosaurian phylogeny. There
were no teeth on the palate, but there was a full array of sharp teeth
around the margins of the jaws, in the premaxillary and maxillary
bones of the skull, and in.the dentary bone of the lower jaw. These
teeth were set in sockets—the thecodont type of tooth implantation
so characteristic of the archosaurs.

Some of the pseudosuchians retained this primitive archosaurian
plan. Thus *Ornithosuchus* of Europe and *Hesperosuchus* of North
America, both upper Triassic genera, adhered to the pattern estab-

lished by *Euparkeria*. These reptiles were characterized by two rows of armor plates down the middle of the back, a common character among the pseudosuchians.

The development of armor reached an extreme in some of the later quadrupedal pseudosuchians, as in the small genus *Aetosaurus* of the upper Triassic of Europe, and the large reptiles *Typothorax* and *Desmatosuchus* of the upper Triassic of North America. These reptiles were literally encased with heavy plates that covered their bodies, making them well-nigh impregnable to attack.

THE PHYTOSAURS

The Triassic phytosaurs, named from the characteristic genus *Phytosaurus*, departed radically from the ancestral archosaurian pat-

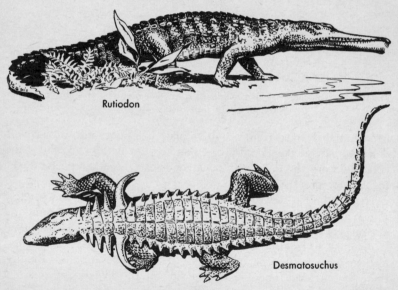

Rutiodon

Desmatosuchus

FIGURE 49.   Thecodont reptiles.   *Rutiodon* was a phytosaur, *Desmatosuchus* was a pseudosuchian.   These were large reptiles, ten feet or more in length.

tern that has been described above, for these reptiles trended toward large size at an early stage in their history, and correlatively they returned secondarily to a four-footed pose, as had some of the armored pseudosuchians. The skull and the body became elongated and very crocodilian-like. Rather it would be better to say that the crocodiles subsequently became phytosaur-like, for the phytosaurs developed special adaptations that were later imitated by the crocodiles.

The phytosaurs, such as *Rutiodon*, were highly predaceous, aggressive reptiles that lived in streams and lakes, and preyed upon fishes or any animals that they could catch. The front of the skull and the lower jaws were elongated and studded with sharp teeth. Unlike the crocodiles, however, the nostrils in the phytosaurs were set far back, just in front of the eyes, and in many phytosaurs were raised upon a volcano-like eminence that protruded above the level of the skull roof. Consequently these reptiles could float down stream with only the nostrils exposed, which was most advantageous to a water-living predator.

The legs and feet were strong, for progression on land, and although the front legs were large they were smaller than the hind legs, thus revealing the ultimate bipedal ancestry of these reptiles. The body was protected by heavy bony scutes, which in life must have been covered with horny epidermis. All in all, the phytosaurs were strikingly similar in appearance to modern crocodilians, and it seems reasonable to think that their habits were likewise crocodilian-like. They were the dominant reptiles of upper Triassic times, and some of them reached gigantic proportions.

THE FIRST DINOSAURS

Although the Mesozoic era was the Age of Dinosaurs, it was not until late in Triassic times that the first dinosaurs appeared. They became well established during the later phases of Triassic history, but even so they were not the dominant land animals that they were to be during the Jurassic and Cretaceous periods.

The first dinosaurs were saurischians, belonging to the suborder Theropoda. They were well represented by the North American genus, *Coelophysis*, in recent years made known by extraordinarily complete and beautifully preserved fossil skeletons, found in the upper Triassic sediments of northern New Mexico. *Coelophysis* was an animal about eight feet in length, so lightly built (the bones were hollow) that in life it probably did not weigh more than forty or fifty pounds. It was strictly a bipedal reptile, with the hind legs very strong and bird-like and well adapted for walking, and with the short front limbs bearing mobile hands that must have been useful for grasping and tearing food. The body was balanced at the hips, and the tail was long and slender. The neck was rather long, and it carried at its end a delicately constructed skull equipped with sharp teeth.

From this account it is apparent that *Coelophysis* inherited the basic archosaurian features that had been established during early Triassic times by the primitive thecodont reptiles. Beyond these characters, however, were the structural modifications that made *Coelophysis* a theropod dinosaur. The skull was long and narrow with large temporal and preorbital fenestrae, in which respects it had developed features that were to be particularly characteristic of the later theropod dinosaurs. The jaws were provided with sharp, serrated, laterally compressed teeth, set in deep sockets. These teeth indicate that *Coelophysis* was strongly carnivorous, probably preying upon small or medium-sized reptiles.

The pelvis is a key to dinosaurian relationships, and *Coelophysis* demonstrates an early example of the saurischian type of pelvis. In this dinosaur the ilium was expanded fore and aft and there was a long sacral attachment involving several vertebrae. From the ilium on each side the pubis extended forward and down, and the ischium extended backward and down. Both these bones were long, the pubis especially so, and their juncture with the ilium was effected by bony processes rather than by a solid attachment, so that the socket or acetabulum for reception of the ball-like head of the femur was open or perforate, not closed as in the more primitive thecodonts.

Coelophysis probably represents the basic adaptations of the theropod dinosaurs, of reptiles adjusted to a life on the dry uplands, where the ability to run fast and move quickly was of prime importance, not only for the capture of food in the form of small animals but also for escape from enemies. From such a beginning the later saurischian dinosaurs had their phylogenetic growth.

Coelophysis and its carnivorous relatives were not the only dinosaurs of the Triassic, for even in this early stage of dinosaurian history some of the derived types of saurischians had appeared. Of particular interest are the rather specialized saurischians known as prosauropods, which, though clearly of theropod relationships, show strong trends toward the giant sauropod dinosaurs of the Jurassic period. The genus *Plateosaurus* is especially characteristic. This dinosaur was in many ways an enlarged model of *Coelophysis*, perhaps twenty feet in length, but in evolving into a large reptile it had lost many of the delicate features of the more primitive theropods. The bones were no longer hollow as they were in the smaller dinosaurs, because the weight of the body had increased to such an extent that hollow bones, though comparatively strong for a small animal, were not

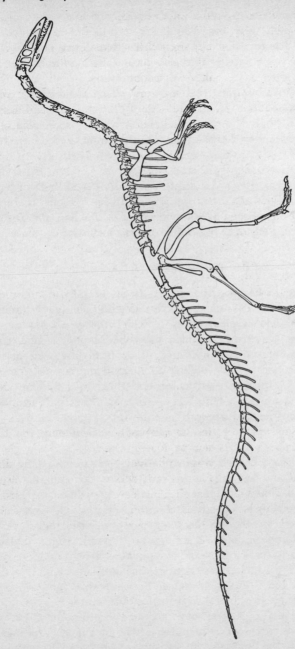

FIGURE 50. Skeleton of the upper Triassic theropod, *Coelophysis*, illustrating the structure in an early and generally primitive dinosaur. About eight feet in length.

sufficiently strong for an animal of this size. The legs were heavy, and the hind feet were broad and less bird-like than the feet of *Coelophysis*. The fore limbs were secondarily enlarged and it seems likely that *Plateosaurus* was able to walk on all fours as well as on the hind legs alone. The skull was comparatively small and light, but the teeth were blunt and flattened, not sharp, meat-eating teeth. Obviously *Plateosaurus* was a plant-eating dinosaur. This dinosaur was widely distributed during late Triassic times; its remains have been found in central Germany, in South Africa, and in western China.

This glimpse at *Coelophysis* and *Plateosaurus* gives us a preview of dinosaurian evolution and indicates the approximate state of dinosaurian development at the end of Triassic times. Briefly, theropod dinosaurs were established as components of the faunas, and already these théropods were evolving along diverse evolutionary lines.

THE PROTOROSAURS

The protorosaurs had their beginnings in the Permian period probably as early derivatives from the cotylosaurs, and continued through Triassic times. The Permian forms, of which the genus *Araeoscelis* is characteristic, were rather small, lizard-like reptiles (again this oft-repeated comparison with lizards) that probably lived in the undergrowth of that period, feeding upon small reptiles and insects. The pelvis was a plate-like structure, and the euryapsid skull was characterized by an upper temporal opening on either side, bounded below by a very deep squamosal bone.

In Triassic times the protorosaurs followed several lines of adaptive radiation. In the late Triassic of North America was the genus *Trilophosaurus*, an enlarged version of *Araeoscelis*, in which the skull was very deep and the jaws were provided with teeth that were transversely broadened into chisel-like blades. We can only speculate as to the food of this late protorosaur; probably it was a plant-eater, and the blade-like teeth were used for chopping vegetation.

In central Europe is found a strange protorosaur, *Tanystropheus*, noted particularly for its grotesquely elongated neck, in which each vertebra was greatly lengthened—giraffe fashion, an adaptation difficult to understand. (Recent evidence indicates that *Tanystropheus* may be an ancient lizard, rather than a protorosaur.)

These widely divergent specializations in the protorosaurs of Triassic times may represent a final burst among animals that were competing with the burgeoning diapsids. If so, the protorosaurs lost out. They became extinct at the close of the Triassic period, whereas the diapsids, especially the archosaurs, rose to ever greater heights of reptilian evolution.

END OF THE TRIASSIC

The association of Paleozoic holdovers and of new progressive forms in the Triassic faunas gave to these assemblages a distinctive, heterogeneous appearance that sets them off from the faunas preceding and following them. Indeed, the mixture of labyrinthodont amphibians and cotylosaurs with progressive mammal-like reptiles and archosaurs, including the early dinosaurs, was a meeting of the old and the new that involved various cross-currents of struggle and competition. This was truly a time of transition.

In the course of the competition between these varied groups of tetrapods some were bound to fall by the wayside, so that during and at the end of Triassic times there were rather extensive extinctions among the amphibians and reptiles. In general the progressive types prevailed, and the archaic forms disappeared under the pressure of competition from highly developed animals with which they were unable to contend.

As will be shown later on, the end of the Cretaceous period was a time of broad extinctions, when five orders of reptiles, containing numerous genera and species, were completely effaced. It is not so generally realized that the close of the Triassic period was also a time of great extinctions, when one large order of amphibians and at least four orders of reptiles disappeared. Perhaps the extinction of genera and species was not so great in late Triassic times as at the end of the Cretaceous period, but the suppression of several orders of tetrapods must be viewed as a series of evolutionary events of considerable significance.

In the first place, the close of the Triassic period saw the disappearance of the widely distributed and numerous stereospondylous labyrinthodonts, certainly a successful group of Triassic tetrapods. Their exit was comparatively sudden, complete, and dramatic. The cotylosaurian reptiles of the Triassic, unlike the labyrinthodonts, were a mere remnant of their Permian forebears, so that their passing at the end of Triassic times was a matter of small consequence. Nevertheless it marked the extinction of an order of reptiles that had been upon the earth for many millions of years. The protorosaurs, likewise, were a small group of relatively small importance in Triassic faunas, but again their extinction at the close of the Triassic period removed still another order of reptiles from the earth. The thecodonts can be regarded in a somewhat different light. These were progressive reptiles that disappeared at the close of the Triassic period, because

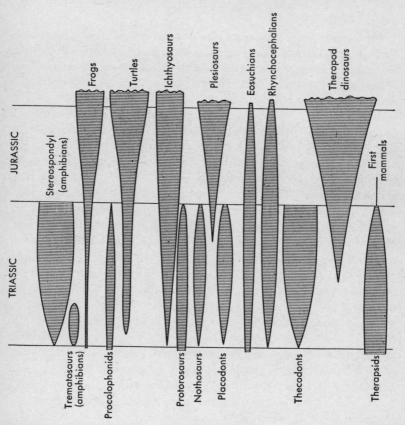

FIGURE 51. Range and relative abundance of tetrapods within and beyond the Triassic period.

of competition from the new reptiles of which they were the ancestors. In a similar fashion, most of the mammal-like reptiles, which disappeared even before the close of the Triassic period, vanished because of the highly progressive nature of their descendants. They evolved themselves into oblivion. One group of therapsids, the dicynodonts, continued to the end of the Triassic, when they seemingly were caught in the wave of extinction that affected various other tetrapod groups.

With the extinction of the labyrinthodonts, cotylosaurs, protorosaurs, therapsids, and thecodonts at the end of Triassic times the stage was set for a new chapter of Mesozoic history. Tetrapod evolution was oriented along new and progressive lines of great variety. For the next hundred million years there were to be giants on the earth.

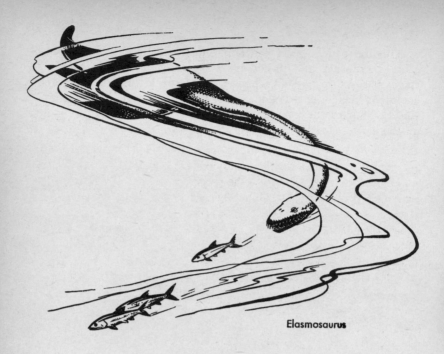

Elasmosaurus

12 · Marine Reptiles

TETRAPOD ADAPTATIONS TO LIFE IN THE SEA

It might be logical, after having discussed the thecodont reptiles and the early dinosaurs in the last chapter, to proceed to a consideration of their descendants, the dominant dinosaurs of Jurassic and Cretaceous times. Instead it is proposed to postpone the description of dinosaurian evolution while some attention is given to certain other reptilian groups that lived during the Mesozoic era, the reptiles that swam in the oceans and those that flew in the air, where they dominated their respective environments almost as completely as the dinosaurs dominated the land. In this chapter we shall be concerned with the marine reptiles.

The Triassic period marked the first time during the evolution of the vertebrates that land-living tetrapods turned in any appreciable numbers to a life lived in the sea. Since then this trend has been several times repeated, but in the Triassic period it was something new in vertebrate history. Of course many amphibians of late Paleozoic and Triassic times were aquatic, but few of the amphibians were marine; the first widely developed marine tetrapods were reptiles.

During their long evolutionary history the tetrapods had freed themselves from an aquatic existence, to become, as reptiles, animals that throughout their entire life history were completely independent of the water. Now some of them went back to the water, and all the various adaptations that had made reptiles efficient and independent land-living animals must needs be modified. These animals no longer had to contend with the problems of gravity or desiccation; no longer did they have to propel themselves across a dry land surface. Rather, we might say, they assumed the old problems with which their fish ancestors had contended many millions of years past—the problems of buoyancy, of propulsion through the water, and of reproduction away from the land.

The reptiles had efficient lungs. These lungs were not abandoned when reptiles went to sea, but rather were used for breathing, in place of the gills that had long since been lost. The reptiles had legs and feet. These were transformed into paddles, similar in function to the fins of the fish. The old fish tail had long since disappeared, so that some of the marine reptiles evolved substitute tails for propulsion, tails that imitated the fish tail to an astonishing degree. The old fish method of reproduction by eggs viable in sea water had been abandoned, so the marine reptiles, many of them unable to come out on the land, developed substitute methods, such as live birth of their young, for continuing their kind in an environment where there was no place to lay an egg in a protecting nest. It can thus be seen that among these reptiles there was a reversal in the trend of evolution—from distant aquatic fish ancestors, through intermediate land-living amphibian and reptile ancestors, to aquatic reptilian descendants.

THE ICHTHYOSAURS

The ichthyosaurs, in many respects the most highly specialized of the marine reptiles, appeared in middle Triassic times. Their advent into the geologic history of the reptiles was sudden and dramatic; there are no clues in pre-Triassic sediments as to the possible ancestors of the ichthyosaurs. It is only through an interpretation of the anatomical structures of these highly specialized reptiles that we are able to make some deductions as to their probable origin, which undoubtedly was from cotylosaurian ancestors. It may be that between the basic cotylosaurian stock and the first ichthyosaurs there were connecting links related in a general way to some of the aquatic pelycosaurs, such as the ophiacodonts.

The ichthyosaurs adhered closely throughout their history to a single pattern of adaptation so that the description of one genus of ichthyosaur applies in most respects to a majority of the other genera. The genus *Ichthyosaurus* from the Jurassic sediments of many widely separated localities around the world serves very well as a charac-

Ichthyosaurus

FIGURE 52.   Ichthyosaurs like this, similar to modern porpoises in size and habits, lived in the oceans of the world during Jurassic and Cretaceous times.

teristic member of the group.   Its remains are frequently found in black shales, in which not only the bones but also the body outline are occasionally preserved; therefore we have definite information as to the body shape and some of the soft parts in this interesting reptile.   From such fossils we know that *Ichthyosaurus* was a fish-like reptile, ranging up to ten feet or more in length.   It had a stream-lined body, increasing in size from the head to a point not far behind the shoulder region and then decreasing uniformly from here back to the tail.   There was no neck in the true sense of the word, and the back of the elongated head merged into the body without a break of the streamlining, as is essential in a fast-swimming vertebrate. The four legs were modified into paddles, and at the posterior end of the body there was a caudal fin, strikingly similar in shape to the caudal fin of many fishes.   In addition, as shown by imprints in the rock, there was a fleshy dorsal fin, a new structure to take the place of the bony dorsal fish fin.

From this it is apparent that *Ichthyosaurus* was essentially like a big fish in its mode of life, and the various adaptations that were described in a previous chapter as advantageous for the fast-swimming fishes can be cited at this place as being applicable to the ichthyosaurs. In short, these animals moved through the water by the rhythmic oscillation of the body, the muscular waves going from the front to the back and then being transmitted to the tail to scull the animal through the water. The four paddles were used as balancers, to control movements up and down through the water, to aid in steering, and to assist in braking. The dorsal fin was a stabilizer to prevent rolling and side slip. In the shape of the body and the caudal fin, the ichthyosaurs showed many similarities to some of the very speedy fishes, such as modern mackerel or tuna, so it would seem obvious that these reptiles were fast swimmers, pursuing their prey through the wide expanses of Mesozoic seas.

It may be useful to note some of the details of various tetrapod structures that were modified in *Ichthyosaurus*. Since this reptile was buoyed up by the water, the vertebrae had lost their interlocking joints and were simplified as flattened discs, bearing neural spines. The double-headed ribs articulated to these discs and flared out to form a body that was deeply rounded in cross-section. Posteriorly the backbone turned down suddenly, to occupy the lower lobe of the fleshy tail fin; hence the tail in the ichthyosaurs was of the reversed heterocercal type. The bones of the limbs were shortened, while the wrist and ankle bones and the bones of the fingers and toes were modified into flattened hexagonal elements, closely appressed to each other. The bones of the fingers were increased in number (hyperphalangy) and often there was an increase in the rows of phalanges (hyperdactyly), thereby adding to the length and width of the paddle. In life the whole structure was enclosed within a continuous sheath of skin.

As noted above, the skull was elongated, principally by a lengthening of the jaws. The jaws were provided with numerous teeth, which had the labyrinthine structure that was so characteristic of the labyrinthodont amphibians and the primitive cotylosaurian reptiles, and this is one clue as to the ultimate ancestry of the ichthyosaurs. The enormous eye is evidence that the ichthyosaurs depended very largely on the sense of vision. The nostrils, as is so common in aquatic tetrapods, were set far back on the top of the skull, thereby facilitating breathing when the ichthyosaur came to the surface. The back of the skull was compressed, and there was a single upper temporal opening, bounded below by the postfrontal and supratemporal bones—the parapsid condition.

How did the ichthyosaurs reproduce? It is probable that these reptiles were unable to come out on land, just as modern porpoises and whales are unable to leave the water. Therefore they could not lay their eggs in the sand or in nests, as did their reptilian cousins. Fortunately for us some fossils of *Ichthyosaurus* from Germany show unborn embryos within the body cavity of the adult, and in one specimen the skull of an embryo is located in the pelvic region, as if the little ichthyosaur were in the process of being born when death overtook the mother. So it is evident that these reptiles were ovoviviparous—that they retained the egg within the body until it was hatched, as do some modern lizards and snakes.

This description of *Ichthyosaurus* indicates the high degree of specialization for marine life that was attained by the ichthyosaurs in general. What has been said for *Ichthyosaurus* applies with but few modifications to all the Jurassic and Cretaceous ichthyosaurs. The Triassic ichthyosaurs were somewhat more primitive than their descendants in that the skull was not quite so elongated, the paddles were not so broad or so long, and the downcurving of the tail was less pronounced.

THE SAUROPTERYGIANS

It will be remembered that in Permian and Triassic times there was a group of reptiles, the protorosaurs, characterized among other things by an upper temporal opening bounded below by a very deep squamosal bone. It is quite probable that these reptiles were ancestral to the sauropterygians, a large group of marine reptiles of Mesozoic age. The sauropterygians, having their beginnings in Triassic times, evolved along three distinct lines, represented by the suborders Nothosauria, Placodontia, and Plesiosauria, the first two being confined to the Triassic period, the plesiosaurs ranging from the upper Triassic to the end of the Cretaceous period.

Adaptations in the sauropterygians for life in the ocean were quite different from those characteristic of the ichthyosaurs. Whereas the ichthyosaurs were fast-swimming, fish-shaped reptiles that swam by a sculling movement of the body and tail, using the paddles for balance and control, the sauropterygians were comparatively slow-swimming animals that rowed through the water with large, strong paddles.

THE PLACODONTS

In early Triassic times the placodonts, a group limited in age to this geologic period, became specialized for life in shallow, marine waters, where they fed upon mollusks that they picked off the sea bottom. These reptiles were rather massively constructed, with a stout body, a short neck and tail, and paddle-like limbs. In the genus *Placodus* there was a strong, ventral "rib basket" of bony rods that helped to support the viscera as well as to provide protection for the lower surface. On the back there was a row of bony nodules above the vertebrae, indicating that the upper surface of the body in this reptile was armored. In the pectoral and pelvic girdles the ventral bones were comparatively strong, but the bones in the upper portions of the girdles were reduced. The limb bones were moderately long and the feet were flattened to form rather small paddles.

The skull was short, with the squamosal bone and other bones beneath the upper temporal opening very deep. The nostrils were not terminal, but had retreated to a position immediately in front of the eyes. In the lower jaw there was a high coronoid process, for the attachment of strong masticating muscles that originated on the powerful temporal arch of the skull. The teeth of *Placodus* were specialized in a most interesting fashion. The front teeth in the premaxillary bones and in the front part of the dentary protruded almost horizontally, and it is evident that they formed efficient nippers. Behind them the teeth of the maxillaries and the palatine bones in the skull and of the back portion of the lower jaw were reduced in numbers but broadened to form huge, blunt grinding mills, which when brought together by the strong jaw muscles must have been capable of crushing tough sea shells. Evidently *Placodus* swam along slowly, plucking various mussels and other shells off the sea floor and crushing them with the strong jaws and teeth.

In some placodonts like *Placochelys* and *Henodus*, the body became very broad and heavily armored by dorsal scutes that coalesced to form a heavy carapace over the back, giving to these reptiles a form and in general a series of structural adaptations somewhat similar to those characteristic of the large sea turtles of later ages.

THE NOTHOSAURS

Contemporaneous with the placodonts were the nothosaurs, which reached the height of their development in late Triassic times. These

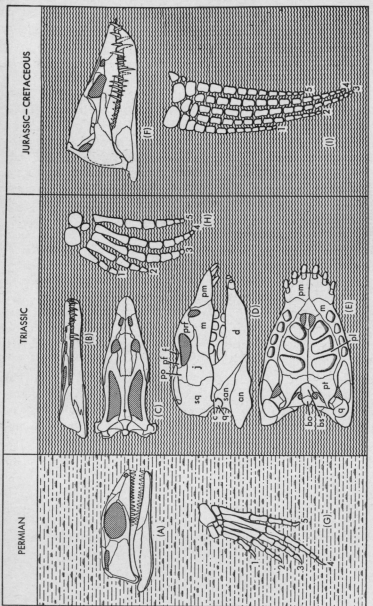

FIGURE 53.

were small to medium-sized, elongated reptiles, with very long, sinuous necks. In them the ventral portions of the girdles were heavy, as in the placodonts, and, similarly, there was a well-developed rib basket. The limbs were somewhat elongated and the feet were modified as short paddles. Limbs and feet were rather strong in the nothosaurs, however, and it is quite probable that these animals could come out on land, as do modern seals and sea lions. The skull was comparatively small and flat, and instead of a deep squamosal beneath the temporal opening the arch was emarginated on its lower surface to form a rather slender rod. The external nares were slightly retreated, and the internal nares, piercing the front of an almost solid palate, were beneath the outer nostrils. The margins of the long jaws were set with numerous sharp teeth.

The nothosaurs, of which the genus *Nothosaurus* is typical, paddled through the water as did the placodonts. The jaws and teeth in these reptiles were clearly fish traps, so it is apparent that as the nothosaurs swam along they darted the long, flexible neck from side to side or forward, thus catching fish that came within their range.

THE PLESIOSAURS

This method of living and feeding was obviously successful, for the Triassic nothosaurs were followed by the plesiosaurs, which became numerous and of world-wide extent during Jurassic and Cretaceous times. In essence, the plesiosaurs followed the nothosaurian pattern, but became specialized through an increase in body size, a great increase in the size and efficiency of the paddles, and improvements of the fish-catching jaws.

The increase in size among the plesiosaurs began during early Jurassic times and continued through the remainder of the Mesozoic era, reaching its culmination in late Cretaceous times. Many of the Jurassic plesiosaurs were ten to twenty feet in length, whereas some of the late Cretaceous forms reached lengths of forty feet or more. In a great many plesiosaurs much of this length was represented

---

FIGURE 53. Euryapsids. (A) Side view of skull and jaw of *Araeoscelis*, a land-living protorosaur, about two-thirds natural size. (B) Side view of skull and jaw and (C) top view of skull of *Nothosaurus*, a nothosaur, one-ninth natural size. (D) Side view of skull and jaw and (E) palatal view of skull of *Placodus*, a placodont, one-sixth natural size. (F) Side view of skull and jaw of *Styxosaurus*, a plesiosaur, one-twelfth natural size. (G) Hind foot of *Araeoscelis*. (H) Hind foot of the nothosaur, *Ceresiosaurus*. (I) Hind foot of the plesiosaur, *Trinacromerum*.

by a very long neck, so that the body remained comparatively short. The body was broadened by the lateral extension of the ribs, each of which had a single articulation with the vertebrae instead of the two articulations that are general in reptiles. The vertebrae had flattened ends on the centra, weak zygapophyses and tall spines, making for a flexible backbone with adequate surfaces for the attachment of strong back muscles. There was a strong ventral rib basket.

The ventral portions of the girdles were very large in the plesiosaurs, whereas the upper elements, the scapula in the pectoral girdle and the ilium in the pelvis, were much reduced. The strong ventral portions of the girdles extended back and forward of the articulations for the limbs, giving origins for powerful muscles that not only pulled the paddles back with great force, but also moved them forward with almost equal force. Consequently the plesiosaurs could row forward or backward, or they could combine these motions among different paddles, to rotate quickly. We might compare swimming in a plesiosaur with a rowboat manned by two skillful oarsmen.

The paddles in the plesiosaurs were very large. The upper limb bones were heavy and elongated, for attachment of the strong rowing muscles, but the lower limb bones and the bones of the wrist and ankle were short. The phalanges of the digits were multiplied in number, thus adding to the length of the paddles, but were always cylindrical, never flattened into discs as in the ichthyosaurs.

The skull was in effect a derivative of the nothosaur skull, with large eyes and temporal openings, an emarginated squamosal bone, nostrils in front of the eyes, an almost solid palate, and jaws that were provided with very long sharp teeth for catching and holding slippery fish.

From the beginning of their history the plesiosaurs followed two lines of evolutionary development. In one line, that of the pliosaurs or short-necked plesiosaurs, the neck was comparatively short, but the skull became much elongated, especially through elongation of the jaws. Such plesiosaurs are typified by *Pliosaurus* of the Jurassic and *Trinacromerium* of the Cretaceous. One of the pliosaurs, *Kronosaurus*, from the Cretaceous of Australia, reached huge dimensions with a skull about twelve feet in length!

In the other line, the long-necked plesiosaurs, the trend in evolution, apart from increase in size, was toward great elongation of the neck. These plesiosaurs evidently continued the nothosaur habit of rowing through shoals of fish, to catch their prey by darting the head this way and that. In Jurassic genera, such as *Muraenosaurus,* the paddles were very large and the neck was elongated so that it equaled the body in length. However, the culmination of this branch of plesiosaurian evolution was reached by the elasmosaurs of upper Cretaceous times, characterized by the genus *Elasmosaurus,* in which reptiles there was a prodigious increase in the length of the neck, so that it was frequently as much as twice the length of the body and contained no fewer than sixty vertebrae!

The plesiosaurs, both the short-necked and the long-necked types, continued with unabated vigor to the end of Cretaceous times. Then they became extinct, as did so many of the dominant upper Cretaceous reptiles.

THE MOSASAURS AND THE GEOSAURS

Two other groups of Mesozoic marine reptiles will be briefly considered at this place, even though the reptilian orders to which they belong will not be discussed until a later chapter. The geosaurs or thalattosuchians were members of a family of Jurassic crocodilians that went to sea. In these crocodiles a reversed heterocercal tail evolved, by a sharp downturning of the caudal vertebrae, and the

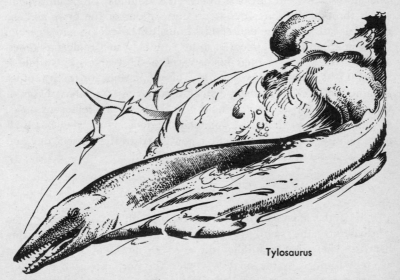

Tylosaurus

FIGURE 54. A mosasaur, a Cretaceous marine lizard, twenty feet or more in length.

limbs were modified to form paddles. With these specializations added to the characteristic crocodilian structures the geosaurs were well suited for life in the sea, but their existence was a short one, confined mainly to the Jurassic period.

The dolichosaurs, aigialosaurs, and mosasaurs were nothing more than varanid-type lizards that became dwellers in a marine habitat. The first two of these three groups, which appeared in early Cretaceous times, were generally small forms, only partially adapted for life in the sea. However, the aigialosaurs appear to have been ancestral to the late Cretaceous mosasaurs, which evolved as highly specialized marine reptiles. In so doing the mosasaurs followed a trend toward giantism, as have so many ocean-living vertebrates, so that some of the last and most specialized of these marine lizards, such as *Tylosaurus,* were animals thirty feet or more in length. Adaptations in the mosasaurs for life in the oceans were brought about by a retreat of the nostrils to a rather posterior position on the top of the skull, by the transformation of the limbs into flat paddles, as might be expected, and by a deepening of the long tail, to form a scull. However, there was no bending of the backbone either up or down, and it would appear that the tail in these reptiles extended back in a straight line from the pelvic region to the tip. The mosasaurs were obviously efficient swimmers, propelling themselves through the water by lateral undulations of the body and the powerful tail, using the paddle-like limbs for balancing and steering.

The marine lizards appeared quite suddenly in Cretaceous times, and like the geosaurs their history was a short one. But while it lasted it was a highly successful line of adaptation, for these reptiles became world wide in their distribution during the later phases of Cretaceous history. They died out near the close of Cretaceous times, as did so many of the large, dominant Cretaceous reptiles, but their close relatives, the varanid lizards, continued to the present day and are now widely distributed in the Old World.

CONCLUSION

This is the story of the marine reptiles of Mesozoic times, the ichthyosaurs, the sauropterygians, the geosaurs, and the marine lizards. These reptiles fulfilled the rôles during the Mesozoic era that are now fulfilled by the smaller whales, the porpoises, and dolphins, by sea cows, by seals, sea lions, and walruses, and by the modern sea turtles. Certainly they were dominant over the marine fishes of Triassic and Jurassic times, and it was not until late in the Cretaceous period, when the marine teleosts began their unprecedented evolutionary history, that there was any real challenge to the sea-going reptiles.

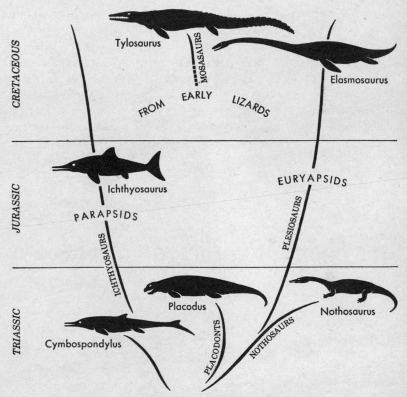

FIGURE 55. Relationships of Mesozoic marine reptiles.

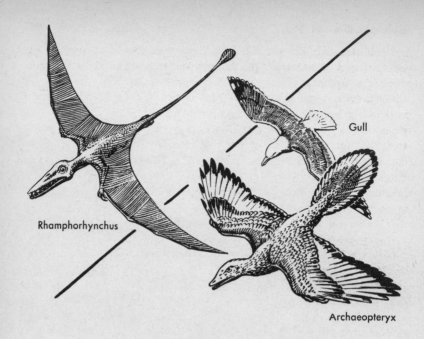

Gull

Rhamphorhynchus

Archaeopteryx

13 · Flying Reptiles and Birds

PROBLEMS OF FLIGHT

During Triassic times the first invasion of the oceans by air-breathing tetrapods took place. That this event did not occur before the Triassic period is probably owing to the fact that until then the tetrapods had not attained a degree of evolutionary development sufficiently advanced to become adapted to the rigorous requirements for complete aquatic life. Similarly it is interesting to see that flight among the vertebrates was not established until Jurassic times, probably because until then tetrapod anatomy was not sufficiently advanced to permit adaptations in these animals that could satisfy the extremely rigorous requirements for flying. Then two groups of tetrapods, the flying reptiles and the birds, quite independently took to the air.

The requirements for flight in vertebrates are indeed restrictive, and only a few groups of tetrapods have been able to meet them during the last two hundred million years of evolutionary history. In the first place, the flying animal must overcome the downward pull of gravity. The problem is not particularly serious for small invertebrates like the insects, but for vertebrates, the smallest of which exceed all but insect giants, gravity has been and is a problem of the first importance.

For instance, the flying vertebrate must be comparatively light, particularly in relation to the strength of the muscles that move the wings. Because of the physical limitations of muscle strength, bone strength, the relationships of wing surface to body weight, and the like, there are definite upper limits in size beyond which the flying vertebrate cannot go, and in this respect it is rather different from the man-made airplane, which continues to increase in size as the powers of motors increase. To achieve lightness, the bones of flying vertebrates are commonly hollow, with thin outer walls. Up to a certain point this type of skeletal structure is strong, and it gives sufficient areas for the attachments of large muscles, so necessary to the flying vertebrate.

The aerial vertebrate must have wings, and throughout vertebrate history these wings have been developed by transformations in the front limbs. It must have a strong backbone as a girder for the support of the flying machine. It must have powerful arm muscles to move the wings up and down, and this means that some of the areas for attachment of the muscles, generally the breast bones, must be tremendously enlarged. There must be a landing gear of some sort, usually supplied by modifications of the hind limbs.

Of course other parts of the anatomy are involved in flight beside the skeleton and the muscular system. For instance, the flying vertebrate must have a flight surface, either a membrane as was developed in the flying reptiles and as in the present-day bats, or modifications of the body cover, like the feathers of birds. Flight involves the senses, too. Flying vertebrates either have very powerful vision, as do the birds, and as probably did the flying reptiles, or they have some other method of guiding their flight, such as the sonar system of the bats. Flight presupposes a delicate sense of balance and nervous control, with consequent high specializations of the cerebellum in the brain, and of the entire nervous system.

Finally, flight, so far as we know it in the living tetrapods, requires a high rate of body metabolism. Whether this stipulation can be applied to the flying reptiles is a moot point.

Adaptations for flight carry certain disadvantages, particularly those that go along with comparatively small size. On the other hand, flight frees the tetrapod from the trammels of earth-bound locomotion; the flying vertebrate is free to move about over areas of considerable size and to cross many barriers that limit the movements of land-living animals. These advantages of flight need no elaboration; the distribution and success of the modern flying birds are indications of the benefits of being able to fly.

THE PTEROSAURS

The pterosaurs were archosaurians that became adapted for flight at the beginning of the Jurassic period. They evolved in considerable variety during Jurassic times, and some of them continued through the Cretaceous period, near the end of which they became extinct.

Perhaps the pterosaurs can be described by outlining the principal characters of the Jurassic form, *Rhamphorhynchus*. This was a reptile about two feet in length, with a characteristic archosaurian skull. Thus there were two temporal openings behind the large eye, and in addition a large preorbital fenestra. The front of the skull and the jaws were elongated and were supplied with long, pointed teeth that projected forward to a considerable degree, probably as an adaptation for fish-catching.

The skull was borne upon a fairly long and flexible neck. The back behind the neck was short and solid, and there was a continuous series of ribs between the pectoral and pelvic girdles. In *Rhamphorhynchus* there was a very long tail, perhaps twice the length of the backbone in front of the pelvis, and impressions in the rock indicate that it was supplied with a rudder-shaped membrane at its end.

In the fore limbs the humerus was strong, the radius and ulna rather elongated, and the fourth finger tremendously elongated to form the principal support for a wing membrane, the presence of which is amply proved by impressions in the rocks. The fingers in front of the fourth digit were reduced to small hooks that probably served the pterosaur as hangers for roosting in trees or on cliffs, while the fifth finger was lost. Projecting forward from the wrist was a spike-like bone, the pteroid bone, that helped to support the wing membrane. The scapula and coracoid were strong, and the coracoid was attached ventrally to an enlarged sternum, which served as an area for the origin of the large pectoral muscles that moved the wings. In some advanced pterosaurs (but not *Rhamphorhynchus*) the upper end of the shoulder blade was attached to the backbone by a special bony element, the notarium, thus giving added strength to the shoulder girdle.

The hind limbs in *Rhamphorhynchus* were comparatively small and weak, as they were in all the pterosaurs, and it is probable that the wing membranes were attached to them.

Such is the picture of a typical pterosaur. It was evidently a reptile capable of sustained flight, an aerial carnivore that probably

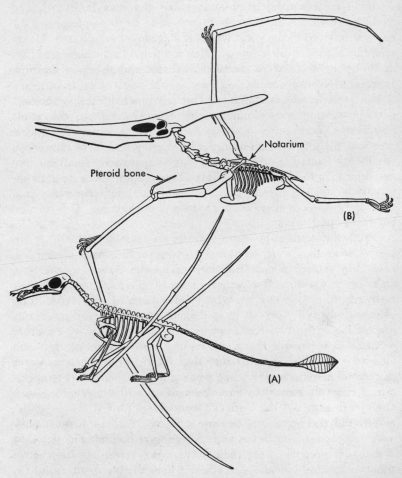

FIGURE 56. Pterosaurs or flying reptiles. (A) *Rhamphorhynchus* of Jurassic age, with a wing spread of about two feet. (B) *Pteranodon* of Cretaceous age, with a wing spread of about twenty feet. The pteroid bone in the wrist of *Pteranodon* was a support for the wing membrane; the notarium served to attach the upper edge of the scapula to the backbone, thus making a strong base for the great wing. Note the large fenestra in front of the eye of this reptile.

fed by swooping down to the water of lakes or lagoons to catch fish swimming at the surface. Like the modern bats, it must have been exceedingly awkward and comparatively helpless on the ground.

During Jurassic times there were various pterosaurs similar to *Rhamphorhynchus*—the rhamphorhynchoids. However, in late Jurassic times another group of pterosaurs, the pterodactyloids, appeared as derivatives from the rhamphorhynchoids. In these pterosaurs the tail was reduced to the point where it was almost suppressed. Likewise the dentition was reduced so that in the most advanced members of the group teeth were completely absent and the jaws took the form of a bird-like beak.

The pterodactyloids continued through much of the Cretaceous period, reaching the culmination of their evolution in the genus *Pteranodon,* found in the Niobrara formation of Kansas. This pterosaur was the giant of the group, with a wing spread of more than twenty-five feet! Even so, the body was comparatively small, bulking no larger than the body of a turkey. The jaws formed a long, toothless beak, and the back of the skull was extended posteriorly into a crest, the purpose of which is a matter of conjecture. This was the last of the pterosaurs.

Certain interesting questions arise in connection with the pterosaurs. Since they were reptiles, and since reptiles have a comparatively low rate of metabolism, how could the pterosaurs maintain flight for any appreciable length of time? Perhaps much of their flight was of a soaring type, which did not require the expenditure of much energy. Even so, it is difficult to imagine the pterosaurs functioning without sources of energy beyond those known for other reptiles. Is it possible that these reptiles were independently warm blooded? Is it possible that they evolved an insulating body cover that would help them maintain a more or less constant body temperature? Hair-like structures have been described in association with some pterosaurs, but the evidence is indefinite at best.

Why did the pterosaurs become extinct? Perhaps because they were in competition with the birds, which were becoming modernized in late Cretaceous times. The birds were warm-blooded, active animals, obviously much more efficient than the pterosaurs, and it is quite likely that their perfection brought about the end of the flying reptiles.

BIRDS

It may seem incongruous to introduce the birds into our discussion at this place, but actually it is not. The birds have been called "glorified reptiles"; as a matter of fact, we can be more specific and designate the birds as "glorified archosaurians." With such a concept in mind, it is quite pertinent to consider the birds along with the archosaurians, and particularly with the pterosaurs, since this gives an opportunity of comparing adaptations for flight in the two groups.

If we were to do justice to the marvelous adaptations and the interesting facts of distribution that characterize modern birds, an entire volume would be required. Such is not possible nor is it suitable in a discussion like this one; consequently our attention will be limited to the major characteristics of the birds and to a short résumé of their evolutionary history.

In spite of an archosaurian ancestry, common with the ancestry of the pterosaurs, birds have solved the problems of flight differently from the flying reptiles. In the birds there are feathers that not only form the flight surfaces but also serve to insulate the body from its environment. The hind legs are very strong in most birds, giving to these vertebrates the double advantage of being able to run or walk on the ground as well as to fly in the air. Indeed, some of the water birds, such as ducks and geese, have the distinction of being able to move around proficiently in the water, on land, and in the air, a range of natural locomotor ability that has never been attained by any other vertebrates.

As we know from modern birds, these vertebrates are highly organized animals, with a constant body temperature and a very high rate of metabolism. In addition, they are remarkable in having evolved extraordinarily complex behavior patterns, such as those of nesting and song, and the habit among many species of making long migrations from one continent to another and back each year.

JURASSIC BIRDS

The first birds, like the first pterosaurs, appeared during Jurassic times. These birds are known from two very good skeletons, and a few miscellaneous additional fragments from the Solenhofen limestone of Bavaria, Germany. This fine-grained rock, which is extensively quarried for lithographic stone, was evidently deposited in a shallow coral lagoon of a tropical sea, and fortunately for us flying vertebrates occasionally fell into the water and were buried by the fine limy mud, to be preserved with remarkable detail. In this way the two Jurassic bird skeletons, which have been named *Archaeopteryx*, were fossilized. And not only were the bones preserved in these skeletons, but also imprints of the feathers.

If the indications of feathers had not been preserved in association with *Archaeopteryx* it is likely that these fossils would have been classified among the reptiles, for they show numerous reptilian characters. These were animals about the size of a crow, with an archosaurian type of skull, a long neck, a compact body balanced on a pair of strong hind limbs, and a long tail. The fore limbs were enlarged and obviously functioned as wings.

The skull had the two posterior temporal openings so characteristic of the archosaurians, but they were reduced by enlargement of the bones surrounding the brain. There was a very large eye opening, containing a ring of sclerotic plates, and in front of the orbit there was a large antorbital opening. The front of the skull and the lower jaws were elongated and narrowed into a beak, in which were well-developed teeth.

The neck was long and flexible, and the back was comparatively short and compact. A short, strong back is, of course, essential to a flying animal. The sacrum was long, giving a strong attachment between the elongated ilium of the pelvis and the backbone. The two other bones of the pelvis on either side, the pubis and the ischium, were transformed into rods, and the pubis had rotated to a posterior position paralleling the ischium, showing an arrangement similar to that of the ornithischian dinosaurs. The hind limbs were strong and very bird-like, with three clawed toes pointing forward on each foot and one short toe directed to the rear. This type of hind limb and foot was typical also of the theropod dinosaurs. Evidently *Archaeopteryx* was able to walk and run in much the same fashion as a chicken. The bony tail was characteristically reptilian and about as long as the rest of the vertebral column. In the fore limb the scapula was slender, the bones of the arm were also long and slender, and the hand, composed of the first three digits, was much elongated. All the bones of the skeleton were delicately constructed.

As preserved, the skeletons of *Archaeopteryx* show long flight feathers extending out from the hand and the lower arm bones, whereas other feathers are indicated on the body. The tail was unique in that it had a row of feathers down either side.

Here was a truly intermediate form between the reptiles and the birds. The skeleton alone was essentially reptilian, but with some characters trending strongly toward the birds. The feathers, on the other hand, were typical bird feathers, and because of them *Archaeopteryx* is classified as a bird—the earliest and most primitive member of the class. The feathers would indicate not only that this animal was able to fly, but also that it was warm blooded. The expanded brain case would indicate that it had already evolved a comparatively complex central nervous system, which is so important to a flying animal.

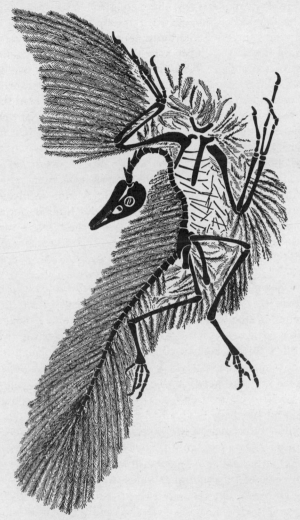

FIGURE 57. A skeleton with impressions of feathers of the earliest known bird, *Archaeopteryx*, as it was found. One-third natural size.

What were the intermediate steps in the evolution of these first birds from archosaurian reptiles? Two theories have been put forward to account for the evolution of flight in the birds. On the one hand it has been argued that bird flight was an outgrowth of rapid running on the ground. According to this theory, the first birds were fast runners that flapped their feathered fore limbs to help them along, as do many modern birds that run rapidly. Gradually the wings enlarged through the processes of mutation and selection, so that in the end they became organs of flight rather than accessories to running. The other theory postulates that the first birds climbed trees, from which they glided to the ground or to other trees, as do modern flying squirrels. At first the feathered fore limb was too small to allow for more than gliding, but as time went on it enlarged and eventually was able to support the animal in flight. Thus flight was an outgrowth of climbing and gliding.

Such is our evidence of Jurassic birds. Birds were still in an early stage of adaptation, and at best they must have been rather poor flyers. At that time they faced strong competition from the flying reptiles, which for the limited duration of the Jurassic period were probably more adept on the wing than were these first birds.

CRETACEOUS BIRDS

By Cretaceous times the birds had progressed far along the evolutionary road that was to lead to modern birds. In most respects the skeleton of the Cretaceous birds had become "modernized." There was a coalescence of the skull bones so characteristic of modern birds, with a further reduction of the temporal openings. There was the development of a high degree of pneumaticity in the bones of the skeleton. The pelvis and sacrum were strongly coalesced to make a single structure, serving as an anchor between the strong hind legs and the body. The bones of the hand were also fused as in modern birds, not free from each other as they were in the Jurassic birds. The long, bony tail was suppressed. In some of the Cretaceous birds there was a great enlargement of the sternum for the origin of powerful pectoral muscles, sure proof of the perfection of flight. However, the Cretaceous birds were primitive in that they retained some teeth in the jaws. One of the best-known of the Cretaceous birds is the genus *Hesperornis* from the Niobrara chalk of Kansas. This was a bird specialized for swimming and diving, very much in the fashion of the modern loons and grebes. The body was somewhat elongated, the jaws were long, the feet were adapted for paddling, and the wings were suppressed.

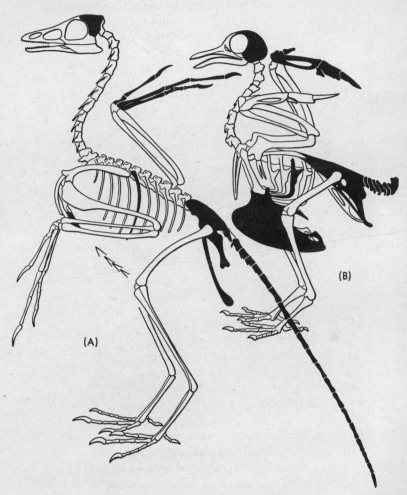

(B)

(A)

FIGURE 58. A comparison of the skeletons in the earliest known bird, *Archae-opteryx* of Jurassic age, and in a modern pigeon. Comparable regions of the skeleton (brain case, hand, sternum, rib, pelvis, tail) are shaded black. Not to scale. In the modern bird the brain case is expanded, the bones of the wing are coalesced, the pelvis is fused into a single, solid structure, the bony tail is reduced, the ribs are expanded, and the sternum or breast bone is greatly enlarged for the attachment of strong wing muscles. All these adaptations, and many others, make the modern bird an efficient flying animal.

CENOZOIC BIRDS

By the beginning of Cenozoic times the birds were completely modernized. They had reached their present high stage of skeletal structure, and so far as we can tell there has been little structural evolution among the birds during the last fifty to seventy million years. However, there have been certain events in the history of birds during Cenozoic times that are worth noting. Perhaps the most striking fact about early Cenozoic avian history was the rapid radiation of large, ground-living birds. It has been suggested that for a time there was active competition between the large terrestrial birds and the early mammals. If so, it was a passing phase, and the mammals soon became the dominant land animals. From then on birds developed for the most part as flying vertebrates, although a few large, flightless birds, the so-called ratites, have continued to the present day in most of the continental regions. The ostriches lived in Eurasia during late Cenozoic times and still inhabit Africa, the rheas are found in South America, the emus and cassowaries in the Australian region, and within the last few thousand years the so-called elephant birds inhabited Madagascar and the moas New Zealand. All these birds have been marked by growth to great size, a secondary reduction of the wings accompanied by a flattening of the sternum and a strengthening of the legs.

Most of the modern birds are remarkably similar to each other in structure. Their great variety has been brought about by adaptations to many different types of life, which in turn has entailed changes in proportion, differences in coloration, and a wide range of differentiation in behavior patterns. Certainly the birds are at the present time highly successful vertebrates, sharing with the teleost fishes and the placental mammals the fruits of evolutionary achievement, as indicated by numerous species showing wide ranges of adaptation, by great numbers of individuals, and by a wide distribution throughout the world. It has been estimated, quite conservatively, that there are perhaps one hundred billion birds in our modern world.

Because of the structural uniformity of Cenozoic and modern birds, their classification is a difficult subject. Modern birds are classified to a large degree upon external characters, which of course cannot be utilized for fossil birds. Moreover, characters that in other vertebrates would be regarded as of comparatively minor importance are accorded ordinal rank in the classification of birds. Yet in spite of the relatively small differences that separate many of the major groups of birds, these vertebrates none the less show a wide range of adaptive radiation.

FIGURE 59.   Some major lines of adaptation among the birds.   This figure is not comprehensive.

For instance, Cenozoic and modern birds range in size from some hummingbirds that are among the smallest of land-living vertebrates to the giant moas and elephant birds, now extinct. They range in their powers of locomotion from flightless, ground-living birds to the masters of the air, like the albatross or the swallows. They range in their adaptations to diet from the strictly plant-eating and seed-eating birds, like some of the fowls and songbirds, to aggressive birds of prey like the owls and hawks. Their colors range from very plain birds to the brilliant birds of paradise that live in the tropics. Their songs range from modest chirps to the remarkably complex songs of some of the perching birds. Their nests range from simple affairs to very elaborate structures. In their distribution they range from sedentary birds to migrants that fly back and forth across almost half the circumference of the globe.

These statements, so well known as to need no elaboration at this place, merely point up the fact that there has been a great deal of evolution in the birds during Cenozoic times, in spite of the general structural similarity of these vertebrates. It must be remembered that the basic avian structure was determined at an early stage in the evolutionary history of birds because of the rigorous limitations placed upon a flying vertebrate. Consequently adaptations in the birds have been along lines that are not always indicated by the details of anatomy, a fact that makes these vertebrates highly interesting to the student of recent animals but difficult subjects for the paleontologist.

The classification of birds by orders is presented at the end of this book.

BIRDS IN THE FOSSIL RECORD

Of all the classes of vertebrates, the birds are least known from their fossil record. As we have seen, knowledge of Jurassic birds is based on two skeletons, whereas our information about Cretaceous birds, though more extensive, is none the less very scanty. Fairly numerous fossils of Cenozoic birds are known, but for the most part they consist of fragmentary bones. Only in unusual fossil deposits, such as the tar pits of the Pleistocene, are Cenozoic fossil birds found with any degree of completeness. These conditions restrict our knowledge of the evolution of birds through time. The study of modern birds is followed in great detail by many professional zoologists, and amateur bird watchers can be numbered by the millions. The study of fossil birds is one of the most restricted aspects of paleontology.

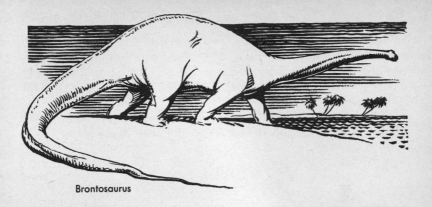

Brontosaurus

14 · Triumph of the Dinosaurs

INTRODUCTION

We come now to a consideration of the dinosaurs, the great reptiles that were dominant on land through one hundred million years of Mesozoic history. What were the dinosaurs?

The word "dinosaur" was invented by Sir Richard Owen more than a century ago to designate certain large fossil reptiles that were then being recognized and described for the first time. The word is a combination of Greek roots meaning "terrible lizard," a purely descriptive term, which, like so many scientific names, must not be taken literally. Many of the dinosaurs undoubtedly were terrible animals when they were alive, but they were not lizards, nor were they related to lizards except in a most general way. In the early days of paleontological science the Dinosauria were regarded as a natural group of reptiles, but as knowledge of these long extinct animals was expanded it became apparent that the term includes two distinct reptilian orders. Consequently the word dinosaur is now a convenient vernacular name, but not a systematic term.

In discussing the life of the Triassic period a brief account was given of the first dinosaurs that appeared during late Triassic times. These early dinosaurs, typified by such genera as *Coelophysis* and *Plateosaurus*, belonged to the dinosaurian order Saurischia, in which the pelvis was a triradiate structure as seen from the side, with the pubic bone extending down and forward beneath the ilium, and the ischium extending down and backward. In addition to the structure of the pelvis, there were other characters diagnostic of the saurischian dinosaurs. In almost all these dinosaurs the teeth either extended around the margins of the jaws, above and below, or were limited to the front portion of the jaws. Most of the carnivorous saurischians retained the general adaptations and pose of their thecodont ancestors, so that they were bipedal, with the body pivoted at the hips and supported on strong, bird-like hind legs. Among the herbivorous saurischians, however, there was a secondary return to quadrupedalism. In the saurischians the toes generally bore strong claws.

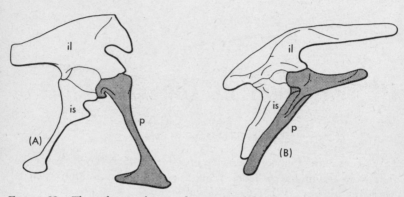

FIGURE 60. The pelvis in the two dinosaurian orders. (A) Saurischian pelvis, with a forwardly directed pubis. (B) Ornithischian pelvis, with the pubis parallel to the ischium.

The other dinosaurian order, which appeared much later in Mesozoic times than the Saurischia, was the Ornithischia. In these dinosaurs the pubic bone of the pelvis had rotated backward so that it occupied a position parallel to the ischium. This contiguity of the pubis and ischium is similar to the arrangement of these bones in birds, hence the name Ornithischia or "bird-like pelvis." In many of the ornithischians the ilium was greatly extended both front and rear, and there was a large anterior process of the pubis reaching forward beneath the front of the ilium. Consequently the pelvis as seen from the side was a tetraradiate structure, its four processes or prongs being formed by the anterior and posterior extensions of the ilium, by the prepubis, and by the closely appressed ischium and pubis. The ornithischians had lost the teeth in the front of the mouth in both upper and lower jaws, and generally this portion of the skull and jaw took the shape of a beak of some sort, whereas in most of these dinosaurs there was a single new bony element on the front of the lower jaw, the *predentary*, that formed the lower portion of the cutting beak. The teeth, limited to the sides of the jaws, were often highly modified for cutting or chewing vegetation, for all

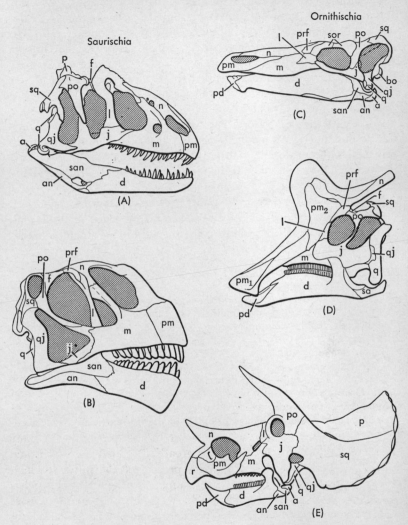

FIGURE 61. Skulls of dinosaurs. Saurischian skulls. (A) *Allosaurus*, a large, carnivorous theropod, one-eighteenth natural size. (B) *Camarasaurus*, a gigantic, herbivorous sauropod, one-tenth natural size. Ornithischian skulls. (C) *Stegosaurus*, an herbivorous stegosaurian, one-eighth natural size. (D) *Lambeosaurus*, an aquatic ornithopod, one-sixteenth natural size. (E) *Triceratops*, an herbivorous, horned ceratopsian, one-twentieth natural size. For abbreviations, see page 449.

the ornithischians were herbivorous. Generally speaking, the ornithischians were never so completely bipedal as were many of the
saurischians, most of these dinosaurs showing a secondary return to
a four-footed pose at an early stage in their history. The ends of
the toes usually bore flat nails or hooves, rather than claws. Whereas
the history of saurischians extended from the upper portion of the
Triassic period to the close of the Cretaceous period, that of the
ornithischians was virtually confined to the Jurassic and Cretaceous
periods, with the bulk of ornithischian evolution taking place during
Cretaceous times. Although the known history of the ornithischians
was therefore considerably shorter than the history of the saurischians,
it was much more varied, and the range of adaptations in these dinosaurs was wider than in the saurischians.

Each of the two orders of dinosaurs may be divided into suborders
that indicate the evolutionary divergence taking place in these reptiles. Perhaps it will be useful to list the suborders of dinosaurs at
this place.

Order Saurischia
    Suborder Theropoda
        The first known dinosaurs, and the one group of persistent carnivorous
        types. These dinosaurs retained the bipedal mode of locomotion
        through their evolutionary history. Upper Triassic through Cre-
        taceous.
    Suborder Sauropoda
        Giant, semi-aquatic, herbivorous saurischians, secondarily quadru-
        pedal. The largest of the dinosaurs. Jurassic and Cretaceous.
Order Ornithischia
    Suborder Ornithopoda
        Among these were the most primitive of the ornithischians, the camp-
        tosaurs, and the highly specialized trachodonts or duck-billed dino-
        saurs, which were large, semi-aquatic herbivores, with the front of
        the skull and jaws broadened into a flat bill. The ornithopods were
        dominantly bipedal, but most of them had strong fore limbs, capable
        of being used for quadrupedal locomotion. Jurassic and Cretaceous.
    Suborder Stegosauria
        Heavy, quadrupedal herbivores, perhaps adapted for life on "uplands"
        away from marshes and rivers. The hind legs were always much
        longer and heavier than the fore legs; the skull was camptosaur-like.
        Plates, spikes, and scutes formed dermal armor and protuberances
        on the body and tail. Principally Jurassic, extending into the lower
        Cretaceous.
    Suborder Ankylosauria
        Heavy, quadrupedal herbivores, similar in adaptations to the stego-
        saurs, but very strongly armored with thick bony plates that com-
        pletely encased the back and sides of the body and tail. Cretaceous.

Suborder Ceratopsia
  Quadrupedal herbivores, with subequal development of fore and hind
limbs. The skull was greatly enlarged, particularly by an extension

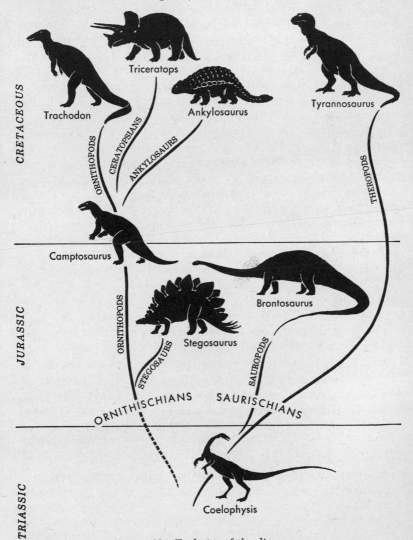

FIGURE 62. Evolution of the dinosaurs.

of some of the posterior elements to form a large frill that extended
back over the shoulders. The front of the skull was narrow and
deep like a parrot's beak, and there were generally horns on the
nose, above the eyes, or in both locations. Upper Cretaceous.

THE CARNIVOROUS THEROPODS

The description in Chapter 11 of *Coelophysis,* a theropod dinosaur of late Triassic age, outlined the essential characters of the ancestral saurischian dinosaurs known as coelurosaurs. Briefly, these were small, hollow-boned, lightly built dinosaurs having a bipedal pose. The strong, bird-like hind limbs supported the body at the hips, and there was a long tail to counterbalance the body in front of the pelvis. The fore limbs were comparatively short, and the hands were adapted for grasping. The neck was rather long and flexible, and it bore a pointed, narrow, archosaurian skull with long jaws, in which were sharp, blade-like teeth. The skull was remarkably open, not only because of the large size of the temporal openings but also because of large fenestrae in front of the orbits.

From an ancestor more or less like this the theropods evolved along three general lines of adaptation. In the first place, certain theropods remained small, and retained for the most part the primitive aspect of the ancestral types. Such was *Ornitholestes,* a little coelurosaurian about five or six feet in length, that lived during late Jurassic times. The description that has been given above for *Coelophysis* applies in a general way to *Ornitholestes.* Perhaps the most striking specialization to be seen in this persistently small, primitive carnivore, as compared with its Triassic predecessors, was in a certain degree of elongation of the fore limbs, particularly the hands, not for a secondary return to four-footed locomotion as in many of the other dinosaurs, but rather as an adaptation for increased efficiency of grasping. In addition to elongation, there was suppression of the fourth and fifth digits, so that the hand consisted of three very long, flexible fingers, terminating in sharp claws. A hand like this was obviously very useful for catching small animals, probably reptiles for the most part, but perhaps insects too. Certainly the teeth of *Ornitholestes* indicate that this active little dinosaur ate all sorts of small game. It probably frequented the undergrowth of the late Jurassic forests, where it was able to hunt successfully by reason of its agility.

A second line of theropod adaptation, taking place among the coelurosaurians during the Cretaceous period, was marked by an increase to moderate size and high specialization of the skull. The late Cretaceous genus, *Ornithomimus,* a dinosaur about the size of a large ostrich, exemplifies this adaptational trend. *Ornithomimus* had very long, slender hind limbs and very bird-like feet, which indicate that it must have been a rapid runner, much as are the modern ostriches. The fore limbs were relatively even more elongated than were those of its coelurosaurian relative, *Ornitholestes*, and it too had the hand limited to three long, grasping fingers. The

Allosaurus

Ornithomimus

Ornitholestes

FIGURE 63. Theropod dinosaurs, drawn to the same scale. *Allosaurus*, a giant carnosaur, was about forty feet long; *Ornitholestes* and *Ornithomimus* were light, running dinosaurs.

most remarkable specializations of *Ornithomimus* were in the skull, which, borne at the end of a long and sinuous neck, was very small and completely toothless. The jaws were specialized as a beak, much like the beak of an ostrich. Indeed, the comparisons of this dinosaur in various aspects of its anatomy to an ostrich are so striking that it is often called the "ostrich-dinosaur," which of course does not imply any direct relationships but does indicate that *Ornithomimus* during late Cretaceous times lived a life that is paralleled by the large flightless birds of today. It probably ate many things—small reptiles, insects, fruits, and any other food that it could catch and handle. At the slightest sign of danger, this dinosaur was able to run away, to live and feed another day; so it survived until the close of the Cretaceous period.

The third line of theropod evolution, the carnosaurians, a group separate from the coelurosaurians, attained its culmination in late Jurassic and Cretaceous times. Here the trend was toward gigantic size. The carnosaurs, typified by the genera *Allosaurus* of the upper Jurassic and by *Gorgosaurus* and *Tyrannosaurus* of the Cretaceous period, grew to be the largest land-living meat-eaters of all time. In so doing they retained the bipedal pose that had typified the ancestral theropods; in fact, bipedalism was intensified among the carnosaurs, because in these dinosaurs the hind limbs became tremendously strong and heavy, and the fore limbs and hands were inordinately reduced. In *Allosaurus* the arms and the clawed hands, though relatively small, were still capable of being used as an aid to feeding; but in *Tyrannosaurus,* a giant, some forty feet in length, that stood about twenty feet high to the top of its head and that had a probable weight during life of six or eight tons, the fore limbs were reduced to such a degree that they must not have been very useful. Since there was this reduction in the fore limbs, the activities of predation, of killing and feeding, were concentrated in the skull and jaws. Consequently the skull in the carnosaurs became tremendously enlarged, and the long jaws were armed with huge, dagger-like teeth. Long jaws and large teeth gave an effective bite for dealing with large prey, which constituted the food of these dinosaurs. There were greatly enlarged openings in the skull that cut down weight, so that it became a series of bony arches—a frame for muscle attachments—in which the brain case was comparatively small. Even with such adaptations, the skull with its large, strong muscles to operate the jaws was obviously heavy, and because of this weight the neck in the carnosaurs was shortened, which served to avoid adverse leverages. All in all the giant carnosaurs of late Mesozoic times were remarkably well adapted for hunting and killing other large reptiles, especially other dinosaurs.

THE GIANT SAUROPODS

It will be remembered that *Plateosaurus* was a fair-sized theropod some twenty feet in length, living during late Triassic times and showing definite trends away from the theropod dinosaurs of that age. Thus in *Plateosaurus* the legs were heavy and the hind feet were broad, having lost the bird-like structure so typical of most theropods. The front legs were secondarily enlarged so that this dinosaur was able to walk in a quadrupedal fashion as well as on the hind legs. The neck was elongated and the skull was comparatively small; it had broadened leaf-like or spatulate teeth, rather than the sharp cutting blades so typical of other theropods.

This line of development culminated during Jurassic times in the large sauropod dinosaurs, exemplified by such genera as *Brontosaurus*, *Diplodocus*, and *Brachiosaurus*, and was carried through the Cretaceous period by similar sauropods. Here we see the dinosaurs reaching their greatest size, attaining lengths of sixty to eighty feet and probable body weights during life of thirty to fifty tons or more. These were the largest land-living animals ever to have lived, although it must be remembered that they have been greatly exceeded in size by some of the large modern whales. It is very likely that the giant sauropod dinosaurs represent the maximum size that can be reached by land-living animals, owing to the physical limitations of bone, muscle, and ligament.

The sauropods were essentially similar to each other, differences being those of size and proportion and of details in the skeleton, especially in the skull. Since they had become giants they were completely quadrupedal, for their bulk was too great to permit a bipedal pose. Even so, the fore limbs were considerably smaller in most of the sauropods than the hind limbs, thereby indicating the bipedal ancestry of these animals. The limbs were extraordinarily heavy, and the bones were dense and solid, to give strong support to the great weight of the body. The feet were very broad, with large foot pads, like those in the feet of elephants, making a strong, elastic cushion to take up the impact of each step and to give support and traction. The toes were accordingly short, and not all of them bore claws. In *Brontosaurus,* for instance, there was a single large claw on the inner toe of each front foot, and claws on the inner three digits of the hind foot. Some brontosaur footprints recently discovered in lower Cretaceous rocks in Texas give graphic and dramatic evidence of the size of the feet, the length of the stride, and the manner of walking in these big sauropods.

The pelvis was a huge structure for strong support and muscle attachments, as might be expected in dinosaurs weighing many tons, and the shoulder blades were likewise very long and heavy. The vertebrae were large, particularly in the neck and back, and, as an adaptation to achieve strength and size without being inordinately heavy they contained deep hollows in the sides of the centra and neural arches, thus eliminating bone where it was not needed yet at the same time allowing for expanded articular surfaces. Both the neck and the tail were very long, and the vertebrae had strong spines that allowed large surfaces for muscle attachments.

The skull was comparatively small. In many sauropods the nostrils were raised to the top of the skull, as an adaptation for breathing with only the top of the head protruding above the water, whereas teeth were generally limited to the front portion of the jaws. In some sauropods such as *Diplodocus* the teeth seem surprisingly weak for so large an animal, being pegs no greater in diameter than pencils. In other sauropods, *Brontosaurus*, for example, the teeth were leaf shaped or spatulate.

This description, which applies to almost any of the sauropods, indicates herbivorous dinosaurs of great size that probably fed upon soft, lush vegetation. Certainly their relatively small jaws and weak teeth would not permit them to feed upon very tough plants. We wonder how such a small mouth could take in enough food to keep such a large animal alive, but it must be remembered that these were reptiles, with a comparatively low rate of metabolism; consequently their food requirements were probably small as contrasted with those of the large mammals we know today, elephants, for instance. It seems likely that the sauropods frequented swamps and rivers and lakes, and fed largely upon the vegetation in these habitats, either along the shore or under water. And these waters were not only places for the sauropods to feed; they also afforded protection to the great beasts. If attacked or threatened by the giant theropods, like *Allosaurus* or his relatives, the sauropods might retreat into the water, where they could wade or swim, with only the head exposed above the surface, and where the big carnivores could not follow them. The sauropod adaptations were strikingly successful, for these dinosaurs persisted until the end of Mesozoic times and became widely distributed over all the continental regions of the earth.

THE ORNITHOPODS

Among the most primitive of the ornithischian dinosaurs, although not the earliest to appear in the geological record, were the camptosaurs, belonging to the suborder of the ornithopods. *Camptosaurus*, occurring in upper Jurassic sediments, is typical, and demonstrates the basic adaptations from which later and more specialized ornithischians evolved.

This was a small to medium-sized dinosaur, sometimes no more than six or seven feet in length, sometimes as much as twenty feet long. It was a predominantly bipedal animal, with strong hind limbs, but the front legs were sufficiently robust so that this dinosaur could, if it so desired, walk around on all four feet. Perhaps the quadrupedal method of locomotion was utilized when *Camptosaurus* was moving about slowly to feed, whereas reliance was placed on the long hind legs alone when this animal needed to run away—to escape attacks from large, carnivorous dinosaurs and other predatory reptiles. In its general build *Camptosaurus* was a heavier animal than the theropod dinosaurs of similar size, and it seems likely that this primitive ornithopod was not a particularly rapid runner. The hind feet were rather broad and the four functional toes (the fifth toe was much reduced) pointed forward. The fingers of the hands were short and terminated in blunt nails, which makes it seem likely that the hands were not used for grasping, as they were in the meat-eating dinosaurs. The pelvis was of the ornithischian type already described; the tail was heavy.

Camptosaurus was an inoffensive plant-eater, as were all the ornithischian dinosaurs, and this is reflected in the various adaptations of the skull and dentition. The skull was comparatively low, and rather long. The temporal openings were large, but the opening in front of the eye was relatively small, thereby instituting a trend of development among the ornithischians that commonly led to the reduction or even the complete suppression of this particular fenestra. The lower jaw was somewhat shorter than the length of the skull, because of the forward and downward extension of the quadrate bone on which the lower jaw articulated. Because of the ventral extension of the quadrate, the articulation of the lower jaw was placed at a level below the line of the teeth, so that the articulation of the jaw on the skull was offset. This had the mechanical advantage of bringing the cheek teeth together at approximately the same time, like a crushing mill, when the mouth was closed, rather than shearing them past each other like scissors, as was the jaw action in the theropod dinosaurs. This adaptation has proved very useful to plant-eating vertebrates through the ages, since it allows a maximum amount of dental surface to be applied to the food in a minimum amount of time and with a minimum amount of motion, a factor of importance to animals that must needs ingest a great quantity of green vegetable food.

Correlated with the offset jaw articulation in *Camptosaurus* was an elevated coronoid process on the jaw, allowing for the attachment of strong temporal muscles. There were broad, leaf-like teeth in the sides of the jaws, serving admirably as choppers to cut the food, but in the front of the jaws there were no teeth at all. The pre-maxillary bones of the skull were somewhat broadened around a very

Corythosaurus

Pachycephalosaurus

Camptosaurus

FIGURE 64. Ornithopod dinosaurs, drawn to the same scale. *Corythosaurus* was about thirty feet long.

large opening for the nostrils to form a flat beak, and there was a single predentary bone on the front of the lower jaw, shaped to bite against the upper beak. Evidently leaves and stems were cropped with this beak, which in life had a horny covering, and then passed back by the tongue to the cutting teeth in the sides of the jaws, to be chopped into comparatively small masses that could be easily swallowed.

Even more primitive than *Camptosaurus* was *Hypsilophodon,* a very small ornithopod from the lower Cretaceous sediments of Europe. This small dinosaur was lightly built for an ornithischian, with a long tail and rather long, supple toes in the hind feet, for which reason it has been suggested that *Hypsilophodon* may have been a tree-climbing reptile. There were still teeth in the premaxillary bones, a particularly primitive character found among only a few of the ornithischians.

From a hypsilophodont-camptosaurid stem the ornithopod dinosaurs evolved along three general lines of adaptation. In one line there was a continuation of the camptosaurid type of structure, the principal development being a trend toward increased size in some genera. The specialized forms of this line are typified by the genus *Iguanodon,* found in lower Cretaceous sediments in Europe. *Iguanodon,* incidentally the first dinosaur to be scientifically described, was essentially an enlarged camptosaur that reached a length of thirty feet or more. In this reptile the thumb was enlarged into a sharp spike that may have been used as a weapon for defense.

Another line of adaptation among the ornithopods is seen in the genera *Stegoceras* and *Pachycephalosaurus,* of late Cretaceous age. In these dinosaurs, the first rather small, the second growing to great size, the skull roof became remarkably thickened, to form a tremendous boss of dense, heavy bone above the brain. As a result of this thickening of the skull the upper temporal opening was completely obliterated and the lateral one was reduced almost to the point of suppression, and in the larger genus numerous knobs decorated the margins and the front of the skull. It is difficult if not impossible to guess at the adaptive significance of such a development. Surely there was a great weight of bone added to the skull, and it is hard to see why these reptiles should have needed several inches of dense skull roof above the brain. Perhaps (as a very wild surmise) the skull was used as a sort of battering ram.

The most spectacular and successful ornithopod dinosaurs were the trachodonts or hadrosaurs of late Cretaceous age. Most of the trachodonts, like *Trachodon,* grew to great size, attaining lengths of thirty or forty feet and weights during life of several tons. In spite of their size, these dinosaurs like the other ornithopods were predominantly bipedal, the hind limbs being very heavy and the feet broad. But the most characteristic adaptations in these dinosaurs were in the head.

The skull in the trachodonts was elongated, and in front both skull and lower jaw were very broad and flat, in form rather similar to

the bill of a duck. Consequently they are often known as the
"duck-billed dinosaurs." The lozenge-shaped teeth in the sides of the
jaws were enormously multiplied in number and closely appressed,
forming in each jaw a solid "pavement" that was evidently used like
a grinding mill to crush the food. In all there were about five
hundred teeth in each jaw, above and below, making a total of about
two thousand teeth, a remarkable adaptation for the comminution
of food!

In addition to the extraordinary specializations of the jaws and
teeth, many of the trachodonts were distinguished by unusual adaptations in the nasal region of the skull. In these genera the premaxillary and nasal bones were pulled back over the top of the skull to
form a hollow crest. In Corythosaurus, for instance, the premaxil-
laries and nasals formed a high, helmet-shaped crest on top of the
skull, in Lambeosaurus a sort of hatchet-shaped crest, and in Para-
saurolophus a long tubular crest, extending far back behind the
occipital region. Dissections show that the nasal passage, running
from the external to the internal nares, traversed the crest in a loop.
What was the purpose of this long nasal passage? Perhaps it served
as an accessory air-storage chamber, utilized by these reptiles when
the head was submerged under water.

Certainly there is abundant evidence that the trachodonts were
aquatic dinosaurs. They are generally found in sediments that were
deposited in rivers or lakes, or even in the shallows along marine
coastlines. Because of the manner in which the trachodonts were
buried it is not uncommon to find the impression of the skin fossilized,
as well as the bones; indeed several fossilized "mummies" have been
preserved by a combination of fortunate circumstances, to show,
except for details of color, just what the trachodonts looked like.
These excellent fossils reveal the fact that the trachodonts had webs
of skin between the toes, a bit of evidence to be added to other clues
proving the aquatic habits of these dinosaurs. The skin was leathery
and roughly pebbled. In the backbone there were strong, ossified
tendons, adding to the strength of the vertebral column, and indicating, along with other features, that these animals swam by powerful
sculling movements of the tail.

From the available evidence it is possible to reconstruct in detail
the appearance and the mode of life of the duck-billed dinosaurs.
They probably fed by wading in shallow waters near the shores,
grubbing along the bottom for water plants. Perhaps they came
out on land part of the time, to feed. If danger threatened they

would dash into deep water and swim away. Such adaptations enabled them to survive in a world inhabited by giant, aggressive theropods.

THE STEGOSAURS

The stegosaurs or plated dinosaurs were, we might say, camptosaurs that grew large, reverted secondarily to a four-footed mode of

Stegosaurus

Ankylosaurus

FIGURE 65. Plated and armored dinosaurs, drawn to approximately the same scale. Each of these dinosaurs was about twenty feet long.

locomotion, and developed peculiar plates on the back and spikes on the tail. They are among the earliest of the known ornithischians, appearing in rocks of early Jurassic age. *Stegosaurus*, from upper Jurassic sediments, was a dinosaur twenty feet or more in length, with legs that were heavy and feet that were short and broad. Even though this reptile was permanently quadrupedal the hind legs were much larger than the fore legs, making the pelvic region the highest point of the body. The shoulders were low. The skull was very camptosaurid-like and remarkably small. *Stegosaurus* is famous for having a brain much smaller than the enlargement of the spinal nerve cord in the sacrum, which has given rise to the popular belief that this animal had two "brains."

There was a double row of alternately arranged, bony, triangular-shaped plates down the middle of the back. The edges of these plates were thin; the bases were thickened and obviously were imbedded in the back, so that the plates stood vertical. In life these plates were probably covered by a horny layer. On the tail there were four long, bony spikes. The purpose of the tail spikes is obvious, for *Stegosaurus* could swing them against an adversary with damaging results; but the function of the plates on the back is not so easy to interpret. Were they protective? If so, they left the flanks of the animal completely exposed. Did they serve some physiological function?

The stegosaurs, primarily a Jurassic group, continued into the beginning of Cretaceous times and then became extinct—the first large category of dinosaurs to disappear.

THE ANKYLOSAURS OR ARMORED DINOSAURS

Although some of the adaptations in the ornithopod and stegosaurian dinosaurs are difficult to interpret, those in the ankylosaurs are self-evident. The ankylosaurs were armored ornithischian dinosaurs of Cretaceous age, showing specializations for defense that were imitated by some of the edentates among the mammals, millions of years later.

Ankylosaurus was a bulky, quadrupedal reptile, some twenty feet in length, not very high at the back and very broad. Its legs were heavy; and, like *Stegosaurus*, it had hind limbs that were much longer than its fore limbs, and its feet were short. Its skull was very broad as compared with its length. The top of the head and the entire back were completely covered by a continuous armor of heavy polygonal, bony scutes, and along the sides of the body there were long, bony spikes. The armored tail terminated in a great mass of bone that obviously formed a club or bludgeon. When danger approached, these dinosaurs needed only to go down on the belly to become a sort of pillbox that must have been hard to penetrate. And woe to the daring predator that approached too near; he stood in dire peril of bone-cracking blows from the heavy club on the end of the tail. The teeth were singularly small and weak, indicating that the ankylosaurs must have fed upon soft plants.

THE CERATOPSIANS OR HORNED DINOSAURS

The last of the dinosaurs to evolve were the ceratopsians, appearing in late Cretaceous times. Their evolutionary history, compared to the history of other dinosaurs, was brief, but in the span of the upper Cretaceous these reptiles went through a remarkably varied range of adaptive radiation, to produce some of the most spectacular and interesting of all dinosaurs.

The beginning of the ceratopsians can be seen in a small genus *Psittacosaurus* from the Cretaceous sediments of Mongolia. This was a generally primitive, bipedal ornithischian, in many respects not far removed from some of the smaller ornithopods. It was specialized, however, in that the skull was rather short and deep, with its front portion narrow and hook-like, resembling in some respects the beak of a parrot. This dinosaur may not actually have been ancestral to the ceratopsians, but the modifications in the skull puts it in a position approximating a ceratopsian progenitor.

The first true ceratopsians are represented by *Leptoceratops* of North America and *Protoceratops* of Mongolia. These were small dinosaurs, but they had developed most of the specializations that were to characterize the horned ceratopsians through the extent of their phylogenetic history. Even though small they were definitely quadrupedal, with the fore limbs secondarily enlarged and with the feet rather broad, and quite certainly adapted to the single function of walking.

It is in the skull, however, that these dinosaurs show the greatest specializations, for here there was an adaptational trend quite unlike that seen in any of the other dinosaurs. Briefly, the skull was deep and narrow in its front portion, forming a beak like that of *Psittacosaurus,* and it was enlarged to such a degree as to be about a third or a fourth the total length of the animal. The enlargement of the skull was brought about in part by an actual increase in size of the structure as a whole and in part (particularly in *Protoceratops*) by a backward growth of the parietal and squamosal bones to form a large perforated "frill" at the back of the skull. Because of the great development of the frill, the skull was balanced on the occipital condyle, that portion behind the condylar joint being about equal to the region of the skull in front of the condyle.

What was the function of the frill in the skull of these early ceratopsians? A careful analysis of the anatomy indicates clearly that the frill was primarily an enlarged area for the origin of strong temporal muscles, running from this region in the skull to the lower jaw. Also the frill afforded attachments for strong neck muscles to control the movement of the head. Secondarily it may have had some protective function, since it projected back over the vital neck and shoulder region.

These early ceratopsians were essentially hornless, although in the largest known individuals of *Protoceratops* there was the beginning of a small horn on the nose. Except for the lack of horns, *Protoceratops* and *Leptoceratops* were small prototypes of their giant descendants.

Protoceratops is one of the most completely known of all the dinosaurs, because our information on this dinosaur is based not only on a large series of individuals showing all stages of growth from the newly born infant to the adult, but also on several nests of fossil eggs, some of them containing portions of embryos! These dinosaur eggs are similar in shape to the eggs of lizards, being elongated, and somewhat larger at one end than at the other. The egg shell was evidently calcareous and tough, and its surface was decorated by a pattern of small, sinuous striations. The preserved clusters of eggs show that the female *Protoceratops* scooped out a nest in the sand, in which she deposited the eggs in several concentric rings, much as do present-day turtles. Evidently the eggs were then covered with sand, and were incubated and hatched by the heat of the sun. Luckily for twentieth-century paleontologists, some of the eggs laid so many millions of years ago by this little dinosaur failed to hatch.

From a protoceratopsian ancestry the evolution of the horned dinosaurs was marked first by an increase in size, to such a degree that many of the later members of the group attained lengths of twenty-five feet and body weights of six or eight tons, and second by the development of horns on the skull. In addition, there was in the genus *Triceratops* a secondary closing of the fenestrae in the frill.

The development of horns in the ceratopsians is interesting by reason of the diversity shown in this adaptation. Among some of the horned dinosaurs like *Monoclonius* there was a single large nasal horn on the front of the skull. In another genus, *Styracosaurus*, there was not only a large nasal horn but a series of long, bristling spikes around the borders of the frill. In still other genera, like *Chasmosaurus, Pentaceratops,* and *Triceratops,* the nasal horn was augmented by two large brow horns, one above each eye.

Triceratops

Monoclonius

Protoceratops

FIGURE 66. Three ceratopsians or horned dinosaurs, drawn to the same scale. *Triceratops*, from the Lance formation of North America, was about twenty-five feet long. *Monoclonius*, also from North America, is found in the older Belly River beds, and *Protoceratops*, one of the most primitive of the ceratopsians, is found in the Djadochta formation of Mongolia.

The horned dinosaurs evidently were something like rhinoceroses among modern mammals. They were large, upland-dwelling herbivores that defended themselves by fighting effectively, using the horns as powerful weapons. The large ceratopsians were certainly formidable; the huge skull, provided with long, sharp horns, was thrust forward with tremendous force by the powerful neck muscles and by the momentum of the heavy body, borne upon strong, sturdy limbs. Any dinosaur that attacked one of the large ceratopsians had a fight in store for him.

We are tempted to wonder why there was so much variety in the development of horns in these dinosaurs. Why was not a single pattern of horns sufficient? Here we may compare the horned dinosaurs with the modern antelopes of Africa, which exist today in such a very bewildering array. Perhaps there is an analogy to be drawn between the antelopes and the horned dinosaurs. Both groups of animals evolved horns for protection, and it is possible that in each group there were numerous separate lines of evolution developing from isolated populations in which mutations were taking place. By a process of natural selection through time various horn forms evolved, all for essentially the same purpose.

At the end of the Cretaceous period the ceratopsians were among the most numerous of the dinosaurs, and it would appear that *Triceratops,* the last of these reptiles in North America, roamed in great numbers across the face of the continent. But with the transition to Tertiary times these numerous and highly successful dinosaurs died out, as did all the other members of the two great orders of reptiles that dominated middle and late Mesozoic lands.

DINOSAUR GIANTS

The dinosaurs evolved in great variety along widely divergent lines, as we have seen, and became adapted to many modes of existence, so that there were dinosaurs of various forms and sizes living during the Mesozoic era, some carnivorous, some herbivorous, some large and some small. Size range among the dinosaurs ran the gamut from reptiles no larger than big lizards or medium-sized crocodiles to huge animals eighty feet in length and weighing during life up to forty or fifty tons. Although mere size cannot be cited as a universal dinosaurian character, since there were many small dinosaurs, these reptiles nevertheless were typified by a preponderance of giants. Of all the dinosaurs certainly the great majority were giants, if we define giants as animals more than twenty feet in length and weighing several tons.

Why should there have been so many giants among the dinosaurs? This is a difficult question. It is probable, however, that giantism in the dinosaurs is to be correlated in part with Mesozoic environments. The herbivorous dinosaurs lived at a time when there was an abundance of tropical or subtropical vegetation over many of the continental areas of the earth. There was an adequate food supply, and this favored evolution to great size among the herbivores. As the herbivores grew into giants, the carnivores that preyed upon them likewise became giants.

For any animals, and especially reptiles, there are certain advantages in being a giant. Large size is a measure of protection. Moreover, the ratio of surface area to mass decreases as size increases; consequently the large animal has proportionately less surface to absorb heat and radiate heat. This means that the large animal requires less food in proportion to its size than the small animal, which is important for a reptile, with a low rate of metabolism and a varying body temperature. Moreover body temperature in a large reptile fluctuates more slowly than it does in a small reptile, because a large mass requires more time to heat up and to cool off than a small one. Therefore it is probable that the dinosaurs, being reptiles and being giants, were more efficient in many ways than smaller reptiles. Certainly giantism among reptiles was a successful evolutionary trend during Mesozoic times.

Consequently the Mesozoic era was an age of giants, when things were on a big scale. The ecological relationships between hunted and hunter were similar to those we see at the present day, but magnified. Instead of antelopes and lions, or bison and wolves, there were herbivorous and carnivorous dinosaurs.

Then near the close of Mesozoic times environmental changes began to take place. There were changes in topography and climates and consequently in vegetation. These changes, though fairly rapid in geologic time, were very slow in terms of years, and we would suppose that the dinosaurs might have adjusted themselves to such changes. Yet they failed to do so, and they became extinct. A new pattern of land life became established, where the advantage of size no longer was of great importance. In this new world, where agility and the power of sustained activity were paramount, the dinosaurs vanished, and the mammals became supreme.

Jurassic Scene

15 · Years of the Dinosaurs

VARIED FAUNAS OF THE TRIASSIC PERIOD

It has already been shown that the Triassic was a period of transition, a time when various groups of tetrapods, persisting from the Permian period, lived side by side with numerous new reptiles, evolving along lines that were to be characteristic and dominant during the middle and later portions of the Mesozoic era. Consequently the Triassic vertebrate faunas were marked by the variety of animals composing them, retaining on the one hand certain aspects of the late Paleozoic tetrapod assemblages and containing on the other many progressive Mesozoic elements. In addition to the zoological variety of early Mesozoic faunas there was a great range of ecological adaptations, brought about by the many different land environments of Triassic times.

It will be remembered that the Permian period was a time of varied climates and environments, which favored the development of the reptiles, so that they became the truly dominant land animals. The evidence seems to indicate that this was true for the Triassic period to an even greater degree than it had been for Permian times. Lands were emergent and widely distributed through the early portion of the Mesozoic era, with the result that the land-living tetrapods ranged around the world through almost all degrees of latitude. Closely related amphibians can be found in Triassic sediments from Spitsbergen, through the middle latitudes of the northern and southern hemispheres, to the tips of the southern continents. Closely related reptiles enjoyed world-wide ranges; thus dicynodonts, thecodonts, and early dinosaurs are discovered in all the continents, extending north and south almost as far as the uttermost limits of the land masses. Evidently there were extensive continental connections during the Triassic period, enabling the land-living tetrapods to spread from one region to another. At the same time climates were sufficiently amenable, even though locally varied, so that amphibians and reptiles became distributed far and wide.

In at least two regions of the world the lower Triassic continental sediments and their fossils form a record continuous with upper Permian sediments and faunas, showing that life on the land went on with scarcely any interruption, even though other evidence indicates a major break in earth history at this point. These two regions are South Africa, where in the Karroo series the Triassic upper Beaufort beds, containing a great host of mammal-like reptiles, succeeds the Permian lower Beaufort beds with an orderly sequence of sediments and faunas, and northern Russia, where the lower Triassic Zone V of the Dvina series follows the upper Permian Zone IV. In these areas we are given a glimpse of the truly continuous history of the earth and its life that would be general rather than exceptional if the geologic record were complete.

In other parts of the world there are of course breaks between the Permian and the Triassic sediments and their faunas, making for contrasts in the life of the two periods. The classic threefold sequence of the Triassic, which gives this name to the period, is found in central Europe, where lower, middle, and upper Triassic sediments are represented respectively by the Bunter, the Muschelkalk, and the Keuper series. In the Bunter and the Keuper are found characteristic land-living tetrapods, described in a preceding chapter, whereas the Muschelkalk, being a marine facies in this area, has yielded some of the early marine reptiles. In England only the lower and upper Triassic are present.

Lower Triassic faunas are found also in Asia, in the Panchet beds of India and in the reptile-bearing sediments of Sinkiang. In North America the Moenkopi formation of the southwestern United States has in recent years produced a fauna composed largely of labyrinthodont amphibians, the age of which is generally regarded as early Triassic. It is quite possible, however, that the Moenkopi sequence extends up into middle Triassic times. In Australia, which in the Mesozoic was without much doubt connected to the Asiatic mainland, some Triassic vertebrates have been found in the lower Triassic Narrabeen beds, the middle Triassic Hawkesbury beds, and the upper Triassic Wianamatta beds.

Middle Triassic tetrapods are less well known than those of lower and upper Triassic age, possibly owing to the spread of marine environments during the middle phase in this period of earth history. The Muschelkalk of central Europe has been mentioned. In Greenland and in Nevada there are middle Triassic marine sediments containing the fossils of primitive ichthyosaurs, and in the alpine region of Europe there are sediments of this age, the Besano beds, containing fish faunas. However, some land-living tetrapods of middle Triassic age are known, especially as represented by the Santa Maria fauna of Brazil, the upper Ruhuhu and Manda faunas of southern Africa, and reptiles discovered in the province of Shansi, China.

It is perhaps in the upper Triassic sediments that the early Mesozoic tetrapods reach their widest distribution and their most varied development. Throughout the world, sediments of Keuper age reveal closely related faunas that contain numerous stereospondyls, varied thecodonts in the culminating phases of their evolutionary development, and the early theropod dinosaurs. Such is the Keuper fauna itself, found in central Germany and in England. Such are the upper Triassic faunas of North America—the Newark fauna of the eastern seaboard, the Chinle fauna of the southwestern states, the Dockum fauna of Texas, and the Popo Agie fauna of Wyoming. From these sediments come some of the most complete fossils of upper Triassic tetrapods, to give a rather well-documented record of what land life was like at that time. These faunas contain aquatic facies too, as revealed not only by the amphibians but also by numerous fresh-water fishes. Related faunas are found in the Maleri beds of India, in the Lufeng series of Yunnan, China, and in the Stormberg series of the South African Karroo sequence.

As pointed out in Chapter 11, the close of the Triassic period was marked by significant extinctions that brought an end to various groups of characteristic Triassic vertebrates, especially those that had persisted from the Permian into the Triassic period. Consequently there were distinct faunal breaks between vertebrate animal assemblages of the Triassic period and those of the succeeding Jurassic period. However, in the southwestern states the sedimentary transition between the two periods was a gradual one, so much so that it has been a debated question for years as to where Triassic sediments end and Jurassic beds begin. Unfortunately the fossil record of the lower Jurassic sediments in this area is so scanty that the nature of the faunal transition cannot be accurately determined.

In Europe there is an horizon and a fauna that in a sense is transitional between typical Triassic conditions and those characteristic of the Jurassic period. This is the Rhaetic of southwestern England, a level marked by a stratum containing numerous small bones and fragments of land-living reptiles. Some students regard the Rhaetic as representing the end phase of Triassic sedimentary history, others as the beginning of Jurassic events, and still others consider it as truly transitional between the Triassic and the Jurassic.

JURASSIC ENVIRONMENTS AND FAUNAS

The opening of the Jurassic period is marked by a remarkable paucity of land-living tetrapods in the geologic record, and this scarcity extends from the lower Jurassic through middle Jurassic horizons. It can be attributed in part to the fact that with the advent of the Jurassic period there seems to have been a spread of marine waters, so that lands that had been extensive during late Triassic times became restricted, whereas shallow seas advanced across many continental regions. Moreover, lower Jurassic continental sediments, where preserved, are frequently almost barren of fossils. For instance, in the western part of North America there are extensive formations of lower Jurassic age, specifically the Wingate and Navajo formations, but these are commonly ancient dune sands in which fossils are rarely found. It is therefore obvious that in addition to the spread of lower Jurassic seas there were in some regions prevalent desert environments, in which reptiles were probably comparatively rare, and in which conditions were not favorable for the burial and fossilization of those reptiles that did live in such habitats.

So it is that about the only good evidence for lower and middle Jurassic vertebrates comes from Europe, mainly from marine sediments along the Channel coast of England. Here is the well-known sequence of Lias, Dogger, and Malm, representing the lower, middle, and upper Jurassic respectively. Along the Dorset coast of England, across the channel in the vicinity of Caen, France, and in southern Germany at Holzmaden are lower Jurassic beds containing fossils of ichthyosaurs and plesiosaurs, together with many marine invertebrates. A few scattered remains of dinosaurs have been found in the Wingate sandstone of Arizona, and lower Jurassic vertebrates are known from some localities in Australia. An important middle Jurassic horizon is the Stonesfield slate of southern England, in which are found jaws and teeth of primitive mammals.

In upper Jurassic times there were evidently broad lowlands in various parts of the world. The Morrison formation, exposed over great areas in western North America, consists of stream channel and lacustrine sediments that were deposited over a large portion of this continent. In Europe it would seem that there were probably numerous low islands and perhaps long peninsulas from mainland areas, so that this region was like the modern East Indian archipelago. Here, various land-living and marine tetrapods lived, died, and were buried in close association with each other. For instance, the Malm of southern England, containing in ascending order (among other horizons) the Oxford clays, the Kimmeridge beds, and the Purbeck beds, has yielded marine reptiles, theropod, and sauropod dinosaurs, stegosaurians, crocodilians, and other land-dwelling or semi-aquatic tetrapods. The Purbeck is notable especially because it is an horizon from which a considerable fauna of primitive mammals has been collected. The Tendaguru beds of east Africa are related to the Purbeck of England and to the Morrison of North America.

The upper Jurassic of England, the Morrison, and the Tendaguru contain dinosaurian faunas that show strong similarities. In these widely separated regions are large carnivorous theropods, numerous gigantic sauropods, small camptosaurs, and stegosaurs. In addition these faunas contain various crocodilians and turtles. It is evident that in spite of the general spread of Jurassic seas there were intercontinental connections in late Jurassic times, by means of which the large dinosaurs migrated from one continent to another. From the nature of these faunas and from other evidence it would seem that environmental conditions were closely similar in North America, Europe, and Africa; that in these regions lands were low and covered with tropical jungles, that swamps were extensive and temperatures uniformly warm. In brief, this was a period of world-wide climatic and environmental uniformity, as shown by the land-living reptiles, and therefore can be contrasted sharply with the late Triassic, when lands were emergent and environmental conditions were varied.

Interesting light is thrown upon late Jurassic landscapes and environments by the famous lithographic limestone deposits at Solenhofen, Germany. Here are sediments that were obviously deposited in the still, shallow waters of a coral lagoon, in an environment rather similar to the coral atolls and lagoons of our modern South Sea islands. In these sediments various invertebrates found their final resting places, as occasionally did some of the flying reptiles that fell into the quiet waters. And providentially two Jurassic birds also dropped into the Solenhofen lagoon, to be preserved as the two known skeletons of *Archaeopteryx*.

Such surroundings were most favorable for the evolution and deployment of the giant dinosaurs. Vegetation was lush and abundant, furnishing an ample food supply for the plant-eating dinosaurs. As a result the sauropods grew to great size, as to a lesser degree did the stegosaurians. The carnivorous dinosaurs that preyed upon these large herbivores also became giants. It was an age of giants.

THE LOWER CRETACEOUS WORLD

It would appear that the extensive marine incursions and the low, tropical lands of late Jurassic times extended into the lower portion of the Cretaceous period. Consequently land-living faunas are not numerous, though perhaps more so than those of late Jurassic age. Of particular interest are the reptiles, especially the dinosaurs, found in the lower Cretaceous Wealden beds of southern England and Belgium. These are the beds containing *Iguanodon*, a camptosaurid of historic interest, and one known from numerous skeletons. Some faunas containing dinosaurs are known from other regions; from the Cloverly formation of western North America, from the Nequen formation of southern Argentina, from the Uitenhage beds of South Africa, from the dinosaur beds of Shantung, China, and from the Rolling Downs beds of Australia. Even so, our knowledge of lower Cretaceous tetrapod faunas is imperfect.

THE DINOSAUR FAUNAS OF LATE CRETACEOUS TIMES

In contrast to the incomplete record and our consequent inadequate knowledge of tetrapod faunas during much of Jurassic and early Cretaceous times, the record of the late Cretaceous is comparatively abundant and extensive. This was a time of earth change, when lands were beginning to rise, and continents were being extended in area. It was a time of modernization in the plant world, when the flowering plants and the deciduous trees became established and widely distributed over the lands. It was probably a time of comparatively varied environmental conditions, at least as contrasted with much of Jurassic history. All in all, conditions were favorable for the spread of land-living tetrapods and for their preservation as fossils. In addition, marine and lacustrine deposits were accumulated on an extensive scale, and some of these contain not only the record of late Cretaceous marine reptiles but also evidence as to the great radiation of modern types of bony fishes—one of the important aspects of the history of life during Cretaceous times.

In upper Cretaceous sediments of several continents are preserved the richest known dinosaurian faunas, exhibiting these great reptiles in the culminating phases of their evolutionary history. Also, these sediments contain abundant records of other reptiles and of other vertebrates. The upper Cretaceous dinosaurian faunas of North America, especially those preserved in the western states and provinces of the United States and Canada, are very probably the most extensive of any in the world, and they give us a comprehensive picture of the course of tetrapod evolution during the final phases of Mesozoic history. In Alberta are the Belly River and Edmonton series, and in Wyoming and adjacent states the Lance formation; and these horizons, together with correlative formations in other western areas, represent in a general way a sequence showing a succession of genera and faunas through late Cretaceous times. In various instances it is possible to follow the evolution of phyletic lines of dinosaurs and other reptiles from the Belly River through the Edmonton into the Lance, this last representing the final stage of Cretaceous history. To supplement this record of land-living tetrapods, there are marine formations, notably the Niobrara limestone and the Pierre shale, giving evidence of the plesiosaurs, ichthyosaurs, and mosasaurs of that time, as well as the developing marine teleost fishes. These sediments make western North America a happy hunting ground for the student of Cretaceous vertebrates, the scene of numerous expeditions and collecting trips, many of them famous in the history of paleontology, that have taken place during the last three-quarters of a century.

North America was probably a continental region during much of late Cretaceous times. Europe, on the other hand, was more broken up, as it had been in the Jurassic period, and it is likely that there

CORRELATION OF MESOZOIC VERTEBRATE-BEARING SEDIMENTS

		Europe	North America	South America	Africa	Asia	Australia
Cretaceous	Upper	Transylvania; Maestricht	Lance; Edmonton, Belly River; Ojo Alamo, Kirtland, Pierre, Niobrara; Aguja	Patagonia	Baharije	Trichinopoly, Ariyalur, Mt. Lebanon; Djadochta, Iren Dabasu, Oshih	Opal Beds
Cretaceous	Lower	Wealden	Cloverly	Nequen, Bahia	Uitenhage	Shantung	Rolling Downs
Jurassic	Upper	Malm; Purbeck, Kimmeridge, Oxford, Solenhofen	Morrison		Tendaguru		
Jurassic	Middle	Dogger; Stonesfield	Navajo				
Jurassic	Lower	Lias; Holzmaden	Kayenta (possibly U. Triassic)				Talbraggar, Durham Downs
Triassic	Upper	Rhaetic; Keuper; Hossel-kus	Moenave, Wingate, Chinle, Shinarump; Dockum; Popo Agie; Newark	Santa Maria	Stormberg — Cave sandstone, Red Beds; Molteno; Upper Ruhuhu Manda	Lufeng, Maleri	Wianamatta
Triassic	Middle	Muschelkalk				Shansi	Hawkesbury
Triassic	Lower	Bunter, Dvina-V	Moenkopi; Red Peak		Upper Beaufort	Sinkiang, Panchet	Narrabeen

were many islands dotting the tropical seas in that region. Certainly marine deposits predominate in the upper Cretaceous of Europe, and here is found the chalk of England from which the name for the Cretaceous period is derived. Marine reptiles are known from various localities, perhaps the most famous being the mosasaurs from the Maestrichtian deposits of Belgium. In Transylvania are sediments containing dinosaurs, and fossils of these reptiles have also been found during recent years in France and in Portugal.

As a result of expeditions during the last three decades, a considerable array of dinosaurs has been found in Cretaceous beds in Mongolia, in the formations known as the Ondai Sair, Oshih, Iren Dabasu, and Djadochta. It may be that the Mongolian formations make a sequence in approximately the order given above, but this is a point that cannot be clarified at the present time. These deposits were laid down in separate inland basins of the Asiatic Cretaceous continent; consequently there is no direct way of linking them, to determine in what order they may have been accumulated. Moreover the fossils have not thrown any truly significant light on this problem. We may say only that they are all of Cretaceous age—possibly all of late Cretaceous age.

Other upper Cretaceous sediments of importance are the red beds of Patagonia, from which a considerable dinosaurian fauna has been described, the Baharije beds of north Africa, and the Opal beds of Australia. In recent years dinosaurs have been discovered in French Morocco, but as yet they have not been fully described.

In the limestones of Mount Lebanon, Syria, are found great quantities of teleost fishes, constituting one of the best-known Cretaceous fish faunas.

The correlative relationships of Mesozoic vertebrate-bearing sediments, briefly described and discussed in the foregoing paragraphs, are illustrated by the accompanying chart.

THE END OF THE MESOZOIC ERA

With the close of the Mesozoic era the years of the dinosaurs came to an end. These great reptiles, dominant on the land for more than one hundred million years, failed to survive the transition from Mesozoic to Cenozoic times, as did likewise the marine reptiles— the ichthyosaurs, the plesiosaurs, and the mosasaurs. In addition the pterosaurs or flying reptiles became extinct. It is probable that these several groups of ruling reptiles did not die out at the same time; in fact we know that the stegosaurs had disappeared during lower Cretaceous times, and evidence seems to indicate that the ichthyosaurs and the pterosaurs may have vanished a little before the end of the Cretaceous period. Nevertheless the extinction of the dominant Cretaceous reptiles was, on the whole, sudden in a geological sense, and dramatic. A great host of reptiles, many of them giants, vanished into limbo, leaving as survivors only the turtles, the crocodilians, the lizards and snakes, the very restricted rhynchocephalians, and for a short time during early Cenozoic times some eosuchians.

What brought about the extinction of the great Mesozoic reptiles? This is a most difficult question for which no ready answer is apparent. We would think that if the crocodiles could survive the transition into Cenozoic times, certainly some of the smaller dinosaurs might have continued. The environmental changes from late Cretaceous into early Paleocene times were not sudden nor were they drastic, and it would seem that some of the dominant reptiles might have adapted themselves to new conditions as these changes took place. Indeed, many changes, such as the establishment and deployment of the angiosperms or flowering plants, and the beginnings of continental uplifts, had already occurred during the latter part of the Cretaceous period, and to such developments the dinosaurs had adjusted themselves with no seeming difficulty.

Yet the fact remains that all the dinosaurs, the ichthyosaurs, the plesiosaurs, and the flying reptiles had vanished from the earth by the beginning of the Cenozoic era. All that can be said is that conditions changed, and for some reason the ruling reptiles were unable to adapt themselves to the changing world. These changes probably involved the establishment of more varied temperatures than had existed during much of the Mesozoic era and the sharpening of zoned climates from the equator to the poles, with consequent effects upon the complexion and distribution of plant life. However that may be, the result was to bring an end to the ruling reptiles of the Mesozoic era.

As soon as the dinosaurs and the other ruling Mesozoic reptiles vanished, the mammals came into their own. Although the first mammals appeared during the Jurassic period, and although modern placental mammals inhabited the Cretaceous world, these vertebrates remained as small, minor members of the middle and late Mesozoic faunas. It would seem that the presence of the varied reptiles of the Mesozoic "held down" the first mammals, and it was not until the dominant reptiles had vanished, to vacate numerous ecological niches, that the mammals enjoyed their first great burst of evolutionary adaptation. By the opening of the Paleocene epoch the world was abundantly inhabited by the mammals, and from that time until today the mammals have reigned supreme.

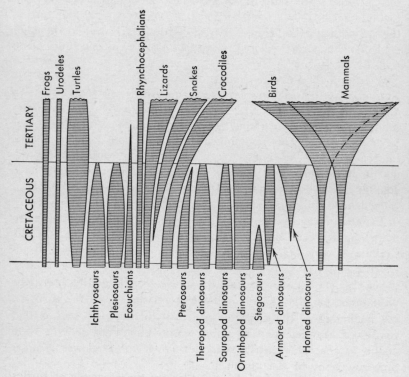

FIGURE 67. Range and relative abundance of tetrapods within and beyond the Cretaceous period.

Sphenodon

16 · Surviving Reptiles

REPTILES SINCE THE CRETACEOUS

In late Cretaceous times varied reptiles belonging to ten orders inhabited almost every conceivable environment on the continents, and ranged far and wide over the surface of the oceans. At the beginning of the Tertiary period the reptiles, now overshadowed by the mammals and birds, were included within five orders, of which one, the Eosuchia, was to disappear not long after the advent of this new age, leaving four orders of reptiles that have survived from early Cenozoic times to the present.

These four orders of modern reptiles are the Chelonia or turtles, the Crocodilia or crocodilians, the Rhynchocephalia, and the Squamata or lizards and snakes. Of these orders, the rhynchocephalians are now represented by the single genus, *Sphenodon*, confined to a very limited range in New Zealand. Since the evidence of the fossils would seem to indicate that the rhynchocephalians have probably been a restricted group of reptiles ever since the end of Triassic times, the truly abundant reptiles that survived the close of the Mesozoic era have therefore been the tropical and subtropical crocodilians, and the widely distributed turtles, lizards, and snakes. Consequently these three orders of reptiles, even though not dominating the earth as did the reptiles of Mesozoic days, have nevertheless been very successful tetrapods, persisting through a long span of geologic time as competitors of the "higher" vertebrates.

The origins of the surviving reptiles go far back in geologic history. The turtles appeared during the Triassic period, as did the rhynchocephalians, when these latter reptiles enjoyed an almost world-wide distribution. The crocodilians arose at the close of the Triassic period, to occupy the ecologic niche vacated by the phytosaurs. The ancestors of the Squamata had appeared in Triassic times, and from these ancestors the lizards became defined and well established during the Jurassic period. By Cretaceous times the snakes had developed the highly specialized adaptations so characteristic of them. Therefore it is necessary to look back to early and middle Mesozoic times, or earlier, to begin the survey of surviving reptiles that will form the subject of this chapter.

THE TURTLES

From the Permian beds of South Africa there has been described a rare and all too fragmentary fossil that gives a possible inkling of the origin of the turtles. This is the genus *Eunotosaurus,* a very small reptile only a few inches in length. Little is known of the skull, but the palate and lower jaw are sufficiently well preserved to indicate that *Eunotosaurus* was well supplied with small teeth around the margins of the jaws and on the palate. The dorsal vertebrae and the ribs, which are nicely fossilized, indicate a remarkable degree of specialization in the trunk region of this reptile, for the elongated vertebrae between the shoulder region and the pelvis in *Eunotosaurus* were limited in number to nine, whereas there were but eight ribs, each so broadly expanded that it was in contact with its neighbor before and behind. There is no certainty on the basis of this fragmentary evidence that *Eunotosaurus* was ancestral to the turtles, but such adaptations in the vertebrae and the ribs might very well have been on the evolutionary line leading to the specialization of the turtle shell.

The first true turtles made their appearance by the middle or late part of the Triassic period, by which time they were far advanced along the lines of adaptive radiation typical of modern turtles. In *Proganochelys,* a characteristic Triassic genus, the bones of the skull had been reduced in number, teeth were absent from the margins of the jaws, and the body was protected by a heavy shell. These are the basic turtle adaptations, and evolution among the turtles since Triassic times has been mainly a matter of refining the characters that were established in *Proganochelys.* For instance, the later turtles were completely toothless, whereas the Triassic forms still retained teeth on the palate. Also, the more advanced turtles developed the power to retract the head, legs, and the tail within the shell, which may not have been possible in *Proganochelys*.

The turtles are obviously direct descendants of the cotylosaurs, and through their evolutionary history they have tended to retain the

Cryptodire

Pleurodire

Amphichelydian

FIGURE 68. Three phases in the evolution of the turtles. The first true turtles were the amphichelydians (now extinct), here represented by *Proganochelys*. The late Mesozoic and Cenozoic pleurodires and cryptodires diverged as two branches from an amphichelydian ancestry.

solid skull roof of the primitive reptiles, though with a reduced complement of bones. In many advanced turtles, however, there have been secondary emarginations and reduction of the skull roof. In other respects the turtles show various adaptations that have served them well in their long struggle for survival. The jaws early became devoid of teeth, as mentioned, and covered with a horny beak. This beak makes a strong shearing mechanism, as we know, equally effective for eating meat or plants. The limbs are heavy, and in the land-living forms the feet are short, with the bones of the toes reduced in number from the primitive reptilian condition. In the marine turtles the feet have become modified as large, flipper-like paddles.

But the truly characteristic specialization in the turtles is the development of the shell. In these reptiles the ribs, by a process of differential growth, have enveloped the girdles and upper limbs segments to support the protective bony carapace. On the ventral surface the bony plastron has been developed. Both carapace and plastron are covered with horny sheaths, and are connected to each other along the sides. In this fashion the turtles have evolved into completely armored reptiles. Turtles are frequently cited as examples of slowness and general stupidity in the animal world, yet their adaptations for heavy protection at the expense of mobility have stood the test of time, for these are among the most ancient of the existing tetrapods.

The first turtles belonged to the suborder of amphichelydians, a group that was widely distributed during Mesozoic times and that held on into the Cenozoic era. From the amphichelydians two suborders of turtles evolved during late Mesozoic times, to continue until the present day. One of these, the pleurodires, is characterized, among other things, by the fact that the neck is bent laterally when the head is pulled into the shell. The pleurodires were rather widely distributed in Cretaceous and early Tertiary times, but during the later phases of their evolutionary history they have been restricted primarily to the southern hemisphere. For example, *Podocnemis* is a pleurodire, now living in South America and Madagascar, that during Cretaceous times ranged through many continental regions. At the present time pleurodires inhabit South America, Africa, southern Asia, and Australia.

By far the most numerous and successful of the turtles have been the cryptodires, which today are found throughout the world. In these turtles the head is withdrawn into the shell by a vertical, S-shaped flexure of the neck, and the cervical vertebrae are highly specialized to accomplish this. These turtles have been prominent in tetrapod faunas since Cretaceous times, and have evolved along many lines of adaptive radiation. Thus there are cryptodires that live in rivers and marshes, whereas others are suited for life on dry land. Some live in forests, others on plains and in deserts. Some turtles spend their lives in the sea, coming on land only for the purposes of breeding. Some are very small; others, like the modern Galapagos tortoises, *Testudo*, or the giant *Colossochelys* of the Pleistocene of Asia, have attained very great size. Some are completely carnivorous, some completely herbivorous, and others omnivorous. By reason of their structural adaptations and the wide range of their adjustments to the changing environments of the world, the turtles have endured for many millions of years; and, if man does not disturb them completely, it looks as if they will be on the earth for a long time to come.

THE CROCODILIANS

In looking at a crocodile or an alligator we are in a way looking back into the Age of Dinosaurs. These, the largest and most aggressive of modern reptiles and the close relatives of the dinosaurs, give us a faint idea of what the dominant reptiles of the Mesozoic era may have been like in the flesh.

The best known of the early crocodilians is the genus *Protosuchus*, from rocks of uppermost Triassic or lowermost Jurassic age (the stratigraphic relationships of these sediments is a matter of argument among geologists) in the northern part of Arizona. It is doubtful whether *Protosuchus* was a contemporary of the large phytosaurs, so characteristic of late Triassic times, but if not it followed immediately after the extinction of the phytosaurs.

Protosuchus was a moderately small reptile, some three or four feet in length, and obviously of thecodont ancestry. It was quadrupedal in pose, but the hind limbs were considerably larger than the fore limbs, indicating the descent of this animal from bipedal ancestors. The legs were strong, and evidently *Protosuchus* was rather well adapted for running around on the land. It may have been something of a swimming animal too, although there is no direct evidence to prove this, beyond certain obvious relationships with the later crocodilians. Its archosaurian skull had certain crocodilian characters, notably a flattening of the skull roof, a reduction in size of the upper temporal opening, and the suppression of the preorbital fenestra. The teeth were sharply pointed, indicating that this reptile was carnivorous. In the front foot the proximal bones of the wrist were elongated, as in all the crocodilians, whereas in the hind foot there was a large calcaneum and astragalus, again a crocodilian trait. Of particular interest is the fact that the proximal end of the elongated pubis did not form any portion of the acetabulum, this being a character peculiar to the crocodilians. Along the midline of the back was a double row of bony, protective scutes.

Protosuchus, which together with several other genera of comparable age can be set apart in a distinct suborder, the Protosuchia, makes an ideal ancestor for the later crocodilians. With the beginning of Jurassic times the crocodiles quickly occupied the ecological niche formerly held by the phytosaurs and have continued in this position through successive ages and faunas down to the present day. The adaptations of the crocodilians have involved phylogenetic growth of the body, so that these reptiles range from medium-sized animals to veritable giants, and the development of specializations for swimming and for an aggressive, carnivorous mode of feeding. Thus the crocodilians as a group have been characterized through their history by strong and frequently elongated jaws equipped with sharp teeth, by rather short but strong legs terminating in broad, webbed feet, by a long, deep, powerfully muscled tail making a strong propeller for swimming, and by heavy armor over the back and the sides, partly in the form of bony scutes, partly as horny external plates.

The first crocodilians to evolve from protosuchian ancestors were the mesosuchians, the most numerous and generally dominant crocodilians of Mesozoic times, living abundantly from lower Jurassic times to the end of the Cretaceous period, and straggling into the Tertiary period. The mesosuchians differed from the protosuchians and from modern crocodilians in that the upper temporal opening was very large, perhaps as an adaptation for the accommodation of particularly strong temporal muscles. The external nostrils, as in all crocodilians, was at the tip of the snout, whereas the internal nares were located at the posterior borders of the palatine bones. Between these two openings the nasal passage was separated from the mouth cavity by a median junction of the premaxillary, maxillary, and palatine bones, forming a bony tube to enclose the nasal passage.

Since the lower and middle portion of the Jurassic period was a time of great marine inundations, when lands were restricted, it is not surprising to find that many of the early crocodilians were well adapted for a life either along the shores of the seas or entirely in the open oceans. Such are the genera *Teleosaurus* and *Steneosaurus*. One family of mesosuchian ancestry, the Metriorhynchidae or geosaurs, became highly adapted for marine life. They lost the heavy bony armor, and, as mentioned in Chapter 12, the limbs were modified into paddles, and the vertebrae of the tail were abruptly downturned to form a reversed heterocercal tail fin. In spite of their high specializations this group of marine crocodilians died out during lower Cretaceous times.

From the mesosuchians two lines of advanced crocodilians evolved during the Cretaceous period. One of them was the suborder Sebecosuchia, unknown until a few years ago, and now represented by two genera, *Sebecus* and *Baurusuchus*. Both these forms are found in South America, *Sebecus* in the Eocene of Patagonia and *Baurusuchus* in the Cretaceous of Brazil. It is possible that this line of crocodilian evolution may have been restricted to the South American continent. These crocodilians differed from other members of the order largely by reason of the fact that the skull was very much compressed from side to side and rather deep, and the teeth were likewise laterally compressed. In *Baurusuchus* the teeth were much reduced in number, and some of the anterior teeth were greatly enlarged, like canines, giving to the skull an appearance superficially similar to that of a mammal-like reptile.

The more familiar line of advanced crocodilians is the line of the eusuchians, the crocodiles of the modern world. Eusuchians made their appearance in Cretaceous times, and evolved rapidly to displace their ancestors, the mesosuchians. In the eusuchian crocodiles the internal nares have moved far back in the palate so that they are completely enclosed by the pterygoid bones. This position causes the nasal passage to traverse a long tube from the external nostrils to the back of the throat, completely separated from the mouth cavity. In modern crocodiles there is a special flap on the back of the tongue, which together with a fold of skin from the back of the palate separates the respiratory passage from the mouth, a useful adaptation for an aquatic animal.

Since the beginning of the Cretaceous period the eusuchians have evolved along three lines, characterized by the crocodiles, the gavials, and the alligators. The crocodiles are narrow-snouted crocodilians with a wide distribution in the tropical and subtropical zones of the earth. The alligators are wide-snouted crocodilians, characteristic of North and South America, with one species in China. The gavials are very narrow-snouted crocodilians, living in India.

During Cretaceous and Cenozoic times the eusuchians were much more widely distributed than they are today, an indication of the greater extent of tropical and subtropical conditions in past ages as compared with the present. Perhaps the culmination of eusuchian evolution was attained by the late Cretaceous genus, *Phobosuchus*, the largest of all crocodiles, known from fossils collected along the Rio Grande River in Texas. The huge skull was six feet in length and broad in proportion, making *Phobosuchus* the possessor of some of the largest and most powerful jaws of all late Cretaceous reptiles. *Phobosuchus* must have had a total length of forty or fifty feet, and it is quite likely that this giant crocodile preyed upon the dinosaurs with which it was contemporaneous.

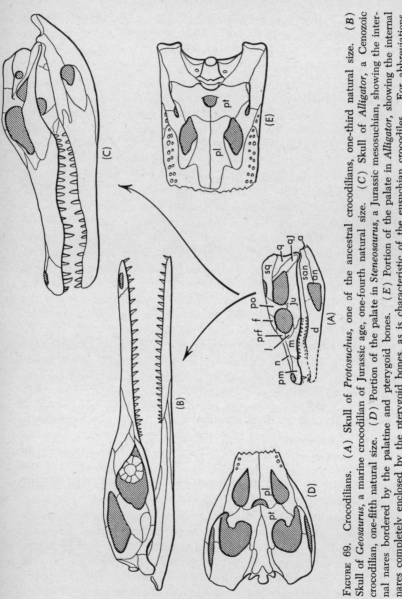

FIGURE 69. Crocodilians. (A) Skull of *Protosuchus*, one of the ancestral crocodilians, one-third natural size. (B) Skull of *Geosaurus*, a marine crocodilian of Jurassic age, one-fourth natural size. (C) Skull of *Alligator*, a Cenozoic crocodilian, one-fifth natural size. (D) Portion of the palate in *Steneosaurus*, a Jurassic mesosuchian, showing the internal nares bordered by the palatine and pterygoid bones. (E) Portion of the palate in *Alligator*, showing the internal nares completely enclosed by the pterygoid bones, as is characteristic of the eusuchian crocodiles. For abbreviations, see page 449.

The largest modern crocodilians reach lengths of twenty feet or more, but such dimensions are rare. Even a ten-foot or a twelve-foot alligator or crocodile is a formidable animal, well able to hold its own in this modern world against all adversaries except man. Unfortunately, the great crocodilians, the impressive remnants of the Age of Dinosaurs, are being constantly reduced in numbers and range by modern firearms.

THE RHYNCHOCEPHALIANS

On a few islands near the coast of New Zealand lives *Sphenodon*, also known as the tuatara, the sole surviving rhynchocephalian. Before the coming of white men *Sphenodon* inhabited much of New Zealand, but with the advance of modern civilization it disappeared at an alarming rate and was on the verge of extinction. Happily the tuatara is now rigidly protected. This reptile, about two feet in length, looks very much like a large lizard; but, unlike any lizard, it has two large temporal fenestrae, making it a true diapsid reptile. The teeth are fused to the jaws rather than being set in sockets. In *Sphenodon,* as in all rhynchocephalians, the front of the skull forms a sort of overhanging "beak," set with teeth.

The rhynchocephalians made their appearance at the beginning of the Triassic period, and according to the fossil record the Triassic was the time of greatest deployment and variety among these reptiles. During the Triassic period rhynchocephalians spread throughout the world. One family, known as the rhynchosaurs, consisting of rather large rhynchocephalians, was especially numerous at the beginning of the Mesozoic era.

After the Triassic the rhynchocephalians were very much restricted, and it would seem that they continued as a limited evolutionary line from then until the present day. The genus *Homoeosaurus*, of Jurassic age, is close to the modern *Sphenodon,* indicating that there has been little change among the rhynchocephalians over a lapse of more than one hundred million years.

THE LIZARDS AND THE SNAKES

The lizards and the snakes are by far the most numerous and diverse of modern reptiles. Whereas there is a single species of rhynchocephalian, about twenty-five species of living crocodilians, and some four hundred species of turtles, there are probably about thirty-eight hundred species of lizards and three thousand species of snakes. Moreover, it would seem likely that this great preponderance of the Squamata among the reptiles has pertained since the end of the Age of Dinosaurs.

The beginning of the Squamata can be seen in certain Triassic eosuchians, particularly in such genera as *Prolacerta*. Although *Prolacerta* was still an eosuchian and therefore a primitive diapsid, it had developed certain lizard-like characters, notably an incomplete quadratojugal bar below the lateral temporal opening. In the lizards there is a single upper temporal opening, above the postorbital-squamosal bar. Below this bar the cheek region is open, there being no lower bar formed by the quadratojugal between the jugal and quadrate bones, as in other reptiles. It would appear therefore that the lizards are modified diapsids, that the open temporal region below the postorbital-squamosal bar is in fact the lower diapsid opening, no longer enclosed below by a bony bar. Since the lower bar is lacking in these reptiles, the quadrate bone is free at its lower end, and this gives great mobility to the joint between the skull and the lower jaw. In addition to the quadratojugal, certain other skull bones are absent in the lizards, notably the lacrimal, the postparietal, and probably the tabular. As contrasted with these specializations in the bones of the skull, the lizards commonly retain the pineal opening, which is a primitive character among tetrapods. The teeth in lizards are not set in sockets, but are fused to the edges or to the inner sides of the jaws.

Lizards are quadrupedal reptiles in which the fourth toe of the hind foot is commonly elongated. These reptiles, when running, usually give a strong lateral push with the long, outer side of the foot, and this is the chief propulsive force. Some lizards, such as the collared lizard *Crotaphytus*, of western North America, rise up on the hind legs when running, and thus they parallel many of the extinct bipedal archosaurians in this mode of locomotion.

Lizards vary in size from tiny animals only a few inches in length to the large monitors, *Varanus*, some of which attain lengths of six or eight feet. These reptiles, evolving through upper Mesozoic and Cenozoic times to the present day, are too numerous for detailed consideration in a book such as this. Their chief paleontological interest is in the fact that during Cretaceous times certain varanid lizards became adapted to life in the sea and grew to gigantic size, reaching lengths of thirty feet or more. These were the mosasaurs, already described briefly in the chapter on marine reptiles of the Mesozoic.

The snakes, the last of all reptiles to evolve, are in essence highly modified lizards. Unfortunately the fossil history of the snakes is very fragmentary, so that it is necessary to infer much of their evolution from the comparative anatomy of modern forms.

In the snakes the limbs are lost, and locomotion is accomplished by various movements of the body—by sinuous side-to-side movements, by a straightforward motion in which the body muscles acting in rhythmic waves pull the snake along, and even by a sort of cork-

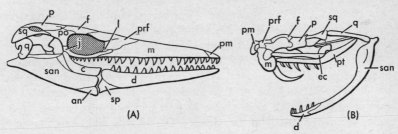

(A)   (B)

FIGURE 70. The skull in the Squamata. (A) *Tylosaurus*, a mosasaur or giant marine lizard. This skull is about three feet in length. Notice the free distal end of the quadrate bone, and the well-defined joint in the middle of the lower jaw. (B) *Crotalus*, a rattlesnake. Notice the reduction of bone in the skull, and the long, movable quadrate. A forward movement of the lower end of the quadrate in the snake increases the gape of the jaws. In the rattlesnake, and many other poisonous snakes, a special muscle pulls the pterygoid bone forward and rotates the maxilla, thus erecting the large poison-carrying fang for striking. For abbreviations, see page 449.

screw looping motion, the so-called sidewinding of some western American rattlesnakes. The body and tail are greatly elongated by an enormous multiplication of vertebrae and ribs, and of course with such an elongated body shape there have been numerous adaptations in the form and arrangement of the internal organs. No less remarkable than the adaptations of the body are those of the skull, which has become a highly kinetic structure, with a long, movable quadrate bone. This gives a sort of double joint to the back of the jaw. In addition, the premaxillae in the skull and the anterior ends of the dentaries in the lower jaw are not coalesced, but loosely connected by ligamental bonds, so that they can be spread apart to a considerable degree. When the snake kills its prey, it engulfs the victim whole, spreading the jaws to swallow an animal often considerably larger in diameter than the snake itself.

The snakes are remarkable by reason of the development of highly toxic poisons in many genera, such as the Old World vipers (*Vipera*) and cobras (*Naja*) and the New World rattlesnakes (*Crotalus*), a late phase of snake evolution possibly not appearing before Miocene times. It is because of this characteristic that snakes are held in such great dread by most people all over the world.

At about the time that snakes arose from their lacertilian ancestors the dinosaurs were in the final stages of their evolutionary history. Then the dinosaurs and the other dominant reptiles of the Mesozoic became extinct, and reptiles were forced to compete with highly efficient and very active tetrapods. This they did, and in so doing they succeeded by diverse means. The turtles continued through the Age of Mammals because of their highly developed protective shells, making them extraordinarily invulnerable to attack. The crocodilians persisted by living in tropical environments, where as aggressive beasts of prey they were relatively immune to attack from all except the largest and boldest of the mammals. The rhynchocephalians continued by retiring to an isolated part of the world, where there were no mammals to bother them. The lizards succeeded largely by following a life spent in the protection of dense foliage and rocks, where they could escape from their enemies. And the snakes succeeded and even perfected their adaptations during the age of mammalian supremacy, in part by becoming secretive animals, living in foliage and among rocks, burrowing under the ground, and retreating to the water, and in part by developing adaptations that made many of them the most dreaded of vertebrates, the carriers of violent death by poison.

Mesozoic Mammals

17 · Beginning of the Mammals

ORIGIN OF THE MAMMALS

The first mammals, descendants of some of the mammal-like reptiles, appeared in Jurassic times. These earliest mammals of the Jurassic period, unfortunately known for the most part only from teeth and jaws, were very small and comparatively insignificant, and all through the remainder of the Mesozoic era the mammals continued as small and minor members of the Jurassic and Cretaceous faunas, completely overshadowed by the numerous and ubiquitous reptiles that populated the lands and waters of the earth. Yet in spite of the littleness of the Mesozoic mammals, theirs was an especially important contribution to the evolutionary history of life, for it was during middle and late Mesozoic times that the mammals were going through the initial stages of their development to establish the basic mammalian types from which arose the tremendous variety of mammals that lived during the Cenozoic era.

As we have seen in Chapter 9 of this book, certain mammal-like reptiles evolved very far along lines leading to the mammals. The theriodonts, and after them the ictidosaurs, had advanced toward the mammalian stage, and with some of these highly evolved reptiles it is truly a matter of definition, based upon a few characters, whether they should be retained within the reptile class or regarded as ancestral mammals. Certainly it was but a short step from these animals to the first undoubted mammals.

It is not easy to determine the precise line of mammalian ancestors among the theriodont and ictidosaurian reptiles. Some theriodonts were far advanced toward the mammals in certain characters, but comparatively primitive in others; and among all the theriodonts the mixtures of advanced and conservative characters are so various that it is not possible to point to any one particular group and define it as progressing most positively in the direction of the mammals. Likewise, the ictidosaurs, although highly advanced toward the mammalian grade, include several diverging evolutionary lines, some of which show specializations of such definite complexity as to preclude them from general mammalian ancestry.

It is quite possible that the mammals may have had a polyphyletic origin—that several groups of mammal-like reptiles contributed to the ancestry of the early mammals. But whatever may have been the origin for the mammals among the mammal-like reptiles, the fact is that during Jurassic times the threshold had been crossed from reptile to mammal; a new and highly significant phase in the evolution of the tetrapods was beginning.

ESTABLISHMENT OF MAMMALIAN CHARACTERS

The diagnostic characters of the mammals are various. Briefly the mammals are active tetrapods in which the body temperature is comparatively uniform and the basic metabolism high, for which reason they are often referred to as "warm-blooded" animals. There is typically a protecting and insulating covering of hair. The young are usually born alive (the monotremes lay eggs) and are nourished during the early stages of their life on milk supplied by the mother.

As for the hard parts, which are of particular concern to the student of fossils, there are various diagnostic characters. Thus the mammals have a double occipital condyle forming the articulation for the skull upon the first vertebra of the neck, there is a secondary hard palate of bone separating the nasal passage from the mouth, and the external nasal opening is a single orifice in the front of the skull. Furthermore, the joint between the skull and the lower jaw is formed by the squamosal and dentary bones, respectively. The quadrate and articular bones, the articulating elements between the skull and jaw in the reptile, have in the mammal retreated into the middle ear to become transformed into two of the three ear ossicles, the incus and malleus, respectively, that together with the stapes (inherited from the reptilian stapes) make a chain to transmit vibrations from the eardrum to the inner ear. This is one of the most remarkable transformations of anatomical structures from one function to another in the history of vertebrate evolution. Of particular importance is the comparatively large brain case in all but the very primitive mammals, a reflection of the growth of the brain and the greatly increased intelligence in these tetrapods. Continuing, the mammals have a differentiated dentition of incisors, canines, and cheek teeth, of which the latter generally have a crown consisting of several cusps, held in the jaw by two or more roots. The mammals have the ribs of the neck permanently fused to the vertebrae, to form integral parts of these bones, whereas in the back part of the body the lumbar vertebrae are free of ribs. In the mammals there is a strong spine running down the middle of the shoulder blade or scapula. The bones of the pelvis, the ilium, ischium, and pubis are fused to form a single bony structure. Finally, the toe bones are reduced in number so that there are but three phalanges in each digit, except for the first one, in which there are two phalanges. Other characters define the mammalian skeleton, but these are some of the more important and obvious ones.

The derivation of these typically mammal characters from advanced mammal-like reptiles can be outlined somewhat as follows.

Mammal-like Reptiles	*Mammal*
Double occipital condyles (cynodonts, ictidosaurs)	Double occipital condyles
Secondary palate (some therocephalians, cynodonts, ictidosaurs)	Secondary palate
Separate external nares	Single external narial orifice
Enlarged dentary (cynodonts, ictidosaurs)	Dentary alone forming the lower jaw
Quadrate-articular joint	Squamosal-dentary joint
Reduced quadrate-articular (especially in ictidosaurs)	Incus-malleus
Restricted brain case	Enlarged brain case
Differentiated dentition	Differentiated dentition
Separate cervical ribs	Fused cervical ribs
Lumbar ribs	Free lumbars
Front border of scapula turned out (cynodonts)	Scapular spine
Pelvic elements separate	Pelvic elements fused
Phalangeal formula 2–3–3–3–3 (in some therocephalians)	Phalangeal formula 2–3–3–3–3

We may only infer some of the other changes that took place in the transition from reptile to mammal. The constant body temperature and the high degree of activity in the mammals are correlated with the four-chambered heart in these tetrapods, in which the arte-

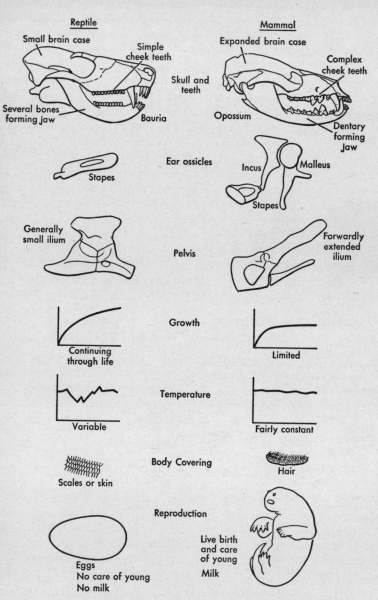

FIGURE 71. Some contrasting characters of reptiles and mammals.

rial blood is kept entirely separated from the venous blood. Perhaps this stage had been attained in some of the theriodonts or the ictidosaurs; certainly we may suppose that it was present in the early Jurassic mammals. It seems probable that the insulating coat of hair evolved along with the constant body temperature in the mammals, to protect them from the cold and from the heat as well. The mammals are characterized by a diaphragm, which separates the thoracic portion of the body cavity from the abdominal region, and assists in drawing air into the lungs and forcing it out. No such structure exists in modern reptiles, and it is reasonable to suppose that the diaphragm developed as a new device that made possible a large degree of oxygen intake for active animals, and that this took place at a late stage during the transition from reptile to mammal. As to the development of new methods of reproduction, it seems likely that these appeared after mammals were firmly established on the earth. The modern monotremes lay eggs, although they suckle their young with milk that is secreted from modified sweat glands on the under surface of the body. Perhaps this was the stage of reproductive development in many of the primitive mammals of middle Mesozoic times.

The marsupials or pouched mammals, in which the young are born alive as tiny, larval animals, to be nurtured for some weeks in the mother's pouch until they have reached a stage of independence, are first found in upper Cretaceous sediments. Likewise the placental mammals, in which the young are born in a comparatively advanced stage of development, first appear in strata of late Cretaceous age. It is therefore probable that these highly developed mammals became established during Cretaceous times.

JURASSIC MAMMALS

Four orders of mammals are known from sediments of Jurassic age, and are represented by fossils discovered in Europe and North America, particularly in the Stonesfield slates and the Purbeck beds of Europe, and in certain phases of the Morrison formation of North America. These are the Triconodonta, the Symmetrodonta, the Pantotheria, and the Multituberculata.

The triconodonts, of middle and late Jurassic age, are known from partial skulls, teeth, jaws, and palates. These animals ranged in size from tiny beasts no larger than mice to animals like *Triconodon* of late Jurassic age, as large as cats. The rather long jaws had a considerable array of differentiated teeth—as many as four incisors, a canine, and nine postcanine teeth. In the mammal-like reptiles the postcanine teeth, commonly designated as cheek teeth, either were all alike or formed a series that gradually increased in complexity from front to back. In the earliest mammals, on the other hand, the postcanine teeth are clearly divisible into anterior premolars and posterior molars, the latter being more complex in structure than the former. The differentiation of the teeth into incisors, canines, premolars, and molars constitutes one of the very important characters of mammals, first seen in the primitive Jurassic forms and carried through from them to the most specialized members of the class. It is indicative of a decided advance over even the most progressive of the mammal-like reptiles, and represents the culminating stage in the differentiation of the teeth for efficient mastication of the food. No mammals have had more than a single canine in the tooth series, but the other teeth have varied in number. A triconodont with nine postcanine teeth had four premolars and five molars. The dental formula would therefore be indicated as 4–1–4–5, meaning four incisors, one canine, four premolars, and five molars. The molar teeth of the triconodonts were characterized by three cusps in a longitudinal row, from which the order derives its name. These primitive mammals would seem to have been an early "experiment in evolution," for most of them failed to survive beyond the close of the Jurassic period.

The symmetrodonts are so named because in them the molar teeth were composed each of three cusps arranged in a rather symmetrical triangle when looked at in crown view. The symmetrodonts of upper Jurassic age, typified by the genus *Spalacotherium,* represent another "experiment in evolution" that failed to survive into Cretaceous times. These animals paralleled the more successful early mammals in the development of their molar pattern.

Of particular importance are the pantotheres, often referred to as the trituberculates. In these middle and upper Jurassic mammals the jaws were long and slender, and there was a large array of cheek teeth. In *Amphitherium,* for instance, there were four incisors, a canine, four premolars, and seven molars. The upper molars in the pantotheres were of triangular shape in crown view, with a prominent cusp, designated as the *protocone,* on the inner apex of the triangle and with various cusps and cuspules on the outer side of the tooth. A row of these molars formed in essence a series of triangles or trigons, with the apices pointing in toward the midline of the mouth. Naturally there were spaces between the teeth along

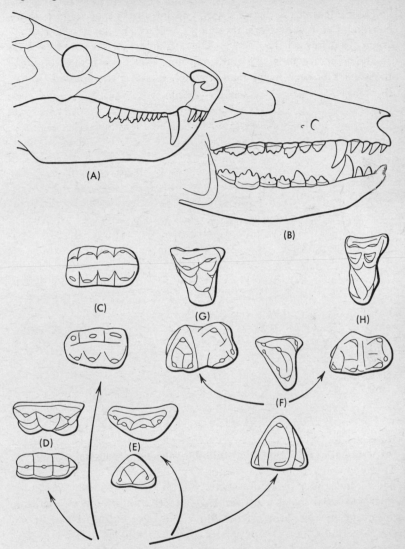

FIGURE 72. (A) *Cynognathus*, a Triassic therapsid reptile, showing the differentiated dentition and the cusped cheek teeth. (B) *Priacodon*, a Jurassic triconodont, with these characters advanced beyond the therapsid condition. (C–H) Crown views of teeth of Mesozoic mammals; upper molars above, lower molars below. (C) *Ctenacodon*, a multituberculate; (D) *Priacodon*, a triconodont; (E) *Eurylambda* (upper) and *Tinodon* (lower), symmetrodonts; (F) *Melanodon* (upper) and *Dryolestes* (lower), pantotheres; (G) *Pediomys* (upper) and a lower molar, marsupials; (H) *Gypsonictops* (upper) an insectivore and a lower molar of generalized therian type. Not to scale.

the inner edges of the dental series, and into these spaces there fitted
the triangular lower molars, in which the apices of the triangles were
directed out toward the cheek. These triangles of the lower molars
are known as trigonids. In addition, there was a low heel or talonid,
on the back of each lower molar, which received the pointed proto-

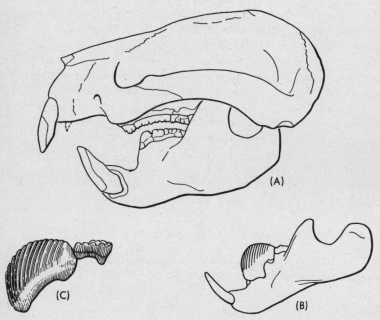

FIGURE 73. Paleocene multituberculates. (A) Skull and jaw of *Taeniolabis*,
one-half natural size. (B) Mandible of *Ptilodus*, somewhat enlarged. (C)
Last lower premolar and first lower molar of *Ptilodus*. Three times natural size.
The premolar was probably used for cutting food, the molar for crushing.

cone of the upper molar. It can be seen that this arrangement of
upper and lower molar teeth formed a rather complicated mechanism
for cutting by the shear of the talons and talonids past each other,
and for grinding by the action of protocone in the talonid like a
pestle in a mortar. Such an arrangement and mechanism of the
molars is exactly what we find in the primitive representatives of
the later mammals, and for this reason it is generally considered that
the pantotheres were the direct ancestors of the marsupial and placental mammals of Cretaceous and Cenozoic times.

The one other order of Jurassic mammals was the multituberculates,
a quite separate group of highly specialized animals. These would

seem to have been the first of the herbivorous mammals, showing in Jurassic times various adaptations for eating plants. The skull was heavy, with strong zygomatic arches for the attachment of powerful muscles to move the massive lower jaws. In the front of the skull and in the mandible was a pair of large, elongated incisors, behind which there was a considerable gap. The molars above and below were characterized by longitudinally arranged rows of cusps, paralleling similar adaptations in the cheek teeth of some of the ictidosaurian reptiles of the Triassic period, previously described. In the primitive multituberculates there were two parallel rows of longitudinal cusps in both upper and lower molars; in the later forms there were three rows of cusps in the upper teeth. The last lower premolar tooth was generally a greatly enlarged shearing blade, with strong vertical ribs on its inner and outer surfaces. In general these adaptations of the skull and dentition in the multituberculates were broadly similar to those seen in the later rodents, and it is reasonable to think that these early mammals lived a type of life that was imitated many millions of years later by the rodents. The Jurassic multituberculates, typified by the genus *Plagiaulax*, were rather small.

CRETACEOUS MAMMALS

Of the Jurassic mammals, only the multituberculates and some triconodonts continued as such into the Cretaceous period. The multituberculates carried on the adaptations that had been established by their Jurassic forebears, living and expanding through the complete span of the Cretaceous period and into the beginning of Cenozoic times. The Cretaceous and early Cenozoic evolution of the multituberculates was marked by certain refinements of the adaptations already outlined for these animals, especially by an increase in size. The culmination of evolution in these mammals was reached after the close of the Cretaceous period in the Paleocene genus *Taeniolabis*, an animal as large as a beaver, with a skull six inches in length and with large, chisel-like teeth, and in certain other forms that survived into early Eocene times.

The pantotheres were mentioned above as being probably ancestral to the marsupial and placental mammals that first appeared in the Cretaceous period. Since these mammals will be described in detail in subsequent chapters they need not be considered here, except to be placed among the Cretaceous mammals. Marsupials closely related to the modern American opossum are found in upper Cretaceous

sediments of North America; and placental insectivores, related to
modern shrews and hedgehogs, have been discovered in upper Cretaceous beds of Mongolia and North America.

THE MONOTREMES

It is pertinent at this place to mention briefly the monotremes,
unknown in the fossil record previous to the Pleistocene period, but
certainly among the most primitive of mammals. The monotremes
are known•from living genera that inhabit Australia and New Guinea.
These are the platypus or duckbill, *Ornithorhynchus,* and the spiny
anteaters, *Echidna* and *Tachyglossus.* Superficially these monotremes
are highly specialized, the platypus for a life in streams and in under-
ground burrows along the banks, and the anteaters for a hedgehog-
like existence in deep forests. In the duckbills the front of the skull
and lower jaw are flattened into a duck-like beak for burrowing in
the mud of streams in search of worms and grubs. The teeth are
shed and replaced by hard pads in the adults. The feet are modified
as webbed paddles. The anteaters are protected by sharp spines that
cover the body. In them the jaws are toothless and elongated into
a long, tubular snout, with which they probe ant hills.

In spite of these specializations the recent monotremes are basically
very primitive mammals. They reproduce by laying eggs, which are
hatched in burrows. The young are suckled on milk that is secreted,
as mentioned above, by modified sweat glands that are homologous
to the mammae or breasts in the higher mammals. The skeleton and
soft anatomy show the persistence of various reptilian characters.
For instance, the shoulder girdle is very primitive, with a persistent
interclavicle, large coracoids, and no true scapular spine. The
cervical ribs are unfused. Various reptilian characters persist in the
skull. The rectum and urinogenital system open into a common
cloaca as in reptiles, not separately as in mammals. There are no
external ears or pinnae as in most other mammals.

There is every reason to think that the monotremes represent quite
a separate line of descent from the mammal-like reptiles, continuing
in an isolated corner of the world, where they have been able to
survive as basically primitive mammals, with an overlay of certain
specializations. In many respects the monotremes give us an excellent view in the flesh of mammals intermediate in their stage of
evolution between the mammal-like reptiles and the higher mammals.

BASIC MAMMALIAN RADIATIONS

This short survey of the primitive mammals of Mesozoic times (plus the monotremes) outlines the first evolutionary developments in the mammals prior to their great expansion that took place at the beginning of Cenozoic times. Though Mesozoic mammals are not numerous or of great variety, they are of the utmost importance because of their bearing upon the later history of the mammals. They lived for a long time—as protracted a time span as that since the close of the Cretaceous period, the Age of Mammals as we usually think of it. And in this long expanse of Jurassic and Cretaceous time the primitive mammals established the primary lines of evolutionary radiation that determined subsequent mammalian history.

We can think of the history of the mammals as consisting of three periods of adaptive radiation.

The first was the Jurassic period, during which four orders appeared, the Triconodonta, the Symmetrodonta, the Pantotheria, and the Multituberculata. Two of these orders, the Symmetrodonta and Pantotheria, became extinct at the close of the Jurassic period, but the Pantotheria was obviously ancestral to the higher mammals of later times. The Triconodonta survived into the Cretaceous period, and the Multituberculata were very successful during late Mesozoic and early Cenozoic times.

The second period of mammalian radiation was the Cretaceous, during which the marsupials and the placentals made their appearance, and the multituberculates carried on.

The third and final period of mammalian radiation was the Cenozoic era, during which marsupials and placentals reached unprecedented heights of evolutionary development, and the multituberculates became extinct. The monotremes, known only during the final stages of Cenozoic history, very probably persisted through all three periods of mammalian radiation. Needless to say, the Cenozoic radiation of the mammals is the most interesting one to students of evolution, since it is during this phase of mammalian history that these tetrapods evolved along the numerous lines that have led to the varied and successful mammals of Tertiary, Quaternary, and recent times. It is to the third phase of mammalian radiation that we shall devote the remainder of this book.

Perhaps the radiation of the mammals as described above can be indicated by a simple diagram as follows.

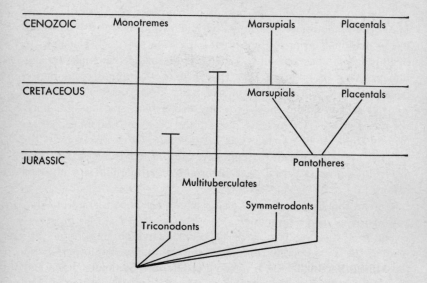

Kangaroos

18 · Marsupials

CENOZOIC CONTINENTS AND MARSUPIAL HISTORY

In order to understand the evolution and the modern distribution of the marsupials it is necessary to give particular attention to the history of the continental land masses during the Cenozoic era. Otherwise it may seem strange that the fossil record of these mammals is so fragmentary and restricted, and their modern distribution so peculiarly limited to the western world and to Australia.

It is probable that during Cretaceous times the marsupials were widely distributed throughout the world, although the evidence of the fossils on this is all too meager. At this period they very likely shared the world (so far as mammals were concerned) with the primitive placentals, and for a time the two groups may have competed on more or less equal terms. But with the advent of the Cenozoic era there was a great evolutionary burst of the placentals that brought about a stringent reduction, if not complete extermination of the marsupials in many continental regions.

In two areas, however, the marsupials continued in isolation from the rest of the world. Australia became completely separated from the Asiatic mainland during or at the end of the Cretaceous period, and here the marsupials lived on with virtually no placental competition. Consequently the marsupials enjoyed a wide range of adaptive radiation in the Australian region, and have continued to the present day as the dominant animals on the island continent. South America became isolated from North America by a breaking of the isthmian link at an early stage in Tertiary history, and it harbored a fauna containing marsupials and primitive placentals before the severance occurred. Once isolated, it too became a haven for the marsupials, since there was no opportunity for advanced placentals to enter the continent from the north. Therefore the marsupials were able to continue their evolutionary development as active competitors with the descendants of the ancient placentals that had been stranded on this continent. They lived on with a fair degree of success until the close of the Tertiary period, when South America once again became connected by an isthmian link with North America. Then there was an influx of highly specialized placentals from the north, and most of the marsupials were exterminated as a result of competition from these invaders. (Likewise, most of the original placentals of South America also disappeared under the wave of new mammals coming in from the north.)

Outside these two Tertiary island continents the development of marsupials was indeed limited. Marsupials managed to hold on in Europe through early and middle Tertiary times, but they eventually became extinct in that region. In North America a few very generalized marsupials have continued, in spite of pressure from the host of placentals evolving in this region. Today the common Virginia opossum, a relic of the Cretaceous period, inhabits a large section of this continent, and within recent years has been increasing its range northward.

MARSUPIAL CHARACTERS

It was mentioned in Chapter 17 that the marsupials are mammals in which the young are generally nurtured by the mother in a special pouch or pocket. Hence the name Marsupialia for the order, derived from the Latin word, *marsupium,* meaning a pouch. Marsupials are born as larval animals after a short period of gestation, and immediately they find their way into the mother's pouch. Here they become attached to the teats, which are located within the pouch. They remain attached to the teats for some time, receiving the milk that is literally pumped into them by the mother. As they develop and take form they finally achieve a degree of independence. Then the young marsupials live a life partly in and partly out of the mother's pouch.

Of course this very specialized method of reproduction and natal care is known to us from the modern marsupials. However there are various osteological characters that distinguish the marsupials,

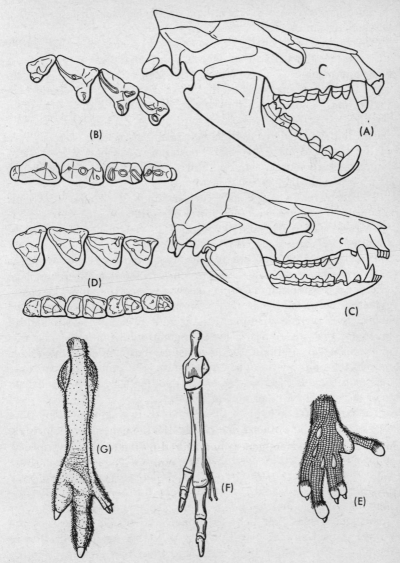

FIGURE 74. Marsupials. (A) Skull and jaw of *Borhyaena*, a large Miocene carnivorous marsupial from South America, about one-third natural size. (B) Upper and lower shearing molar teeth of *Thylacinus*, the recent Tasmanian "wolf," about natural size. (C) Skull and jaw of *Didelphis*, the modern North American opossum. (D) Upper and lower molar teeth of *Didelphis*. (E) Hind foot of the opossum, showing the divergent first toe, an adaptation for climbing. (F) Bones of the hind foot, and (G) the hind foot of a kangaroo, showing the syndactylous second and third toes, for grooming the fur.

making it possible to identify them and trace their history as it is inadequately preserved in the fossil record.

The brain case is small in the marsupials, a character that readily distinguishes them from the placentals and at the same time reflects their low mentality. Consequently the sagittal crest, for the attachment of the temporal muscles that close the jaws, is frequently high and strong. The opening for the eye is confluent with the temporal opening, as it generally is among primitive mammals. The bony palate is perforated by well-defined openings, seldom solid as it is in the placental mammals. The posterior angle of the lower jaw, beneath its articulation with the skull, is usually turned in or inflected, as it rarely is in the placental mammals.

The teeth in the marsupials vary in number. There may be as many as five upper and four lower incisor teeth on each side as compared with the maximum of three in the placental mammals. In primitive marsupials there are commonly three premolars and four molar teeth on each side of both upper and lower jaws, whereas in the placental mammals there are four premolars and three molars. The molar teeth in the marsupials show a triangular pattern of cusps, evidently inherited from the pantothere tooth pattern described above; thus there is an upper trigon with two outer cusps and an inner one that shears past a lower trigonid with one outer and two inner cusps. In addition, the lower molar has a basined talonid, to receive the point of the inner upper cusp, the protocone. In these mammals there is less replacement of milk teeth by permanent teeth than there is in the placental mammals.

The postcranial skeleton of the marsupials is greatly modified from the skeleton in the mammal-like reptiles, and in general is comparable to the skeleton in the placentals. There are seven cervical vertebrae, followed by about thirteen ribbed dorsals and commonly seven lumbar vertebrae, these latter free of ribs. There is generally a large clavicle, but the coracoid is reduced. There is a strong spine on the shoulder blade. In the pelvis there are commonly epipubic or "marsupial" bones that help to support the pouch. The toes are always clawed. Many marsupials show a strange specialization of the hind foot, whereby the second and third toes are very slender, closely appressed and enclosed in a single sheath of skin at their base. These two toes in effect "balance" the fifth toe, and the fourth toe, the largest of the series, serves as the axis of the foot. The slender second and third toes, known as syndactylous digits, make a sort of two-pronged comb with which, as can be seen in modern marsupials, the animals groom their fur.

THE OPOSSUM—A CRETACEOUS MAMMAL

The American opossum was mentioned above as a Cretaceous survivor in the modern world. This is no figure of speech, for the opossum is truly a "living fossil" that has changed very little during the long lapse of time from the Cretaceous period to the present. Therefore we are fortunately able to obtain a very fair idea of a primitive mammal by studying the opossum. This familiar inhabitant of our southern states is a small animal, about the size of a house cat. It is covered with coarse, light gray hair and it has a naked, rat-like tail. The opossum tail is prehensile, which means that it can be used for grasping limbs of trees, like a "fifth hand." The feet are primitive, with all the toes present in an unreduced state, and well provided with claws. The clawed feet and the prehensile tail make the opossums great climbers, and they spend much of their time in trees.

The skull is generalized, showing the various marsupial characters already listed, such as the small brain case, the perforated palate, and the inflected angle of the jaw. The teeth, too, are primitive, with a dental formula of five upper and four lower incisors, a canine, three premolars, and four molars. The pattern of the molar teeth is of the primitive type already described, a series of opposing triangles with basined talonids in the lower molars.

This animal can be taken as representing in essential features the ancestor of the marsupials. From an opossum-like base the marsupials have evolved, especially in the Americas and in Australia, along various lines of adaptive radiation.

EVOLUTION OF THE AMERICAN MARSUPIALS

The marsupials that, like the Virginia opossum, have remained primitive throughout the course of their history are the didelphids of North and South America. It is probably because the didelphids have continued as small and generalized marsupials that they have been able to survive, in spite of the presence of numerous highly specialized placental mammals. The common opossum, *Didelphis*, has already been described. Perhaps some of its ancestors included *Eodelphis*, from the Cretaceous, and *Peratherium*, from the early Tertiary of North America and Europe. Another persistent primitive opossum is the "mouse opossum," *Marmosa*, of Central America.

Chironectes, the modern yapok of Central America, is an opossum that has become adapted to life in streams and rivers.

From didelphid ancestors certain South American marsupials specialized as aggressive carnivores during Tertiary times. These were

Borhyaena and Litoptern

Thylacosmilus

FIGURE 75. Middle and upper Tertiary carnivorous marsupials of South America. *Borhyaena* was as large as a wolf, *Thylacosmilus* equaled a jaguar in size, and paralleled in a remarkable way the large, saber-tooth cats.

the borhyaenids, of which the Miocene genus *Borhyaena* was typical. This was a rather large marsupial, perhaps as large as a wolf or a large dog. The skull was very dog-like, with the canines enlarged as piercing and stabbing teeth, and some of the molars modified into shearing blades. The body was long, and the back was strong and supple. The tail was long. The limbs were strong, and the feet had sharp claws. All in all, *Borhyaena* was like a large, long-tailed dog in its general adaptations, and it obviously preyed upon other mammals, both marsupial and placental, with which it was contemporaneous.

In Pliocene times some of the borhyaenids became remarkably specialized. One genus, *Thylacosmilus*, an animal as large as a tiger, had a short skull and a tremendously elongated, blade-like upper canine tooth, whereas in the lower jaw there was a deep flange of bone to protect this tooth when the mouth was closed. Here we see an uncanny resemblance to the saber-tooth cats of the Pleistocene of North America. In spite of such advanced specializations *Thylacosmilus* and the other carnivorous borhyaenids were unable to withstand the influx of the carnivorous placentals from North America when the two continents became reunited during the Pliocene epoch. Therefore these marsupials, showing close patterns of convergence with the placental carnivores of other continents, became extinct.

In another line of marsupial evolution in South America are the caenolestoids, small and in most respects generalized marsupials that range in age from the Eocene to the present day. The modern representative of this phylogenetic line is *Caenolestes*, the "opossum rat," of Ecuador and Peru, a marsupial without a pouch. There has been an enlargement of the middle lower incisor teeth in these marsupials, with a correlative reduction or complete suppression of the other incisors. In some of the early genera, such as *Polydolops*, from the Paleocene and Eocene, this specialization had reached a high stage of development. Except for the caenolestoids, all the American marsupials can be classified as "polyprotodonts," which means that they had several incisor teeth on either side in the upper and lower jaws. The caenolestoids, however, seem to show some relationship in this respect to the "diprotodonts," the marsupials of Australia that have a single lower incisor on each side of the lower jaw.

ADAPTIVE RADIATION OF THE AUSTRALIAN MARSUPIALS

Australia is (or was until the coming of the white man) the great home of the marsupials, harboring an array of these mammals not equaled elsewhere in the world. Unfortunately the marsupials of Australia are virtually unknown in sediments older than the Pleistocene, so that most of our conclusions as to the evolution of the pouched mammals in Australia must be based upon inferences drawn from studies of recent types. The range of adaptations in the modern

246 Evolution of the Vertebrates

Australian marsupials is great, and indicates a variety of evolutionary lines during Tertiary times.

'There are three groups of marsupials in Australia, the dasyuroids, the parameloids, and the phalangeroids, these last often called the diprotodonts.

The dasyuroids are polyprotodont marsupials that show adaptations for various modes of life. Some of the dasyuroids are carnivorous, like the thylacine or Tasmanian wolf, *Thylacinus,* in which there is a remarkable parallelism with the extinct borhyaenids of South America. The Tasmanian devil, *Sarcophilus,* is a smaller but aggressive carnivore; and still other meat-eaters among the dasyuroids are represented by the numerous "native cats," of which *Dasyurus* itself is an example. Other dasyuroids are *Myrmecobius,* an ant-eating marsupial, and *Notoryctes,* a mole-like animal, living in burrows under the ground.

The parameloids are also polyprotodont marsupials, mostly of small size, in which the hind feet have the second and third toes modified as syndactylous digits, used for combing the fur. These are the bandicoots, long-snouted animals with long hind legs for hopping, rabbit fashion. Some bandicoots feed upon insects or plants, and some of them are omnivorous, eating anything they can get.

The phalangeroids are the diprotodont marsupials in which the hind feet have syndactylous digits. They form a large, varied group that includes some of the most characteristic of the Australian marsupials. Here are the numerous phalangers or Australian opossums, many of them showing squirrel-like adaptations. One of the well-known diprotodonts is the koala or native "bear," *Phascolarctos,* an animal strangely adapted for feeding upon the leaves of certain eucalyptus trees and nothing else. Another is the wombat, *Phascolomys.* Finally, there are the wallabies and kangaroos, so well known as to need no description. These are the herbivores of Australia, adapted for browsing and grazing upon a variety of plants. Instead of running, as do large plant-eating mammals in other parts of the world, the kangaroos sail across the landscape in graceful, prodigious leaps, propelled by their powerful hind legs.

A Pleistocene relative of the modern diprotodont marsupials was the giant animal *Diprotodon.* This marsupial was as large as a large ox, and was a rather clumsy, four-footed beast. In life it may have looked something like a huge wombat.

The modern marsupials of Australia constitute a remarkable example of adaptive radiation and evolutionary convergence. On this island continent, protected from invading placentals by isolation from the mainland, the marsupials have evolved in various directions for many differing modes of life, so that they occupy the ecologic niches that in other continents have been usurped by the Cenozoic placentals. Thus the carnivorous thylacines can be compared with wolves of other regions, the small dasyures with small cats, weasels, and martens. These marsupial carnivores prey upon other mar-

Marsupial "Mouse"

Tasmanian "Wolf"

Wombat

Phalanger

Bandicoot   Koala   Marsupial "Mole"

FIGURE 76. Adaptive radiation among the recent marsupials of the Australian region. All drawn to approximately the same scale.

supials, the thylacines on the larger plant-eaters, the dasyures on the numerous small marsupials that inhabit the grasslands, the thickets, and the trees. The wallabies and kangaroos can be compared with deer, antelopes, and gazelles in other continents, even though they have no physical resemblance to the hoofed animals. Nevertheless these are the larger plant-eaters, most of which live on the plains or in the open forest, and escape by their ability to cover ground at a very rapid pace. The wombats can be compared with large rodents, like woodchucks, and there are numerous small marsupials comparable to the small rodents of other regions. Phalangers can be compared with squirrels, bandicoots with rabbits, and so on.

THE EVOLUTIONARY POSITION OF THE
MARSUPIALS

From this discussion it appears that the marsupials have been and are "second-class mammals" as compared with the placentals, and for this reason it has been common practice for zoologists to regard the marsupials as constituting a sort of lower grade in the heirarchy of mammals—an intermediate step in the evolution of mammals between the ancestral mammals of the Jurassic period and the Cenozoic placentals. However the evidence indicates that although the placentals may have gone through a stage in their early history somewhat comparable to that of the marsupials, the two groups probably arose independently from a common pantotherian ancestry, to evolve side by side. Certainly the fossil record of the placentals is as ancient as that of the marsupials.

It is probably valid to think of the marsupials and placentals as arising at about the same time, during the Cretaceous period. They developed two quite dissimilar methods of reproduction, as well as various anatomical differences. During the early stages of their evolutionary histories they were probably well matched, so that marsupial adaptations were about as efficient in evolutionary terms as placental adaptations. But as time went on, and especially with the opening of the Cenozoic era, the placentals became dominant. There were probably various factors that led to the dominance of the placentals over the marsupials, but of these it is likely that the superior intelligence of the placental mammals was of particular importance.

Dinosaurs and Insectivores

19 · *Introduction to the Placentals*

BASIC PLACENTAL CHARACTERS

The Cenozoic period is commonly referred to as the Age of Mammals. We might with reason call it the Age of Placental Mammals, because these have been the overwhelmingly dominant mammals in almost all parts of the earth ever since the transition from Cretaceous into Cenozoic times. During Cenozoic history the monotremes have been represented by 3 Recent genera, belonging to a single order; the order of multituberculates, by 17 genera of early Tertiary age; the marsupials by 127 genera; fossil and recent, also contained within a single order, and the placentals by 2648 genera belonging to 28 separate orders. On a percentage basis, the Cenozoic placentals total 95 per cent; the non-placentals 5 per cent. These figures, based upon the modern very complete classification of mammals made by George Gaylord Simpson, illustrate placental dominance without the need of further discussion.

The placental mammals or eutherians are, of course, those mammals in which the young go through a considerable period of prenatal growth, to be born in a comparatively advanced stage of development. In these mammals one of the membranes inherited from the old reptilian egg, the allantois, is in contact with the uterus, within which is the embryo; and through this area of contact, the placenta, food and oxygen are carried from the mother to the developing embryo. As a result of this embryonic growth, the placental mammal when born is to a greater or lesser degree a miniature replica of its parents. Even the most helpless of newborn placentals, like baby rodents or carnivores or human beings, are incomparably more advanced than the larva-like newborn of the marsupials. And in many placentals, such as the hoofed mammals or the whales, the young are born as active little animals, fully able to follow their mothers within a few hours after their birth.

In osteological characters the placentals show various distinguishing traits. Perhaps the most important character to be seen in the skeleton of these mammals is the expanded brain case, reflecting the superior intelligence of most placentals as contrasted with the marsupials. Additional features that characterize the skull in the placentals are the solid bony palate, as contrasted with the generally pierced palate of the marsupials, and the usual lack of an inturned or inflected angle in the lower jaws. In the postcranial skeleton the placental like the marsupial is characterized by seven cervical or neck vertebrae, behind which is a thoracic series of vertebrae bearing ribs, and after that a ribless lumbar series. The girdles and limbs in the placentals are basically similar to those of the marsupials, already described, although of course there are many placental specializations that result from adaptations to varied modes of locomotion. The placentals lack epipubic or marsupial bones on the pelvis.

Of all the hard parts, however, the teeth are of particular importance in a study of the placental mammals. It is very probable that if all the placental mammals except man were extinct, and represented only by fossil teeth, their basic classification would be essentially the same as the classification now drawn up on the knowledge of the complete anatomy in these mammals. This is indeed fortunate. Even though many fossil mammals are frequently preserved only as fragments of jaws containing teeth, it is possible to study them and reach valid conclusions as to their evolutionary history and their relationships. For this reason it may be useful at this place to introduce a discussion of the teeth in the placental mammals.

THE TEETH OF PLACENTAL MAMMALS

The basic tooth formula for the placental mammals is three incisors, a canine, four premolars, and three molars, on each side in both upper and lower jaws. This formula, expressed by the notation 3–1–4–3, appears in the first placentals of Cretaceous age, and it persists in many modern mammals. Of course there has been extreme specialization of the teeth in many placentals, and this has frequently led to divergences from the primitive dental formula.

In most of the placental mammals the incisor teeth tend to be comparatively simple, single-rooted pegs or blades, adapted to nipping food. In some mammals the incisors are enlarged, in others they are reduced or suppressed. In a few they become complex, with comb-like crowns. Yet in spite of their various specializations, the incisors always retain the single root that holds them in the jaws.

The canines in primitive mammals are enlarged teeth of spike-like form, obviously used for stabbing and piercing functions. These teeth, like the incisors, remain usually single rooted throughout their many divergent adaptations, but they may show specializations in the crowns, especially with regard to shape and size.

The premolars of the placentals are generally of complex structure, and they commonly increase in complexity from front to back. Thus the first premolar may be a narrow-crowned tooth with two roots, whereas the last member of the series may be broad, with several cusps making up the crown and with three or more roots. It is not uncommon for the posterior premolars to show close resemblances to the molar teeth in many specialized mammals.

It is in the molar teeth, however, that we find a key to eutherian relationships. Indeed, much of our knowledge of the evolution of mammals through geologic time is based upon the close study of the molar teeth.

In discussing the Jurassic mammals it was shown that the panto-theres can be regarded as the probable direct ancestors of the marsupials and placentals by virtue of the construction of their molar teeth. Among the early marsupials and placentals the upper denti-tion consisted of trigons that sheared past the trigonids of the lower dentition. In addition to this shearing action of the upper and lower molars there was a crushing function brought about by the biting of the inner cusp of the trigon into a talonid, located behind the trigonid of the lower molar. Molars of this type are frequently said to be of trituberular, tuberculosectorial, or tribosphenic form. Perhaps the last of the foregoing terms is the preferable one; it will be used in this book. The tribosphenic molar constituted a base from which evolved the multitudinously varied molar teeth of the higher mammals.

The primitive nature of the tribosphenic molar pattern was estab-lished many years ago by the great American paleontologist, Edward Drinker Cope, and the nomenclature of the cusps was proposed by his disciple, Henry Fairfield Osborn. Cope and Osborn considered the tribosphenic molars as opposed, reversed triangles. So Osborn named the three cusps of the upper molar the protocone, the para-cone, and the metacone, the first being on the inner side of the tooth, the other two on the outer side. In addition there are often two intermediate cusps in the upper molar, between the main cusps; these were designated the protoconule and the metaconule. In the lower molar the outer cusp was designated the protoconid, and the two inner cusps were called the paraconid and the metaconid. In the lower molar there are commonly three cusps around the talonid or posterior basin. The outer one of these cusps was called the hypoconid, the inner one the entoconid, and the posterior one, on the back of the basin, the hypoconulid.

These basic cusps, which constitute the upper and lower tribo-sphenic molars, can be regarded as having had a common derivation, thus making them homologous in all marsupials and placentals. Their spatial relationships can be indicated as follows.

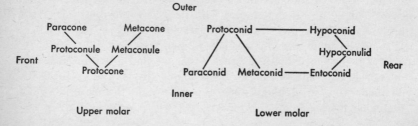

In many of the more advanced mammals there is a fourth main cusp, the hypocone, occupying the back inner corner of the upper molar. This cusp appears as an addition to the tooth during the evolutionary history of various orders of mammals; consequently it is doubtful that the hypocone is homologous in those mammals having the cusp. Finally, in the molars of many mammals there are various crests or ridges, which have been designated as lophs in the upper

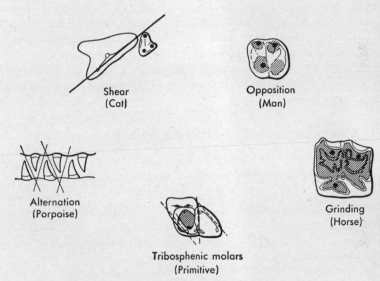

Shear
(Cat)

Opposition
(Man)

Alternation
(Porpoise)

Grinding
(Horse)·

Tribosphenic molars
(Primitive)

FIGURE 77. Types of action in mammalian cheek teeth.

molars and lophids in the lower molars, whereas certain small accessory cusps around the edges of the teeth have been termed styles and stylids in the upper and lower molars, respectively.

In the placental mammals the motions of the jaws involve four types of action between the upper and the lower molar teeth, three of which are present in the tribosphenic molars of the primitive mammals. In the first place there is the alternation of cusps, the biting past each other of these elements in the upper and lower molars, to hold and tear the food. For instance, the protoconid alternates with the paracone and metacone along the outer edge of the dentition, whereas the protocone alternates with the paraconid and the metaconid along the inner edge. Second, there is the shearing of the edges of teeth, or of lophs or crests, past each other, to cut the food. In the tribosphenic molars the front and back edges of the trigons shear past the front and back edges of the trigonids.

In the third place there is the opposition of certain parts of the teeth, which serves to pulverize or crush the food. Such is the action of the protocone biting into the basin of the talonid. Finally, there is the grinding of opposite tooth surfaces against each other like mills, to grind the food. This action is seen in the expanded molar crowns of many of the specialized mammals.

An important part of the discussion in the rest of this book will have to do with the adaptive radiation of teeth from the tribosphenic type in response to the need for preparing the food by the actions of alternation, shear, opposition, and grinding. It may seem that a great deal of emphasis is being given here to the teeth in placental mammals. The fact is, however, that much of the success of mammals during their Cenozoic history can be attributed to the adaptations of the teeth.

THE CLASSIFICATION OF THE PLACENTAL MAMMALS

Twenty-eight orders of placental mammals or eutherians evolved during the Cenozoic era, and of them sixteen orders exist at the present time. The orders of placental mammals can be listed as follows.

Insectivora: the insectivores. Shrews, moles, and hedgehogs.
Chiroptera: the bats.
Dermoptera: the colugos or "flying lemurs."
Taeniodonta: the taeniodonts, an extinct group.
Tillodontia: the tillodonts, an extinct group.
Edentata: the edentates. Anteaters, tree sloths, ground sloths, armadillos, and glyptodonts.
Pholidota: the pangolins.
Primates: the primates. Lemurs, tarsiers, monkeys, apes, and men.
Rodentia: the rodents. Squirrels, beavers, mice and rats, porcupines, cavies, and chinchillas.
Lagomorpha: the rabbits and hares.
Cetacea: the porpoises and whales.
Carnivora: the carnivores or beasts of prey. Creodonts (extinct), dogs, wolves and foxes, bears, pandas, raccoons, weasels, mink, otters, wolverines, badgers, skunks, civets, hyaenas, cats, sea lions, seals, and walruses.
Condylarthra: the condylarths. Primitive hoofed mammals. Extinct.
Notoungulata: the notoungulates. Primitive hoofed mammals of South America. Extinct.
Litopterna: the litopterns. Hoofed mammals of South America. Extinct.
Astrapotheria: the astrapotheres. Large South American mammals. Extinct.

Tubulidentata: the aardvarks.

Hyracoidea: the conies or dassies of Africa and Asia Minor.

Proboscidea: the proboscideans. Moeritheres, dinotheres, mastodonts, mammoths, and elephants.

Desmostyliformes: relatives of the sea cows and the proboscideans. Extinct.

Sirenia: the sea cows, or sirenians.

Pantodonta: the pantodonts. Large hoofed mammals. Extinct.

Dinocerata: the uintatheres. Gigantic hoofed mammals. Extinct.

Pyrotheria: the pyrotheres. Very large mammals of South America. Extinct.

Xenungulata: the xenungulates. Large hoofed mammals of South America. Extinct.

Embrithopoda: the arsinoitheres. Large hoofed mammals of Egypt. Extinct.

Perissodactyla: the perissodactyls or odd-toed hoofed mammals. Horses, titanotheres, chalicotheres, tapirs, and rhinoceroses.

Artiodactyla: the artiodactyls or even-toed hoofed mammals. Dichobunids, entelodonts, pigs, peccaries, anthracotheres, hippopotamuses, oreodonts, camels, tragulids, deer, giraffes, pronghorns, antelopes, goats, sheep, muskoxen, and cattle.

The earliest and most primitive eutherians were the insectivores, and it seems obvious that they were probably the ancestors of all other placental mammals. From an insectivore stem the eutherians have radiated in such a variety of directions along so many evolutionary lines that it is not easy to group the orders into larger categories. However recent work, especially by Simpson, would seem to indicate that the orders of mammals may be combined into four large groups, which he has designated as cohorts.

One cohort, the Unguiculata, includes the direct derivatives of the primitive insectivores. Here can be placed, together with the insectivores, the bats, the edentates, several lesser groups, and the large order of primates. A second cohort, the Glires, includes the rodents and lagomorphs. A third cohort, the Mutica, contains only the porpoises and whales, obviously a quite separate group of mammals since very early times. Finally the cohort Ferungulata includes the carnivores and all the various "hoofed mammals," extinct and living. This large and inclusive cohort, containing mammals showing indications of a common origin, can be broken into several subdivisions of the rank of superorders. One of these is the Ferae, the carnivorous mammals. A second is the Protungulata or primitive hoofed mammals, like the condylarths and various extinct South American mammals, as well as the modern aardvarks. A third superorder is the Paenungulata, the herbivorous mammals that include

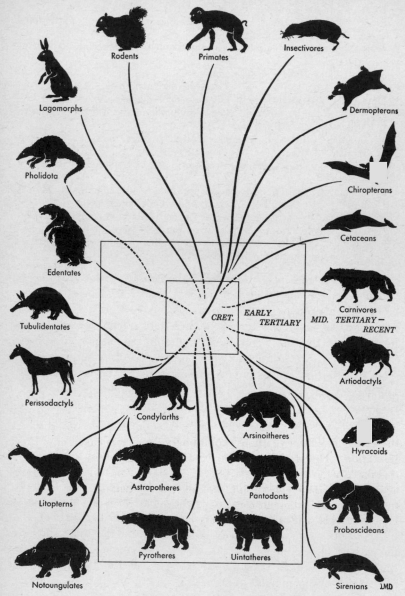

FIGURE 78.   Relationships of the orders of placental mammals.

the proboscideans, sea cows, uintatheres, and their relatives. Finally two separate superorders can be recognized, one each for the perissodactyls and the artiodactyls. On the basis of these groupings, the orders of placental mammals can therefore be listed in the following manner.

EUTHERIA

Cohort Unguiculata.
  Orders Insectivora, Chiroptera, Dermoptera, Taeniodonta, Tillodontia, Edentata, Pholidota, Primates.
Cohort Glires.
  Orders Rodentia, Lagomorpha.
Cohort Mutica.
  Order Cetacea.
Cohort Ferungulata.
  Superorder Ferae.
    Order Carnivora.
  Superorder Protungulata.
    Orders Condylarthra, Notoungulata, Litopterna, Astrapotheria, Tubulidentata.
  Superorder Paenungulata.
    Orders Hyracoidea, Proboscidea, Desmostyliformes, Sirenia, Pantodonta, Dinocerata, Xenungulata, Pyrotheria, Embrithopoda.
  Superorder Mesaxonia.
    Order Perissodactyla.
  Superorder Paraxonia.
    Order Artiodactyla.

In the remaining chapters of this book the various orders of placental mammals will be discussed, but not always according to the sequence by which they have been listed in this outline classification. It is not easy to be completely logical when considering a group of animals as extensive and varied as the mammals, particularly when the time dimension of their evolutionary history is taken into consideration. Therefore it may be expedient in discussing some orders to take up the evolutionary history of certain orders of mammals according to their geographic distribution or their position in time, rather than according to the strict concept of relationships. Let us hope that this will not be unduly confusing to the reader.

Ground Sloth

Mole

Glyptodonts

20 · Unguiculate Mammals

THE UNGUICULATES

The unguiculate mammals, in spite of the diversity of their adaptations, have certain characters in common that demonstrate their direct descent from insectivore ancestors. In general, these are and have been the most conservative of the eutherians, even though some of them are very highly specialized in some respects. The bats are essentially insectivores that have developed specializations for flying. The colugos are primitive mammals adapted for gliding. In the primates, obviously close relatives of the insectivores, a high degree of mental development and manual dexterity has evolved. The edentates are insectivore descendants in which specializations have been in the direction of climbing and digging, of restrictions in the diet with a consequent simplification or suppression of the teeth, and of the development of heavy armor for protection. The Pholidota, as we shall see, have evolved independently in a manner similar to some of the edentates. And the extinct taeniodonts and tillodonts were short-lived orders derived from an insectivore ancestry.

It would be convenient and logical to discuss all the unguiculate orders together, because of their underlying relationships to the ancestral insectivores. However, the primates are so large and varied a group of such great importance that they must of necessity be deferred for separate consideration.

THE INSECTIVORES

One of the very primitive Cretaceous insectivores was the genus *Deltatheridium*, from Mongolia. This was a small mammal, with a low skull less than two inches in length. The canines were comparatively large, piercing teeth; the molars were tribosphenic, with the paracone and the metacone of the upper teeth very close to each other. These molars would appear to be intermediate in structure between the pantothere molar and the molar of the more advanced placentals.

Deltatheridium can be regarded as approximating in structure the ancestral insectivores and through them the basic placentals. None of the insectivores have evolved into large or even medium-sized mammals, and most of them have been and are small. The common shrews are the smallest of all mammals, and it is probable that the secretive habits and the minute size of these insectivores have been instrumental in their long survival with little change from Cretaceous times to the present. All the insectivores have had a small and primitively constructed brain, as we might expect. The teeth have retained much of the ancestral tribosphenic molar pattern throughout the adaptive radiation of these mammals. The tympanic bone, which in higher mammals is frequently inflated to form a sort of capsule around the middle ear, is in the insectivores a simple ring. The skeleton has continued the generalized form typical of the primitive mammal, with an overlay among some groups of specializations for very definite modes of life. For instance, in the moles the limbs and feet are highly adapted for digging. The classification of the insectivores is difficult. Certain insectivores, known as "zalambdodonts," have been characterized through their evolutionary development by triangular upper molars, in which there is a high central cusp, a low inner cusp, and various cuspules along the outer edge. Although these teeth appear to be primitive, they probably are not, but rather represent specializations from the typical tribosphenic molars of the ancestral insectivores. Among these insectivores are the giants of the order, exemplified particularly by *Centetes*, the modern tenrec of Madagascar, an animal almost two feet in length. Among most of the insectivores, often designated as the "dilambdodonts," evolution in the upper molars has been marked by a wide separation of the paracone and metacone on a W-shaped outer ridge or ectoloph. In addition, some of these latter insectivores have a hypocone on the back inner corner of the upper molar. The Old

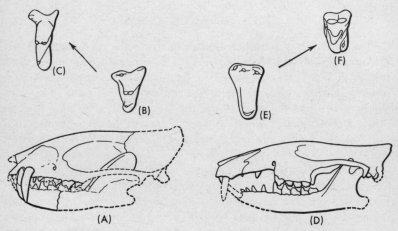

FIGURE 79. Insectivore skulls and jaws, natural size; left upper second molars, three times natural size except for (*F*), which is 3/2 natural size. (*A* and *B*), *Deltatheridium*, a primitive Cretaceous form. (*C*) *Palaeoryctes*, a Paleocene tenrecoid or "zalambdodont." (*D* and *E*), *Zalambdalestes*, a Cretaceous erinacoid. (*F*) *Diacodon*, an Eocene erinacoid or "dilambdodont."

World hedgehogs, typified by *Erinaceus*, illustrate this type of molar structure.

The division of the insectivores into zalambdodonts and dilambdodonts, although common in publications about these primitive mammals, does not indicate adequately their relationships. Perhaps the most logical expression of insectivore classification is the recognition of several groups, regarded by Simpson as superfamilies, which may be listed as follows.

Deltatheroids. Primitive Cretaceous and early Tertiary insectivores.
Tenrecoids. Various primitive extinct insectivores, as well as the tenrecs of Madagascar and *Solenodon*, the alamiqui, of the West Indies.
Chrysochloroids. The golden mole (*Chrysochloris*) of Africa, its progenitors and relatives.
Erinaceoids. Numerous fossil dilambdodonts. The Old World hedgehogs, *Erinaceus*.

Macroscelidoids. The elephant shrews, such as *Macroscelides,* of Africa.
Soricoids. Shrews and moles, exemplified by *Sorex* and *Talpa.*
Pantolestoids. Relatively large, extinct dilambdodonts.
Mixodectoids. Aberrant, extinct insectivores with enlarged incisors.

THE BATS

Because of their habits, bats like birds were not commonly interred
in sediments and fossilized. Therefore the history of these mammals

Insect—Eating Bat

Fruit—Eating Bat

FIGURE 80. Modern bats, representative of the Microchiroptera (left) and the
Megachiroptera (right).

is inadequately known, even though bats are numerous and of world-
wide distribution in modern times. These, the only mammals to have
mastered true flight, probably originated at a relatively early date,
and they must have experienced an initial stage of very rapid evolution, because the first known bats of Eocene age were highly developed and not greatly different from their modern relatives. There
are no known intermediate stages between bats and insectivores.

In the bats, as in other flying vertebrates, the front limbs are
modified to form wings. The limb bones are elongated, as are all
the fingers except the thumb, and these support the membrane that
forms the wing. The thumb is a free digit with a claw on the end.
The hind limbs are weak, so that bats are rather helpless on the
ground. However the feet have clawed digits, and with these the

bats hang themselves upside down when they sleep. The skull may show various specializations, but the molar teeth are usually primitive, rather like those of some of the dilambdodont insectivores, with a W-shaped outer ridge or ectoloph.

Modern bats are commonly nocturnal. In these mammals the sense of hearing is remarkably acute, as indicated by the enormous external ears or pinnae, so characteristic of many bats. Recent experiments show that as they fly bats emit a constant stream of supersonic squeaks. The ears catch the echoes or reflections of the sound from near-by objects, and thus the bats are guided by the sensitivity of their hearing. They are able to fly at night and pursue insects without any reliance upon the sense of vision. This sonar device of the modern bats probably evolved at a fairly early stage in the history of these mammals, and was very likely an important factor in their successful evolution.

The bats may be divided into two large categories or suborders. The Megachiroptera, perhaps the more primitive of the bats, are the large fruit-eating bats of the Old World and the Pacific region, among which are the "flying foxes," largest of all bats. Most of the bats, however, are contained within the suborder Microchiroptera, a group of world-wide distribution. Most of these bats are insectivorous, taking their food on the wing, as they have probably done through the history of the order. Certain modern microchiropteran bats, the so-called vampires of tropical America, have become highly specialized for sucking blood from large mammals.

DERMOPTERA

Another descendant from the insectivores is the colugo (*Galeopithecus*) or "flying lemur" of the East Indies. This animal is not a lemur, and it does not fly. It is an herbivorous, tree-living mammal, about the size of a large squirrel, with broad folds of skin extending between the legs and onto the tail, with which it is able to glide for long distances from one tree to another. A few Paleocene and Eocene fossils from North America may belong to early relatives of the colugo.

THE EDENTATES

The word "edentate," which means "without teeth," has been variously applied to mammals in which the teeth are greatly simplified, reduced, or suppressed, as an adaptation to very specialized diets. In the modern sense, the term Edentata is restricted to an order of mammals that evolved largely in South America and never got beyond the limits of the New World.

The first edentates, known as palaeanodonts, have been found in early Tertiary sediments in North America. Although these fossils do not represent the actual ancestors of the later edentates, they probably are the remains of primitive members of the order that had not diverged very far from the ancestral stock. The Eocene genus *Metacheiromys*, the most completely preserved of the palaeanodonts, was a small animal about the size and proportions of an armadillo. The legs were rather short, and the feet had sharp claws; the tail was long and heavy. The skull was low and somewhat elongated. Of particular significance is the fact that the dentition was modified; the incisors and the cheek teeth were almost completely suppressed, but the canines were retained as relatively large, sharp blades. In some other palaeanodonts the cheek teeth remained but were reduced to simple pegs with almost all the enamel missing. The palaeanodonts survived in North America until about the end of the Oligocene epoch, but it would seem likely that they were never very numerous in the early Tertiary faunas of this region.

In the meantime the early edentates had pushed into South America, where they became well established before the early Tertiary connection between that continent and North America was broken. Then the edentates evolved on the southern continent in complete isolation from the rest of the world. They quickly became prominent members of the South American faunas, and have remained so to the present day.

Certain distinctive characters developed in the South American edentates led to their early specialization for restricted modes of life, and masked the primitive features that had been inherited from their insectivore ancestors. In these mammals were developed accessory xenarthrous articulations between the lumbar vertebrae of the back, making this region of the backbone very strong. In addition the neck was increased among some of the edentates to include as many as nine cervical vertebrae, instead of the usual seven that are almost universal among the mammals. The feet had large claws. In the skull the brain was comparatively small and primitive, and it remains so in the modern edentates. The zygomatic arch or cheek bone was usually incomplete. Finally, the teeth were much reduced and simplified, or completely suppressed.

During Tertiary times the higher edentates evolved along two broad lines of adaptive radiation. One of these lines included the ground sloths, now extinct, the tree sloths, and the anteaters. This group is generally designated as a suborder—the Pilosa. The other evolutionary line, also of subordinal rank, was that of the Cingulata, the armored armadillos and the glyptodonts.

The most distinctive evolutionary development in the armadillos and glyptodonts was the growth of extensive armor to protect these animals against attack. This armor was formed of heavy bony plates covered with horny scutes. In the modern armadillos there are solid shields of bone over the shoulders and the hips, and between these areas are transverse movable bands of scutes, which gives flexibility to the back. There are also scutes on top of the skull and on the tail. The teeth in the armadillos consist of simple pegs without enamel, along the sides of the jaws. The armadillos, which have been very successful mammals from early Tertiary times to the present day, are scavengers, eating insects, carrion, and almost any other food they can find on the ground.

The late Cenozoic glyptodonts like *Glyptodon* were giant cousins and probable descendants of the armadillos, in which the body armor formed a solid bony carapace, like the shell of a turtle. In the largest of these ungainly mammals the shell was a massive, heavy dome, often five feet or so in length. Not only was the body heavily armored, but also the top of the head was covered with a thick shield of coalesced plates, and the tail was encased with concentric rings of bony armor. In some of the glyptodonts the end of the tail was provided with an enlarged, spiked knob of bone, remarkably like the heavy maces that were carried by medieval knights; with this weapon these glyptodonts were able to flail their enemies with deadly force. The legs and feet were very heavy, to support the great mass of the animal. The skull and lower jaw were extraordinarily deep, and the teeth, limited to the sides of the jaws, were tall, each tooth consisting of three columns, joined along a fore to aft line.

Huge ground sloths evolved in South America during late Cenozoic times side by side with the glyptodonts. An evolutionary trend in these edentates was to gigantic size; they never developed any bony armor, although there was a sort of cobble-stone pavement of bones in the skin. In these animals the skeleton became very heavy throughout, and some of the bones of the legs grew to be enormously broad. The feet were very large, with claws that were probably used for digging. It is evident that the ground sloths, like some of their living relatives, walked upon the sides of the hind feet and upon the knuckles of the front feet. The skull was somewhat elongated, and the teeth, limited to the sides of the jaws, were peg-like. The largest of the ground sloths, such as *Megatherium,* were as large as

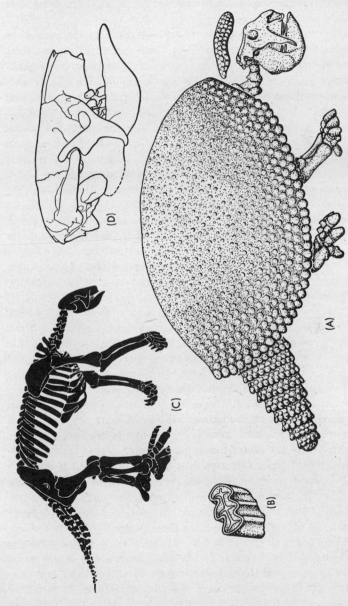

FIGURE 81. (A) *Glyptodon*, skeleton and bony armor. (B) A glyptodont tooth. (C) Skeleton and (D) skull of *Nothrotherium*, a ground sloth. A and C about one-twenty-fourth natural size; D about one-sixth natural size.

small elephants, and in life they must have weighed several tons. These were probably plant-eaters that lived largely upon the leaves of trees and bushes.

In modern tropical America are the tree sloths, the close relatives of the extinct ground sloths. The tree sloths are small to medium-sized, leaf-eating edentates, that live curiously inverted lives hanging upside down from the limbs of trees by their long, hook-like claws. Time means nothing to the sloths, which are proverbially slow and clumsy.

Also in the tropics of America are the anteaters, which evolved from the same ancestors as the tree sloths. *Myrmecophaga* is a ground-living edentate, in which the skull is enormously elongated by the extension of the snout into a long tube, which is used as a probe to investigate ant hills and termite nests. There is a very long protrusible tongue that is utilized for lapping up the insects upon which these animals feed. The teeth are completely suppressed. The claws are greatly enlarged and very sharp, and are used not only for digging into the homes of ants and termites, but also as formidable weapons. Like the extinct ground sloths, the anteaters walk on the sides of the hind feet and upon the knuckles of the front feet.

Thus we see the edentates evolving in South America during Tertiary times as the armadillos and the glyptodonts, on the one hand, and as the ground sloths, the tree sloths, and the anteaters on the other. In late Pliocene times the isthmian link between North and South America was re-established for the first time since the beginning of the Tertiary period, and there was an influx of immigrants from the north into the South American continent. These immigrants brought about the extinction of many South American mammals of ancient lineage, as we have seen, but not of the edentates. These mammals not only withstood the impact of the northern immigrants, but in turn they spread to the north, to invade Central and North America. Consequently certain edentates became characteristic members of the late Pliocene and Pleistocene faunas of North America, and they were so successful that their bones are among the commonest of Pleistocene mammalian fossils.

The glyptodonts and the giant ground sloths ranged widely during Pleistocene times in both North and South America, and the evidence shows quite clearly that these mammals survived until comparatively late dates. There is now ample proof that early man in the New World was contemporaneous with the ground sloths. In addition, the discovery of partial mummies of these great edentates, with

patches of skin and hair intact, is an indication of the fact that the
ground sloths probably persisted to within the last few thousand
years.

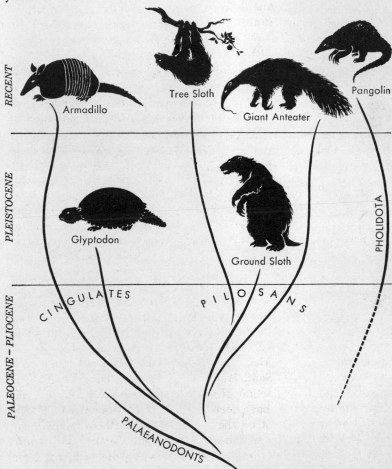

RECENT

Armadillo

Tree Sloth

Giant Anteater

Pangolin

PLEISTOCENE

Glyptodon

Ground Sloth

PHOLIDOTA

PALEOCENE – PLIOCENE

CINGULATES

PILOSANS

PALAEANODONTS

FIGURE 82.   Evolution of the edentates.

The anteaters and the tree sloths never got north of the tropical
region, but the armadillos entered the southern portion of North
America, where they live at the present time.   In fact there has been
a decided northward and eastward spread of these edentates within
the last century.   Armadillos were formerly limited in the United
States to the area immediately north of the Rio Grande, but they

have now extended their range as far north as Oklahoma and eastward along the Gulf coast. These are adaptable mammals, and it looks as if they will continue to prosper and spread, in spite of the perils of modern civilization.

PHOLIDOTA

The pangolins or scaly anteaters live in the tropical regions of Asia and Africa. These mammals, belonging to the genus *Manis*, of Pleistocene and Recent Age, have a remarkable body covering of overlapping, horny scales, which makes them look something like reptiles or perhaps like large, animated pine cones. The skull is elongated and rather similar in some respects to the skull in some of the American edentates. There are no teeth, and these animals subsist upon ants. There are large, powerful claws on the feet for digging, and the long tail is prehensile, as an aid to climbing in trees.

The fossil story of the pangolins is virtually unknown. Evidently these mammals have had a long, independent history, during the course of which they have paralleled the American edentates in various ways. It is even possible that they may have evolved from the same ancestors as the true edentates, but it is equally possible that they represent a completely independent development from primitive insectivore ancestors.

THE TAENIODONTS AND THE TILLODONTS

Here we may consider two "orphan orders" of mammals, primitive placentals that evolved during Paleocene and Eocene times from an insectivore stem, and then became extinct. It seems probable that these mammals were never very abundant; they were early "experiments in evolution" destined to short phylogenetic histories.

The taeniodonts evolved as rather large mammals, especially for early Tertiary times. In the most advanced of these animals, like the Eocene genus *Stylinodon*, the skull and jaws, a foot or more in length, were deep and powerful and the teeth were modified as long, rootless pegs, with a limited band of enamel on each tooth. The limbs were heavy, and on the feet were strong claws. For these reasons it has been suggested that the taeniodonts were related to the edentates. However, as we go back in taeniodont history, we see that the teeth of the earlier forms, like *Conoryctes* of the Paleocene, approached the ancestral tribosphenic type. Therefore it would seem likely that these mammals represent an early and independent specialization quite separate from the edentates.

The tillodonts were also large animals for early Tertiary times, and some of the last of them, such as *Tillotherium*, were the size of large bears. They were like bears, too, in the strong skeleton with heavy, clawed feet. The skull, however, had a curious resemblance to the skull in rodents, with enlarged, chisel-like incisor teeth in both upper and lower jaws. The taeniodonts and tillodonts were successful for a time, but with the rise of large, progressive mammals during the Eocene epoch these strange mammals disappeared from the earth.

Stone Age Man

21 · Evolution of the Primates

THE ORIGIN OF THE PRIMATES

It is common in discussions of vertebrate evolution to consider the primates—the lemurs, tarsiers, monkeys, apes, and men—last of all. This practice is an outgrowth of the idea that man is the crowning achievement of evolutionary history, that man is at the top of the heap, the ruler of the world, and the arbiter of his destiny. According to this view the grand climax of the evolutionary story is achieved with a description of primate evolution. In a sense this is true, for there is no doubt that the higher primates surpass all other animals in their mental development, and man is a phenomenon unique in the history of life on the earth. On the other hand, the evidence is quite clear that the primates are unguiculates, directly descended from insectivore ancestors, and for this reason it is quite logical to discuss them along with the other unguiculates.

The best evidence for the basic relationship of the primates to the insectivores is embodied in the modern Oriental tree shrew, *Tupaia*. This is a small mammal about the size of a squirrel, with a long snout and a long tail, and well adapted to climbing among the lofty branches of tropical trees in search of the insects on which it feeds. *Tupaia* is a very primitive placental, in many respects one of the most generalized of all living mammals, and therefore *Tupaia* and its relatives have been included by many authorities among the insectivores. There are, however, some characters that definitely link the tree shrews with the primates rather than with the insectivores. For instance, there is in these animals a bony postorbital bar separating the eye from the temporal region, as is characteristic of the primates. Of particular significance is the fact that the brain is relatively large, whereas its olfactory region is small. In addition, the middle ear region is similar to that of the lemurs, and, as in primates, the thumb and the great toe are set somewhat apart from the other toes.

From a probable tree shrew or tupaioid ancestry the primates evolved along various lines of adaptive radiation during the course of Cenozoic times. This evolutionary development involved an initial radiation of primitive primates in Paleocene times, so that a suborder, the Prosimii, was established, represented on the one hand by the lemurs and lorises, and on the other by the tarsiers. After the Paleocene divergence of the lemurs and lorises, and the tarsiers, there was a second radiation of primates that would seem to have taken place in upper Eocene and subsequent geologic periods. These later primates, probably derived from lemuroid ancestors, can be included in a second suborder, the Anthropoidea, and are represented by the monkeys, apes, and men.

All of the several large groups of primates have been successful mammals and have survived into our modern age; consequently we are able to follow the successive steps in primate evolution not only from the study of fossil materials but also from first-hand acquaintance with living primates in various stages of advancement. This is indeed fortunate, since throughout their history most of the primates have been forest animals, an environment in which they have not been abundantly buried and preserved as fossils.

PRIMATE CHARACTERS

In many respects the primates are not highly specialized mammals, so that it is not surprising that these mammals should retain many generalized eutherian characters. Nevertheless they show definite specializations along certain lines, and of these the basic underlying trend running through all primate history has been the adaptations for life in the trees. Consequently there has been an emphasis in the primates on those characters important to arboreal life.

Quick reactions are important to active, tree-living mammals. The primates are notable by reason of their activity and restlessness, and especially because of their curious concern with what goes on around them. They are very much aware of the world they live in; they explore their environment with alert eyes. Binocular vision is of particular importance to the primates and is probably more highly developed in them than in any other mammals, giving them a keen visual appreciation of their treetop world. The sense of smell, however, is of no great value to tree-living animals, and so in most of the primates the nose and the olfactory portion of the brain are reduced.

Although there has been a reduction of the olfactory region in the brain of most primates, there has been a converse increase in the rest of that organ, especially the cerebrum. The large brain and the increase in intelligence are the most significant aspects of primate evolution, and they have been of prime importance to the successful progress of these mammals. Primates see things clearly and in detail, they can interpret what they see, and because of their high degree of intelligence and nervous control they are able to use their hands for skillful explorations and manipulations of the things around them. The brain, the eyes, and the hands have made the primates what they are.

Of course these adaptations are reflected in the bony structure. The brain case is large in the primates, and in the more advanced forms it grows to such an extent that it makes up the bulk of the skull. The eyes are also large, and in most of the primates they are directed forward, instead of laterally. They are separated from the temporal region by a bony bar, and in the more advanced primates there is a complete bony wall enclosing the orbit. Since the sense of smell is so greatly curtailed in the primates, the nose is generally small; we might say that it is crowded and pinched between the large eyes.

The jaws are frequently short; the teeth are usually primitive or generalized. The third incisor is lost, as is likewise the first premolar in all but the most primitive primates. In the higher primates the two anterior premolars are lost; therefore the dental formula is generally 2-1-3-3, or 2-1-2-3. The cheek teeth are commonly low

crowned, with blunt cusps, an adaptation that permits the primates
to eat a great variety of food.

The limbs and feet are mobile. Moreover, the joints of the limbs
allow much rotation of the bones. The hands and feet retain five
digits, and the thumb and first toe in most primates are set apart from
the other digits and aid in grasping limbs and manipulating objects.

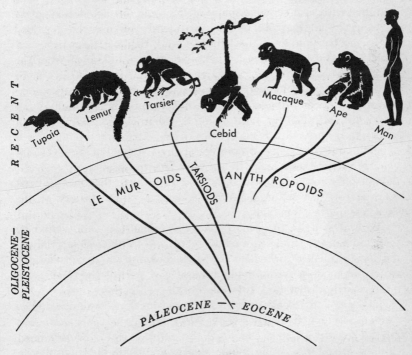

FIGURE 83. Evolution and relationships of the major groups of primates.

In addition to these distinctive anatomical features, the primates
are characterized by certain other traits, of which particular importance may be accorded to the relatively slow postnatal development
that necessitates a long period of intimate association between the
mother and her baby. Family life is therefore well developed in
many of the primates, and of course it reaches its highest stage of
development in modern man.

These are some of the general characters typical of all the primates.
Adaptive radiation, however, has been so diverse in these mammals
that there are many other characters restricted to the various di-

vergent primate groups. Some of them are further perfections of the characters mentioned above, others are special features peculiar to certain groups.

ADAPTIVE RADIATION OF THE LEMUROIDS

The Oriental tree shrew, *Tupaia,* has already been cited as a primitive eutherian showing many of the basic characters that might be expected in stem primates. The tree shrews may be classified as the most primitive of the lemurs (using this last term in a very broad sense). Unfortunately the tupaioids are unknown from the earliest Tertiary sediments and are represented in the fossil record by only one genus, *Anagale,* of Oligocene age. In spite of its comparatively late age, *Anagale* was a primitive tupaioid, an animal that seemingly had persisted with little change from the early stages of eutherian history. For instance, this tupaioid had a full complement of teeth, and there was no complete bony bar behind the eye as is general among the modern tree shrews and the primates. *Anagale,* though an important fossil, is at best only an indication of what may be revealed to us some day about the early history of the stem lemurs, the tupaioids.

The next stage in the evolution of the primates is represented by the lemurs in the strict sense of the word, and by their close relatives the lorises. These primates are well known from a considerable variety of modern forms living in Asia and Africa; the lemurs are rather widely distributed as fossils.

Paleocene and Eocene lemurs are found in North America and in Europe. Among them (the genus *Plesiadapis* is typical) there was a trend toward an enlargement of the anterior incisors into strong, chisel-shaped teeth. The molar teeth were basically tribosphenic, with low cusps, and it is probable that these early lemurs lived upon fruits and small game, such as insects.

Fortunately one Eocene lemur, *Notharctus,* is known from complete skeletons, discovered in western North America. *Notharctus* was a small mammal, resembling the modern lemurs in its general aspects. The skull was about two inches in length, and low, with the eye located about halfway between the front and the back of the skull. The muzzle and the lower jaws were rather long, and supplied with a full set of cheek teeth. The small incisors were of normal shape; there were small, tusk-like canines, and the molars were low-crowned and rather quadrangular, especially by reason of the development of a hypocone in the upper molars. The back was supple, and the tail was very long. The legs were long and slender, and capable of a great range of movement in all directions; and in the hands and feet the first digit was even at this early date set apart from the other toes. It is therefore evident that *Notharctus* was an able climber, grasping limbs and branches with its hands and feet, stretching and reaching with its legs in almost any direction necessary for clambering among the tree tops, and using its long tail as a balancing organ. In Eocene times *Notharctus* and its relatives lived in the tropical and subtropical forests that covered much of North America and Eurasia, and established a mode of life that proved to be very successful. Consequently the lemurs have persisted with little change to the present day.

After the close of the Eocene period the lemurs disappeared from the northern hemisphere. They continued, however, in the tropical parts of the Old World, and today they persist in abundance and variety on the island of Madagascar, as remnants from the Eocene epoch.

In many respects the persistently primitive modern lemurs, such as *Lemur* itself, are very much like the Eocene *Notharctus*. The common lemurs are small animals with very long tails, elongated flexible limbs, and grasping hands and feet. The muzzle is elongated and pointed, giving the face a fox-like appearance. The eyes are large. The molar teeth are primitive, but in the front of the jaws the upper incisors may be reduced or absent, whereas the lower incisors are long and horizontally directed. These teeth form a sort of comb, with which the lemurs groom their fur. Modern lemurs are nocturnal animals, roaming through the trees at night in search of insects and fruits.

As might be expected, there have been various departures from the central lemur stock among the lemurs of Madagascar during their long period of isolation upon that island. Some of these lemurs are very small; others, like the indris, are rather large and monkey-like, walking on their hind legs. In Pleistocene and sub-Recent deposits on Madagascar are found the remains of a giant lemur, *Megaladapis*, as large as a chimpanzee. This lemur lacked a tail, and it had a large, heavy head.

Among the strangest of the lemurs is the aye-aye of Madagascar, *Daubentonia*, in which the incisor teeth are rodent-like, the digits elongated, and the third finger very long and slender. This peculiar finger is used to dig insects from the bark of trees.

The lorises, now living in India and Africa, are often separated as a group equal in rank to the lemurs. These primates, represented by *Loris*, the slender loris of India, and by *Galago*, the "bush baby" of Africa, are specialized in various ways. For instance, the muzzle is reduced, as in higher primates, and the eyes are turned forward as compared with their more lateral direction in the lemurs. Modern lemurs have three premolar teeth, but in the lorises these are reduced to two. The brain case is high. Like the lemurs, the lorises are predominantly nocturnal animals that prowl through the trees in search of fruit and insects.

THE TARSIERS

The third branch of the Prosimii, the lemurs and the lorises being the first two branches, is that of the tarsiers, appearing in Paleocene times and continuing to the present day. Tarsiers have been highly specialized primates through their evolutionary history. They show interesting adaptations, some of which have the appearance of being more or less intermediate between the lemurs and the higher primates. However, it is likely that the specializations of the tarsiers that seem to link them with some of the higher primates represent independent parallel developments.

A single genus, *Tarsius*, living in the East Indies and the Philippines, is the surviving tarsier of modern times. This is a small animal, no larger than a squirrel, covered with soft fur. The enormous eyes are set close together and look directly forward. Indeed, the eyes of the tarsier are so large that they occupy much of the face, giving the tarsier a weird, nightmarish appearance, and they crowd the nose to such an extent that it is very small and narrow. The external ears are also large, and indicate that the tarsier has an acute sense of hearing, as well as of sight. These animals are completely nocturnal, and they rely upon the large, light-gathering lenses of the eyes and the expanded ears that catch faint sounds to guide them through the tops of the trees in the tropical night, where they prey upon insects and other small animals.

The body is compact, but the tail is very long. The hind legs are also long, and the tarsier has a peculiar elongation of the calcaneum and navicular, two proximal bones of the ankle, to make the foot an elongated lever. Elongation of the hind foot usually signifies a running or jumping animal, and the tarsier is noted for its ability to make tremendous leaps through the tops of trees. The fingers and the toes are slender and are supplied with adhesive pads for the purpose of grasping branches very firmly. Such specializations, established at an early date in the phylogenetic history of the tarsiers, have enabled these little primates to survive successfully as alert, quickly moving denizens of high trees, over a span of many millions of years.

The early specialization of tarsiers in Eocene times is indicated by several genera found in North America and Europe, particularly by *Tetonius* of the New World. In this fossil, of which a fairly good skull is known, many of the advanced adaptations so characteristic of the tarsiers had already appeared. *Tetonius* had enormous orbits, an indication that the eyes were large, although not as large as in the modern tarsiers, and it seems reasonable to think that *Tetonius* was an animal of the night, as is its modern relative. The jaws were short, the canines were enlarged, and the molars were primitive.

NEW WORLD MONKEYS

We now come to a consideration of the advanced primates, belonging to the suborder Anthropoidea. This suborder like the Prosimii may be divided into three lesser groups of superfamily status—the New World monkeys, the Old World monkeys, and finally the great apes and men.

All these higher primates have certain characters in common that set them apart from their primitive relatives, the Prosimii. In all the anthropoids the eyes are large and face forward, and are completely separated from the temporal fossa by a solid bony wall, a specialization beyond the simple bony postorbital bar of the primitive prosimians. There are either three premolar teeth (in the New World forms) or two (in all but the most primitive Old World types). The molar teeth, though low crowned, are generally quadrangular, having lost the primitive tribosphenic pattern. The brain is comparatively large, and the cranial part of the skull is rounded.

Most of the anthropoids are able to sit in an upright position, and thus the hands are freed for manipulating objects. The thumb and the great toe are commonly set apart from the other digits, as in the prosimians, but in many anthropoids this character is advanced to a high degree of perfection.

The New World monkeys, the most primitive of the anthropoids, are now found in Central and South America, where they generally live high in the trees of tropical forests. These monkeys retain three premolar teeth, as mentioned above, and some of them are characterized particularly by a prehensile tail, with which they are able to grasp branches. Thus they have a sort of "fifth hand" as an aid for climbing. There are two groups of modern New World monkeys,

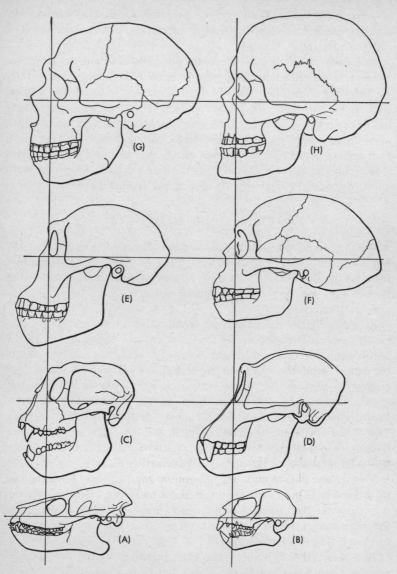

FIGURE 84. Skulls of primates; A, B, and C roughly one-half natural size, the others roughly one-fourth natural size. (A) *Notharctus,* an Eocene lemuroid. (B) *Tetonius,* an Eocene tarsioid. (C) *Mesopithecus,* a Pliocene cercopithecoid or Old World monkey. (D) *Pan,* a modern chimpanzee. (E) *Australopithecus,* a Pleistocene man-ape from Africa. (F) *Pithecanthropus,* a primitive Pleistocene man from Asia. (G) *Homo neanderthalensis,* Neanderthal man. (H) *Homo sapiens,* Cro-Magnon man.

the small, rather squirrel-like marmosets, and the larger cebids, or capuchins, spider monkeys, howling monkeys, and their relatives.

The fossil history of the New World monkeys is indeed scanty. In the Miocene sediments of Argentina and Colombia are found a few genera (such as *Homunculus* and *Cebupithecia*) related to some of the more primitive modern cebids, but beyond this evidence little knowledge of the primates in South America during the Tertiary period exists.

There are two explanations of the origin of monkeys in South America. On the one hand, it is quite possible that the ancestors of these monkeys, perhaps the descendants of northern lemuroids, entered the southern continent from North America in very early Tertiary times, before the two continental masses had been separated. If this is so, they lived during early Tertiary times in South American environments, where their bones were not buried and fossilized. The other possibility is that primates came into South America during middle Tertiary times as waifs, as accidental and unwilling passengers on natural rafts or floating logs. If this be so, we have yet to find their ancestors in other parts of the world.

OLD WORLD MONKEYS

In contrast to the very scanty fossil record of the New World monkeys, fossils of the Old World monkeys or cercopithecoids can be traced from Oligocene times to the present. One of the first and most primitive of the Old World monkeys was the genus *Parapithecus*, found in Egypt in sediments of early Oligocene age. This was a very small monkey, as indicated by a jaw less than two inches in length. The jaw was rather deep, as is characteristic of the higher primates, and the condyle, the joint for articulation of the jaw with the skull, was placed on a high ascending ramus, well above the line of the teeth. There were three premolar teeth, and the canine tooth was comparatively small. All the teeth formed a continuous series, in contact with each other.

Various fossils of monkeys are found in the Old World in deposits of Miocene and later ages, but for the most part they are fragmentary and give us mere glimpses of cercopithecoid history. However, enough material has been found to indicate that the cercopithecoids were widely distributed throughout the Old World in middle and late Cenozoic times. One of the best-known of these fossils is the genus *Mesopithecus*, a Pliocene monkey related to the modern langurs, and known from complete skeletal materials.

The more advanced Old World monkeys, as represented by fossil and recent forms, are small to medium-sized mammals. They have only two premolars, a character they share with the highest of the primates, apes and men. The brain is well developed, perhaps more so than in the New World monkeys, and consequently the brain case is large and rounded. The tail is variously developed; it may be long or it may be very short, but it is never prehensile or grasping, as in some of the South American monkeys. In these primates, as in the New World monkeys, the external ears are comparatively small, pressed close to the sides of the head, with the edges rolled over.

In evolving during middle and late Cenozoic times, the cercopithecoids have followed two trends, represented by the cercopithecines and the colobines. The cercopithecines are the various Asiatic and African monkeys, such as the rhesus monkeys, the guenons, and the baboons. These monkeys are generally omnivorous, eating fruits, berries, insects, lizards, and any other animals they can catch, but some of the highly specialized members of the group are primarily fruit-eaters. They are characterized by cheek pouches, in which they can store considerable quantities of food.

The baboons show an interesting secondary trend in the evolution of the primates away from the basic tree-living life to a life on the ground. In so developing, the baboons have imitated in certain respects some of the ground-living carnivorous mammals, like dogs. This is particularly apparent in the skull. Baby baboons have round heads and short noses, as do most of the higher primates, but in the adults the snout becomes very long and dog-like, and the canine teeth are greatly enlarged. Their elongated jaws and large canine teeth make them aggressive animals, well able to cope with other ground-living mammals. This mode of life has proved very successful for the various baboons, now widely distributed throughout the African continent.

The colobine monkeys are the langurs, slender, long-legged, long-tailed, now inhabiting Asia, with one genus in Africa, but living during Pliocene times in Europe. The colobines are consistent tree-dwellers and are herbivorous.

THE APES

Parapithecus, described above as an early cercopithecoid monkey, has been regarded by many students of the primates as an early ape. Since this little primate is so imperfectly known at the present time, its precise position cannot be determined, and equally strong arguments can be put forward for regarding it as either an ancestral cercopithecoid or an ancestral ape. Perhaps it fulfills both rôles; perhaps it was the common ancestor from which both monkeys and apes arose.

However that may be, it is an interesting fact that in the lower Oligocene sediments of Egypt, the same sediments in which *Parapithecus* was found, another lower jaw was discovered. It was described under the name of *Propliopithecus*, and it certainly represents a primitive ape. *Propliopithecus*, like *Parapithecus*, was very small; the lower jaw was less than three inches in length. This jaw was proportionately much deeper than the jaw in *Parapithecus*, and, whereas there were three premolars in *Parapithecus*, there were only two in *Propliopithecus*, as in all the higher monkeys, the apes, and men. The lower molar teeth had five low cusps, in which respect they resembled the lower molars in the later apes.

Certain trends have characterized the evolutionary history of the apes, and of these a few of the most prominent may be mentioned. For instance, there has been a strong trend toward a great increase in size, so that almost all the apes have been larger than most of the monkeys, and some of them have been the giants among primates. There has been not only a great increase in body size among the apes during the course of their phylogenetic development, but also a marked increase in the size of the brain, with of course a correlative development in the cranial portion of the skull. Consequently the head in the apes is large and rounded to a greater degree than it is in the monkeys. The teeth are low crowned and rather generalized, and in the lower molars there are five cusps (already present in *Propliopithecus*) as contrasted with the four cusps in the lower molars of monkeys. The canine teeth may be very large in some apes, but this is an adaptation for fighting, not for eating meat. Most of the apes are vegetarians, although some of them may eat a little meat.

Since the apes have been for the most part rather large animals, unable to walk along the branches of trees as do monkeys, they have evolved as brachiating animals, swinging by their arms from branch to branch. This type of locomotion is predominant among the apes, and only in the heavy-bodied giant apes has it been abandoned. Because they have been brachiators, the apes have developed long arms and long fingers, the fingers serving as hooks for hanging on to large tree limbs. The hind legs in the apes are short, and most of these animals are rather clumsy walkers.

The apes have no external tail.

The fossil remains of apes are not common, but they are sufficiently numerous to show that these primates were widely distributed throughout Europe, Asia, and Africa during the middle and latter portions of Cenozoic times. The earliest apes to appear after *Propliopithecus* were *Limnopithecus* and *Proconsul,* from the lower Miocene sediments of Africa. It seems probable that *Limnopithecus* represents a form generally ancestral to the gibbons and their relatives, whereas *Proconsul* may indicate the approximate ancestry of the other apes.

The descendants of *Proconsul* were the various dryopithecines, of which the genus *Dryopithecus* is typical, flourishing in Eurasia during the Miocene and the Pliocene epochs. The dryopithecines were generalized apes, in many respects rather similar to the modern chimpanzee, and it is probable that from them there arose most of the modern apes of Pleistocene and recent times.

The modern apes are the comparatively small, long-armed gibbons of Asia, the most skilled brachiators of all primates, the orangs of the East Indies, and the chimpanzees and the gorillas of Africa. The gorillas are the giants among modern primates, far exceeding any men in bulk and strength. However there seem to have been apes living in Asia during the Pleistocene epoch that were even larger than the gorillas. These gigantic apes, named *Gigantopithecus,* and unfortunately known at the present time only from teeth and jaw fragments, were the greatest of all primates, past or present, the nearest things in nature to the giants of fairy tales.

THE AFRICAN MAN-APES

Within recent years important discoveries made in Pleistocene cave deposits in South Africa have revealed the remains of some advanced prehominids that lived during the last great ice age. The first fossil to come to light, the skull of a baby animal, was named *Australopithecus.* Subsequently the skulls and portions of skeletons of adults were found, and, although they received different names, it seems likely that they may all be included within two genera, *Australopithecus* and *Paranthropus,* each representing a separate line of evolution.

The australopithecines (as they may be called) show an interesting mixture of ape and human characters. The skull and the face were ape-like. The dentition was of human aspect, and the canine teeth were reduced in size as compared with these teeth in the apes. The fragmentary fossils of the pelvis and the limbs indicate that these primates were able to walk in an upright posture.

The combination of an ape-like brain with teeth similar to those in men, and the attainment of an upright posture, present a mixture of conservative and progressive characters that indicate the intermediate position of the australopithecines between the dryopithecine apes and the most primitive men. These African man-apes cannot be regarded as the direct ancestors of man because of their late geologic age. Nevertheless they approximate closely what the immediate forebears of men may have been like, and thus they give us some insight into the very beginning of human evolution.

FACTORS OF HUMAN EVOLUTION

Even though human beings may not be descended from the autralopithecines as we know them, it is very possible that man arose from australopithecine-like ancestors. The origin of the human stock probably occurred in late Tertiary times, for man is essentially a Pleistocene animal. Having become differentiated from his primate relatives, man evolved during the Pleistocene period along certain lines that have made him what he is today. The evolutionary development of human beings was not of great magnitude within the course of Pleistocene history; rather it was a matter of the perfection of details that set man apart from all other primates, and from all other animals for that matter.

Four factors have been of prime importance in determining the evolutionary development of man from an ape-like primate. They have been the growth and elaboration of the brain, the perfection of the erect posture, a slowing down of postnatal development, and finally the growth in human populations. Let us consider these four factors of human evolution.

Man has been through the course of his evolution a thinking animal. Structurally and physically man was and is far inferior to many of the large animals that have shared his environments; consequently, most of his phenomenal success in adjusting himself to varied environments and in overcoming his enemies has been the result of his superior intelligence. The largest of the modern apes, the gorilla, has a brain case with a capacity of about 500 to 600 cubic centimeters. In the australopithecines the cranial capacity was approximately 600 cubic centimeters, certainly an advance over their dryopithecine ancestors.· In the most primitive men of Pleistocene age the cranial capacity was about 900 cubic centimeters, whereas in late Pleistocene and Recent men this figure has ranged from a minimum of about 1200 to a maximum of over 2000 cubic centimeters. The size of the brain is a rough index to mental development, and it is reasonable to think that as the brain got larger through time the intelligence of man increased. Of particular significance is the size of the brain in relation to body size. The most primitive men with cranial capacities of about 900 cubic centimeters were about as large physically as modern men; it is evident therefore that the brain of man has about doubled in its relation to body weight within the limits of Pleistocene time. As we follow the evolution of man we can see the brain case getting increasingly larger as compared with the rest of the skull. Since much of the development of the human brain has been a matter of growth in the frontal region, the cranium has bulged in front, giving to men of late Pleistocene and Recent times a high, broad forehead. Correlatively the face has become increasingly vertical and the jaws proportionately short and small. Because of the shortening of the jaws, the bones containing the teeth have changed from a long, U-shaped arch in the ancestral types to a short parabolic curve in the more modern men.

In addition to the physical changes brought about in the skull and jaws as a result of the increase of the brain, there have been the less tangible but very important behavior patterns resulting from the growing intelligence of man as he has evolved. Growth of the intellect has resulted in the ability to communicate ideas by facial gestures and especially by speech. The importance of speech to the quickening evolution of man is so obvious as to need no extended discussion at this place. As a result of his increased intelligence, man became a tool-making animal at an early stage in his history. The manufacture and use of tools, like speech, has been of incalculable effect in hastening the progress of man beyond the status of a mere forest-living animal that competed on more or less equal terms with other animals in wresting a living from the environment.

This brings us to the second important factor in the evolution of man, the development of the upright posture. In this respect man has diverged widely from most of the other primates, which are either completely tree-living animals or ground-living types that walk and run on "all fours" as do baboons and gorillas. The upright posture has freed the hands completely from the necessity of assisting in locomotion and has made them available for handling things, for use in defense, and finally for the manufacture of tools. It is the ability to pick up things and examine them that has helped to make all the higher primates, and especially man, very curious animals that are always experimenting with things and generally learning much as a result of this experimentation.

Physically the upright posture of man has involved a change in the shape of the spinal column. In the ancestors of man, as in the modern apes, the backbone between the skull and the pelvis formed a simple curve, so that the body leaned forward from the hips, and the head was thrust forward from the shoulders. In man the vertebrae are aligned in a complex, S-shaped flexure that throws the body and neck into an upright position, with the head balanced on top of the neck. Naturally this pose is especially efficient for an animal that has freed the fore limbs from locomotor functions, since the entire body from head to heels is aligned along a vertical axis, in line with the force of gravity. Correlative with the development of the upright posture and bipedal locomotion, man has evolved long legs for comparatively fast running over the ground, and arms that are short as contrasted to the arms in most other higher primates.

The third important factor in the evolution of man has been the increase in the process of growing up. A gorilla becomes mature at about the age of ten years, whereas it takes a man about twice as long to reach his full stature and his full powers. This time difference in maturing means that young human beings spend a longer time under the care of parents than other primates, and this longer interval in turn leads to the perfection of family life. This growing-up period, as surely as increased intelligence and the freeing of the hands for tool-making, has been of tremendous import in the advance of man to the high position he now holds in the world.

Finally, the growth of human populations has been of the utmost importance in the evolutionary history of man, particularly in his development during the last few thousand years. From the family group, man progressed to the clan and the tribe, and at length to the complex nations that have developed within the last few millennia. This trend in human evolution, so important to the modern world and the world of the future, has depended upon the social behavior of man, first developed within the family group. It has been made possible by man's capacity for cooperation and by his realization of the necessity for restraint in his behavior. The factor of social relationships, like other physically intangible aspects of evolution, has been of particular importance in making man unique among the animals, a being with a culture.

Neanderthal   Cro-Magnon

Australopithecus   Pithecanthropus

FIGURE 85. The man-ape of Africa and early men of Eurasia.

THE EVOLUTION OF MAN

Perhaps no aspect of evolution has received such intense study as the evolution of man, yet this is a subject concerning which there is much debate, and about which there is much still to be learned. There are various reasons for the incomplete knowledge and controversial nature of human evolution. Fossils are not common. Because of the importance to modern man of fossil men, every specimen has been subjected to close study, and differences that would be regarded as minor in other animals have here been accorded great importance. But even though the imperfections in the record are great, and there is much disagreement among authorities who work in this field of knowledge, the general outlines of the evolution of man are fairly well defined.

As mentioned above, it is possible that man arose from australopithecine-like ancestors. By early to middle Pleistocene times the first true men, the pithecanthropoids, had evolved. These are known from fossils found in Java and in China, near Peking. The Javanese fossils have been designated as *Pithecanthropus,* those from China as *Sinanthropus,* but it is quite evident to an objective observer that these early men were essentially the same, and therefore should be known as *Pithecanthropus.* For the sake of convenience those from the East Indies can be called the Java Man, those from China the Peking Man.

These first known human beings were definitely more primitive than modern men. They had a cranial capacity of about 900 to 1000 cubic centimeters, as compared with an average of about 1500 for the modern European. The cranium was low, especially in the frontal region, and the bony brow ridges above the eyes were comparatively heavy. The jaws were strong and large, and projected farther forward than the jaws in modern man; hence *Pithecanthropus* is said to be prognathous. However the chin was rather receding. The teeth were thoroughly human but they were heavy, and the canine teeth were somewhat longer than the other teeth. Such skeletal evidence that is at hand would indicate that these early men were ground-living, erect-walking primates.

The pithecanthropoids were probably forest men that traveled in small family groups and sought shelter in caves. It seems likely that they knew how to use fire, and that they utilized simple tools and weapons of wood and stone. To our modern eyes they seem like crude people in a low stage of human development, yet they had many advantages over the animals that were around them and with which they had to contend. They had made great strides along the path leading to modern men.

Although pithecanthropoids are unknown in Europe, there are some fragmentary fossils that indicate the presence of men in this region during the first half of the Pleistocene period. One of these fossils is the famous Heidelberg jaw, found in sands of the first interglacial stage near Heidelberg, Germany. It is a very large, heavy jaw, but the teeth are of moderate size and of modern appearance. The Heidelberg jaw may indicate the presence in Europe of a somewhat modernized pithecanthropoid, but this jaw is generally classified in the genus *Homo,* to which modern men belong.

All men other than *Pithecanthropus* can be placed in the genus *Homo*. The most primitive members of this genus were the Neanderthal men, *Homo neanderthalensis*, known from a considerable number of skulls and skeletons found in Europe, Asia, and Africa. Neanderthal man lived during the third interglacial stage in late Pleistocene times, and was a man sufficiently advanced to make tools and weapons and to bury his dead.

Neanderthal man was rather short and stocky, not much more than five feet in height. The shoulders were stooped, the head was thrust forward somewhat, and the knees were slightly bent. The skull showed some traces of pithecanthropoid features. Thus the cranium was somewhat lower than in modern man and the brow ridges were heavy, the face was large and the jaws were prognathous, and the chin was receding.

In spite of his uncouth appearance, Neanderthal man had developed a complex, though primitive, culture. This man was a hunter who used fire. He skillfully fashioned beautiful chipped stone tools and weapons. He lived in a land inhabited by many large aggressive mammals, great cats, bears, wolves, rhinoceroses, and mammoths, and he was able to prevail against them.

Neanderthal man was of the Old Stone Age, the period in the development of human cultures when men relied on chipped flint implements and weapons. One of the last of the Old Stone Age men was the Cro-Magnon man of Europe. Cro-Magnon man was a modern man, belonging to our species, *Homo sapiens*. He was a tall man, with a large brain and a high, wide forehead. The face was straight, not prognathous like his predecessors', and there was an angular point on the chin. Cro-Magnon man lived in rock shelters and caves, and in the deep recesses of many caves in southern Europe he drew wonderful pictures of the animals that lived around him. He was an accomplished artist, and Cro-Magnon pictures and sculptures rank with some of the finest artistic work ever produced by man. It is possible that Cro-Magnon man displaced and finally exterminated Neanderthal man in the Old World.

Man was essentially an Old World animal, but with the close of the Pleistocene period and during sub-Recent times various men spread over most of the earth's surface. Some fifteen or twenty thousand years ago Asiatic men migrated into the New World to populate both North and South America. They were the progenitors of our modern Indians. Other men spread from Asia into the East Indies and the Pacific Islands. As men became proficient with tools they learned how to make clothes and dwellings, and thus were able to escape from the subtropical and tropical lands to which they had originally been limited. They spread north and south as well as laterally, and learned to live comfortably even in the polar regions.

There are four basic stocks of modern men, all belonging to the species *Homo sapiens*. The Australian blacks are the most restricted, and perhaps the most primitive of modern men. The other basic races of modern men are the caucasoids or white men, the negroids or Negroes, and the mongoloids or yellow and red men—the Asiatics and the American Indians. Man is a very restless being, made more so in modern times by the perfection of rapid and easy methods of transportation. Consequently the races of men have been mixing with each other for thousands of years, and within the last century this process has been greatly accelerated. Therefore, although the basic racial stocks of modern men remain distinct, their limits are blurred, and are becoming more and more so as the years progress. This is an age of assimilation.

HUMAN CULTURES

A discussion of cultures properly belongs in a textbook of anthropology. However, since the later evolution of man was affected by his cultural development, perhaps it is pertinent to say a few words at this place about the sequence of cultures.

During most of the Pleistocene period men made chipped stone implements and weapons. This was the Old Stone Age, and it may be divided into a series of type cultural levels, according to the technique and perfection of the stone work. The Old Stone Age or Paleolithic Age was followed by the New Stone or Neolithic Age, which began perhaps about fifteen thousand years ago. Neolithic men made polished stone implements in addition to their chipped stone tools and weapons. In some parts of the world, as in many Pacific Islands and in the New World, the Neolithic stage of culture continued until modern times; it is only now being displaced.

About five thousand years ago man began to learn the use of metals, and the Bronze Age began. The Bronze Age was followed by the Iron Age, when the great Old World civilizations arose and flourished. We are now in what might be called the Steel Age, a relatively new phase of culture, and are entering with much foreboding the Atomic Age.

What of man's future? This question is in the forefront of much of the thinking and planning of modern men, all over the world.

Man has had increasing control over his own fate, even over his evolution during several thousand years; but within the last century, and especially within the last decade or two the degree of this control has increased at a prodigious rate. More than ever before in his history man has assumed crucial responsibilities for himself and for the environment in which he lives, and the manner in which he fulfills these responsibilities will determine to a large degree the course of his history in the years to come.

Gray Squirrel

22 · Rodents and Rabbits

THE EVOLUTIONARY SUCCESS OF THE RODENTS

The criteria of evolutionary success are various. We like to think of ourselves as the most successful of all animals, for in our own way we rule the world. Yet we are but a single species, and the great dominance we now enjoy has been a recent development of the last few thousand years. As contrasted with the evolutionary success of man, or of the order of primates, or of any other mammalian order, the rodents have been supremely successful during most of Cenozoic times. If the range of adaptive radiation, the numbers of species, and the numbers of individuals within a species are criteria of success in evolution, the rodents far outshine all other mammals.

At the present time the species of rodents outnumber all other species of mammals combined, and it is probable that this was true throughout most of Cenozoic times. Moreover, most species of rodents are abundantly represented in their respective ranges, so that in individuals they commonly are more numerous than any other mammals. Indeed, it is probable that their biomass, the total mass of all the rodents in the world, exceeds the biomass of the whales, the largest of all mammals.

Several factors have contributed to the evolutionary success of the rodents. In the first place these mammals throughout their history have for the most part remained small. Small size has been advantageous to the rodents, for it has allowed them to exploit numerous environments not available to larger animals, and to build up large populations. The establishment and continuation of large rodent populations are furthered at the present time, as they probably were in the past, by the rapid rate of breeding in these little mammals, which means that they can quickly occupy new ranges and adapt themselves to changing ecological conditions.

The adaptability of most rodents has also stood them in good stead during the millions of years of mammalian dominance. They live on the ground and under the ground, in trees and rocks, in swamps and in marshes, and they range from the equatorial regions to the polar belts. They have been able to compete successfully with other mammals, and frequently to prevail by the sheer weight of their numbers.

All these factors have brought about the long-continued success of the rodents throughout the world. They have persisted where other mammals have failed, and it is quite likely that when human beings decline, at some unforeseeable date in the future, the rodents will still be making their way on the earth with unabated vigor.

In spite of their importance as the most numerous of all mammals, either as species or individuals, rodents cannot be given adequate consideration in this survey of mammalian evolution. Any discussion of the modern rodents involves such a broad range of families and genera and so much detail concerning adaptations to environments that it necessarily becomes very long and complex. Any consideration of the fossil rodents is painfully inadequate, because the history of these mammals is very incompletely known.

Our unsatisfactory knowledge of the fossil rodents is to a considerable degree a result of the general lack of interest among paleontologists in these mammals. In the earlier collections of fossil mammals rodents are comparatively rare, since the inconspicuous remains of these small mammals were frequently overlooked by collectors who concentrated on the larger animals. Moreover, fossil rodents do not make good museum displays, either for the general public or for teaching purposes, so that the large mammals have in past years been given priority in collecting programs.

Within the last two or three decades, however, several paleontologists have turned their attention to the rodents, so that knowledge of the fossil record of these mammals has increased greatly during this period. The trend is continuing, and it is to be expected that in the years to come the history of the rodents as revealed by fossils will be greatly augmented.

CHARACTERS OF THE RODENTS

From their beginnings to the present time, the rodents have been gnawing animals, and, in line with this basic adaptation, they have the incisor teeth limited to two pairs of large, sharp-edged chisels, one pair in the skull and an opposing pair in the lower jaws. These chisel-like teeth grow from a persistently open pulp cavity, so that the wearing down of their cutting edges is compensated for by the continual growth of the teeth. Along the front edge of each incisor tooth is a broad, longitudinal band of hard enamel, and it is the differential wear between this enamel and the softer dentine composing the remainder of the tooth that brings about the formation and the maintenance of the sharp chisel edge.

The lateral incisor teeth, the canines, and the anterior premolar teeth are suppressed in the rodents, so that there is a long gap between the gnawing incisors and the cheek teeth. Most rodents feed upon plants, although some may eat insects and others are omnivorous. The cheek teeth, which consist of the molars and in some rodents of one or at the most two premolars, commonly take the form of tall prisms; and such teeth, with the grinding surfaces complicated by folding of the enamel, are well suited for grinding hard grain and other plant food. In the more primitive rodents the teeth may be low crowned, with blunt cusps.

The skull is long and low, and the brain is primitive. The articulation between the skull and the lower jaw and the development of the cheek muscles are of such a nature that the mandible can be slid backwards and forwards in relation to the skull, as well as moved up and down and sidewise. The deep portion of the powerful masseter muscle, which in most mammals runs from the cheek bone to the lower edge of the mandible to furnish much of the power for

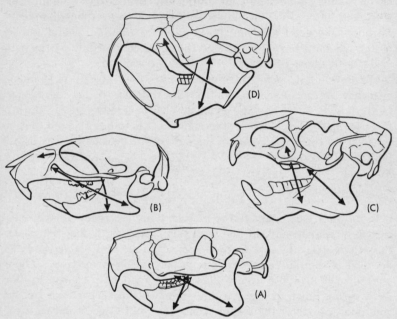

FIGURE 86. Rodent skulls. (A) *Paramys*, a Paleocene and Eocene sciuromorph, one-half natural size. (B) *Cricetops*, an Oligocene myomorph, twice natural size. (C) *Neoreomys*, a Miocene caviomorph, one-half natural size. (D) *Palaeocastor*, a Miocene castorimorph, two-thirds natural size. The arrows represent the courses of the deep and superficial layers of the masseter muscle. In the primitive sciuromorph (A) both layers of the muscle reach from the zygomatic arch to the lower border of the mandible. In the castorimorph (D) the origin of the deep section of the masseter is extended forward onto the face, in front of the cheek region. In the caviomorph (B) and the hystricomorph (C) the origin of the deep layer of the masseter is extended onto the face through the enlarged infraorbital foramen.

closing the jaws, in the rodents is directed forward, thus supplying the forward horizontal pull on the jaws. In the more primitive rodents this deep section of the masseter muscle attaches beneath the front border of the cheek bone or zygomatic arch, but in some of the specialized rodents it extends forward through the infraorbital foramen, an opening at the front of the zygomatic arch commonly for the passage of certain nerves and blood vessels, or upward in front of the arch, to attach to the side of the face. This gives the muscle considerable length and thereby increases the efficiency of its horizontal action.

The skeleton behind the skull is not highly specialized in most rodents. The fore limbs are generally very flexible, for climbing, running, and food gathering, and usually all the toes are retained. These toes, like those of the hind feet, usually have claws. The hind legs are frequently more specialized and less flexible than the fore limbs. Some rodents are adapted for hopping; their hind limbs are long and powerful, and their fore limbs comparatively short.

CLASSIFICATION OF THE RODENTS

It has been common practice for many years to divide the rodents into three large subordinal categories, but recently A. E. Wood, a leading student of these mammals, has suggested that there should be seven rather than three suborders of the Rodentia. Wood's arrangement, which is accepted here, is as follows:

Sciuromorphs
Primitive rodents, aplodonts or sewellels, squirrels, chipmunks, and marmots.
Theridomyomorphs
Scaly-tailed "squirrels" and certain fossil forms.
Castorimorphs
Beavers and their relatives.
Myomorphs
Dormice, voles, rats and mice, pocket gophers, kangaroo rats, jerboas and jumping mice.
Caviomorphs
South American cavies, capybaras, agoutis, chinchillas, spiny rats, and New World porcupines.
Hystricomorphs
Old World porcupines, bamboo "rats," rock "rats."
Bathyergomorphs
Naked "rats" of Africa.

EVOLUTION OF THE RODENTS

One of the earliest and most primitive of the known rodents is *Paramys*, an ischyromyid from Paleocene and Eocene sediments of North America. *Paramys* was rather like a large squirrel, with clawed feet for grasping and climbing and a long tail for balancing. The cheek teeth were low crowned, with rather blunt cusps in the unworn condition. Yet even though *Paramys* was a primitive rodent,

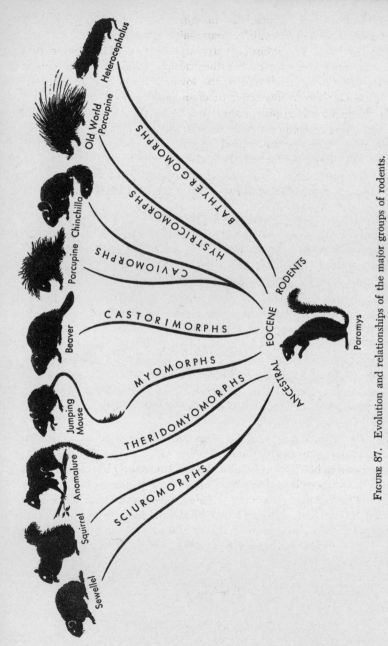

FIGURE 87. Evolution and relationships of the major groups of rodents.

it was none the less a specialized mammal, with no indications of its derivation from more primitive mammals. The skull was elongated and rather low. The incisors were large chisels. There were two premolars and three molars on either side of the skull, one premolar and three molars in each half of the lower jaw, the maximum number of cheek teeth in this order of mammals.

From ancestors approximated by *Paramys* the sciuromorphs evolved along numerous trends of adaptive radiation during Cenozoic times. A conservative stock was the Aplodontoidea, of which the sewellel (*Aplodontia*) of the Pacific Northwest is the only surviving representative. The aplodontoids reached the zenith of their development in middle Tertiary times, when they were represented by several families, among which the Miocene mylagaulids, were particularly abundant. The mylagaulids were small, burrowing rodents. Some members of this group, such as *Ceratogaulus*, had horns on the skull, the only rodents showing this specialization.

The squirrels, the Sciuridae, appear in the fossil record in middle Tertiary times, but it seems obvious that these rodents represent a long-continued and probably little-changed line from ischyromyid ancestors. Most squirrels, like *Sciurus*, have been tree-living types, and this environment has afforded them the safety and the food supply that has insured their long continuation to the present day. However some members of this group of rodents are specialized for life on the ground and in burrows. Such are the various ground squirrels and chipmunks, like *Tamias*, the prairie dogs (*Cynomys*), and the marmots or woodchucks, these last being the largest of the squirrel family.

The theridomyomorphs are a separate group of squirrel-like rodents, of Old World origin and distribution.

The beavers of Pleistocene and Recent times are the sole survivors of the castorimorphs, a group that made its appearance in Oligocene times. The first castorids, such as *Palaeocastor* and *Steneofiber*, were small, burrowing rodents, and their skeletons have been found associated with the natural casts of their burrows. During the course of time the castorids showed a trend toward adaptations to the water, culminating in the beavers, with which we are familiar. In Pleistocene times there were giant beavers in North America, and of these *Castoroides* was one of the largest of all rodents, attaining a size comparable to that of a small bear.

Perhaps the word "rodent" means rat or mouse to most people, since they are the rodents with which we are most familiar, often to our great annoyance. The myomorphs show a considerable range of adaptive radiation, but the central and most abundant types are the various rats and mice. It must not be supposed, however, that the names rats and mice refer only to the unwelcome dwellers in our homes, for there is a tremendous array of rats and mice belonging to numerous genera and species living throughout the world. The rats and mice are at the present time the most successful of the rodents, outnumbering all other rodents in numbers of species and probably in numbers of individuals as well.

The myomorphs may be divided into four groups of superfamily status. The muroids are the rats, mice, voles, and lemmings in their varied manifestations—the most numerous of all mammals. Many genera and species, native to the several continental areas, have been components of mammalian faunas in many regions of the world during much of the latter portion of the Cenozoic era. In addition to the muroids, the myomorphs include the long-ranging geomyoids, represented today by such divergent types as the burrowing pocket gophers (*Geomys*) and the hopping, desert-living kangaroo rats (*Dipodomys*). The glroids or dormice (*Myoxus*), are in some respects, such as the presence of low-crowned cheek teeth and the retention of a premolar, the most primitive of the myomorphs. The fourth group of this suborder of rodents is the dipodoids, consisting of the Old World jerboas (*Dipus*) and the New World jumping mice (*Zapus*). In these myomorphs the hind limbs are greatly elongated for making long hops, whereas the fore limbs are comparatively small. The development of adaptations for leaping in the jerboas and the jumping mice probably took place independently by processes of parallel evolution. Fossils of these rodents are not common, but the evidence for them in the geologic record extends back to Oligocene times.

Caviomorph rodents appear for the first time in the Oligocene sediments of South America. From these beginnings the caviomorphs evolved as the New World porcupines (*Erethizon, Coendu*) plus a great variety of South American rodents. Recent evidence would seem to indicate that the ancestors of the caviomorphs, descended from North American paramyids, entered the southern continent from the north in very early Tertiary times, before the continental connection between North and South America was broken. If this was so, these rodents failed to leave any fossil remains in any part of South America until the Oligocene epoch—a strange circumstance indeed. The alternative to this explanation is that the caviomorph rodents entered South America in Oligocene times, after that continent had become separated from North America. If so, the ancestral caviomorph rodents must have been rafted into South America on floating logs or trees.

In South America the caviomorphs evolved during the interval from Oligocene to Recent times along varied lines of adaptive radiation. One of these lines was the porcupines, a very successful group of rodents that pushed into North America in Pleistocene times, when the two continents had become reunited. The other caviomorphs of South America, a few scattered members of which invaded the northern continent in the Pleistocene epoch, have been the cavies or guinea pigs (*Cavia*), the capybaras (*Hydrochoerus*), and their relatives, some of which are the largest of modern rodents, the agoutis (*Agouti*) and pacas, the chinchillas, and finally the octodonts, which may be designated as the "spiny rats." Until the final stages of the Pliocene epoch these rodents were isolated on the island continent of South America, completely free from competition with any other rodents. Consequently they evolved along many lines, some of them developing as small, rather mouse-like animals, others as running, rabbit-like animals, and others as large, herbivorous rodents. Although the invasion of South America in late Pliocene and Pleistocene times by various North American mammals brought about the extinction of many of the indigenous mammals of ancient ancestry on that continent, it did not so affect the caviomorph rodents, and they continued with vigor into our modern age.

The hystricomorphs or Old World porcupines have a long history going back to the Oligocene epoch. These rodents may have arisen from ancestral paramyids, and probably have nothing to do with the porcupines of South America. They evolved in Asia and Africa and are found in those continents today.

In Africa are also found the peculiar bathyergomorphs, burrowing rodents, among which one genus, *Heterocephalus*, is almost devoid of hair and is adapted for a subterranean existence.

The development of the rodents through geologic time along seven subordinal lines, so briefly summarized in the foregoing paragraphs, indicates a high degree of parallel evolution among these mammals. Such parallelism, involving many of the anatomical features and some of the behavior patterns that characterize the rodents, has in the past confused our understanding of phylogenetic relationships among these most numerous of all mammals. But with the growing recognition of the important rôle that parallelism has played in the evolution of the rodents, and with a constantly increased knowledge of the fossil forms (this, the result of improved field techniques and the increased interest, already mentioned, among paleontologists in these mammals) our knowledge as to the details of rodent evolution should become ever clearer as time goes on.

THE HARES, RABBITS, AND PIKAS

It was long the practice to consider the hares, rabbits, and pikas as rodents, placing them in a suborder, the Duplicidentata, so named because of the two incisor teeth on each side in the skull. This suborder was set against the Simplicidentata, the rodents with a single incisor on either side in the skull. The grouping of the rabbits and their relatives with the rodents was based primarily on the general similarity of adaptations for eating in these two large groups of mammals, for in both rabbits and rodents there are enlarged incisor teeth for gnawing, separated by a long gap or diastema from the grinding cheek teeth. In recent years, however, there has been a growing tendency among students of mammals to regard the rabbits as quite independent of the rodents, and to view such similarities as exist between these mammals as a result of convergent evolution. There is good reason to think that this interpretation is correct. Very primitive rodents and rabbits are found in sediments of Paleocene and Eocene age, and these fossils show that the two groups of mammals were quite distinct from each other at that early stage in the history of the mammals. Moreover, when the seemingly similar characters of the rabbits and rodents are critically examined it soon becomes apparent that the resemblances are superficial rather than basic.

For instance, the rabbits have enlarged incisor teeth, as do the rodents, but this is a character that has developed independently many times in various groups of mammals. As for the cheek teeth, there are no real similarities. In the rabbits there are two or three premolar teeth present, as contrasted with a much greater limitation in the rodents. Moreover, the cheek teeth in the hares and their relatives are tall prisms with transversely ridged crowns for cutting, rather than crushing teeth of the rodent type. The masseter muscle, though powerful in the rabbits, never shows the high degree of specialization so characteristic of the rodents. In the postcranial skeleton there are few similarities between rabbits and rodents. The rabbits are animals specialized for hopping, and as a result the hind limbs are very long and strong. The tail is reduced to a mere vestige.

Thus it would seem probable that the rabbits are an independent order of mammals descended from an ancient eutherian ancestry.

It seems quite possible that this ancestry is to be found among the condylarths, the primitive hoofed mammals from which several orders of herbivorous mammals would seem to have arisen. In line with this concept they may be placed in a separate order, the Lagomorpha.

Pika   Rabbit

Eurymylus

FIGURE 88. Relationships of the two suborders of lagomorphs.

EVOLUTION OF THE LAGOMORPHS

The first indication of rabbits in the fossil record is the genus *Eurymylus,* from upper Paleocene sediments of Mongolia. Although this ancient lagomorph must be excluded from the direct ancestry of later forms, since it had lost the second upper incisor, it nevertheless indicates what the very early Tertiary rabbits were like. These animals are sparsely represented in Eocene faunas, but with the advent of the Oligocene epoch they seem to have become abundant, and to have continued this abundance into modern times.

The lagomorphs became divided at an early date into two separate groups of family rank, and have maintained this dichotomy ever since. On the one hand there are the pikas, of which the modern pika or "cony," *Ochotona,* is typical. Through the extent of their history they have been small, compact, short-legged lagomorphs, with short ears. Contrasted with the pikas or Ochotonidae, there are the hares and rabbits, such as *Lepus* and *Sylvilagus.* These lagomorphs have evolved as swift runners that bound over the ground in long hops. The hind limbs are very long to give power and distance to the leap. The front limbs are adapted for taking up the shock of landing. The ears are elongated, particularly the hares', and serve as acute sound-gathering devices.

RODENTS, RABBITS, AND MEN

The development of man as an agriculturist and as a civilized human being has been inextricably interwoven with the fortunes of the rodents and rabbits. When man was a primitive hunter it is probable that rodents and rabbits were of little concern to him, except as secondary sources of food; but as he established his dominance over the larger animals of the earth, he came into increasing conflict with the rodents and the rabbits.

When man began to grow vegetable crops, cereals, and grains, he discovered that the rodents and the rabbits were eager to share his food supply. So it is that the history of civilized man has entailed, among other things, a long battle with certain rodents and rabbits, which have persisted in invading his premises, to eat his food and to bring disorder into his household. The battle has been going on for a good many thousand years.

Of course the common house mouse and the European rats are virtual parasites on man, going wherever he goes, and eating whatever he eats. The damage done by these rodents each year is tremendous. But various rodents of the fields also are and have been for many centuries annoying and costly to man. Likewise the rabbits cause much damage as a result of their depredations, although these animals are also viewed with favor, since they are for us a source of food.

In addition, the rodents and rabbits are of extreme importance and concern to man as carriers of disease. During past ages rats and lice spread the bubonic plague through Eurasia, with terrifying and disastrous effect, and it is only within comparatively recent times that this great scourge has been conquered. Moreover, it requires eternal vigilance on the part of man in the modern world to prevent the spread of various diseases borne by rodents and rabbits.

All these considerations point up the fact that the rodents and the lagomorphs have been extraordinarily successful animals during the last fifty or sixty million years. From the evolutionary viewpoint these mammals represent in many respects the climax of mammalian success.

Fin-Back Whales

23 · Cetaceans

THE RETURN TO THE SEA

Of all mammals the whales and porpoises, or cetaceans, are certainly the most atypical, and in many ways the most highly specialized in the extent to which they have diverged from their primitive eutherian ancestors. These mammals must have had an ancient origin, for no intermediate forms are apparent in the fossil record between the whales and the ancestral Cretaceous placentals. Like the bats, the whales (using this term in a general and inclusive sense) appear suddenly in early Tertiary times, fully adapted by profound modifications of the basic mammalian structure for a highly specialized mode of life. Indeed, the whales are even more isolated with relation to other mammals than the bats; they stand quite alone. Therefore it seems evident that the whales, having separated from the ancestral eutherians at an early date, enjoyed at the outset a series of extraordinarily rapid evolutionary changes that made them by middle Eocene times completely adapted for life in the ocean.

The whales returned to the sea to imitate the fishes after a fashion and to take the place of the ichthyosaurs, the fish-like marine tetrapods of Mesozoic times. In becoming adapted to a life in the open ocean the whales, as descendants of fully land-living ancestors, were faced with the same problems that had been encountered and overcome millions of years previously by the first ichthyosaurs. These problems have already been discussed in the description of the ichthyosaurs, but perhaps they may be repeated briefly at this place.

The problems to be surmounted by the ancestral whales in their new environment were in short those of locomotion, of respiration or breathing, and of reproduction. The adaptations to locomotion in the water involved a streamlining of the body, the development of a fish-like tail as the main propeller, and the transformation of the legs into balancing paddles. Like the ichthyosaurs of the Mesozoic, the whales retained the lung breathing that was their heritage from land-living ancestors, and in so doing they evolved adaptations that increased the efficiency of respiration. Of course embryonic development in whales posed no particular problems for these mammals, but there were special adaptations for the survival of the young in the water, from the moment of birth on.

The return of whales to the sea is a fine example of convergence in evolution. In following this evolutionary trend the whales have shown many adaptations that are remarkably similar to those of the ichthyosaurs, yet the ancestors of these two groups of tetrapods were quite distinct—cotylosaurian reptiles on the one hand and primitive eutherian mammals on the other. Convergence such as this illustrates the remarkably similar adaptations by dissimilar animals to an environment that imposes stringent limitations upon its inhabitants.

WHALES AS MARINE VERTEBRATES

As already mentioned, whales are fish-like vertebrates, highly streamlined for efficient swimming. The body is torpedo shaped, and there is no visible neck distinct from the trunk. There is no hair on the body of the modern whales, and it is likely that this adaptation developed early in the history of these mammals. The smooth skin makes a sleek surface that offers little resistance to the water as the animal moves forward. Since whales are warm blooded, they have developed a heavy layer of fat or blubber beneath the skin, to give the necessary insulation that in most mammals is furnished by the covering of hair.

The vertebrae are much alike and numerous, making for a flexible backbone, but the neck vertebrae are commonly shortened and fused into a single bony mass. Long muscles and tendons attach to the vertebrae and run back to the tail, to furnish the propulsive force that drives the animal through the water. The whales are unique among marine vertebrates in that the tail terminates in a horizontal fin that moves up and down, rather than in a vertical fin that moves from side to side. The horizontal tail fin of the whale, generally called flukes, is a neomorphic structure in these mammals, and, though stiff and strong, contains no bones. Likewise the whales frequently have a fleshy dorsal fin, another neomorph or new structure. This fin is a stabilizer that prevents the animal from rolling, and may be compared in function with the fleshy dorsal fin of the ichthyosaurs or the bony dorsal fins of fishes.

As in the ichthyosaurs, the limbs in whales have been modified as paddles. However, in all known whales, both fossil and recent, the pelvis and hind limbs are reduced to mere vestiges; only the front limbs remain as functional paddles. The arm bones are short and flattened, the wrist bones are flattened discs, and the fingers are commonly greatly elongated by multiplication of the phalanges as supports for the paddle.

In all but the earliest whales the external nostrils are shifted to the top and the back of the skull, to form the "blowhole" so characteristic of these mammals. The nostrils can be closed by valves, and the lungs are highly elastic and extensible, for taking in great quantities of air. Whales are able to remain submerged for long periods of time—as long as an hour in some of the large whales—and some of them can dive to great depths. In line with these remarkable accomplishments there are profound adaptations in the physiology of the whales.

In addition to the modifications in the skull brought about by special adaptations for breathing, the whales show marked specializations of the ear. The tube to the external ear and the eardrum are drastically reduced, and it is obvious that whales do not hear sounds in the same manner as other mammals. Instead they are very sensitive to vibrations in the water, which are transmitted to a heavy, shell-like bone formed by a fusion of the periotic bone and the auditory bulla, and separate from the rest of the skull. In contrast to this highly developed sense, whales have no olfactory sense. Consequently olfactory lobes are lacking, and the brain is large and rounded. The brain is highly developed in these mammals, and recent experiments indicate that whales are remarkably intelligent. The brain and the sensitive auditory apparatus are telescoped into a small space at the back of the skull; the remainder of the skull is made up of very long jaws.

Whales are and have been throughout their history carnivorous, living upon large invertebrates, fishes, and even other whales, or upon microscopic marine animals known as plankton. In the first category are the toothed whales, ancient and modern. Those in the second category are the whalebone whales, in which the teeth are suppressed and transverse plates of fibrous keratin or baleen hang from the roof of the mouth to strain plankton from the water.

As for reproduction, young whales are very large and well formed when they are born. As soon as they are born, the mother pushes them to the surface so that they can get their first breaths of air. From that time on the baby is able to swim along with its mother. The mammary glands are enclosed in a sort of pocket, so that the young whale can nurse without shipping a lot of sea water.

EARLY WHALES

Whales appear in the geologic record in sediments of middle Eocene age. These first whales, known as archaeocetes, are characterized by the genera *Protocetus* and *Eocetus* of middle Eocene age

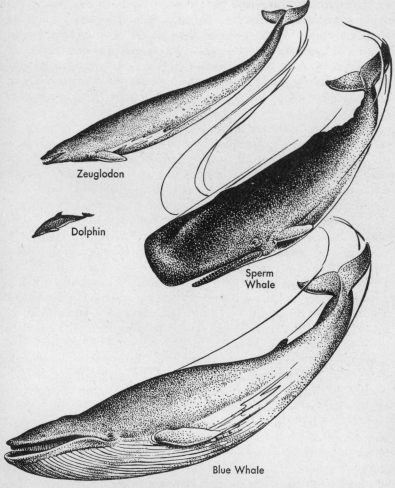

FIGURE 89. An Eocene whale (*Zeuglodon*) and three recent cetaceans, drawn to the same scale. The largest of these is an animal ninety feet or more in length. *Zeuglodon* was an archaeocete; the dolphin and the sperm whale are odontocetes or toothed whales; the blue whale is a mysticete or whalebone whale.

and by *Basilosaurus* (commonly designated as *Zeuglodon*) of upper
Eocene age. The early whales were large, and in this respect they
indicate an evolutionary trend typical of the whales. Many of these
mammals, freed from many of the limiting effects of gravity, have
become the giants of the animal world past or present, and even
Basilosaurus (or *Zeuglodon*) of the Eocene epoch was some sixty
feet in length. In this whale the tail was very long, the fore limbs
were modified into paddles, and the hind limbs were suppressed.
The skull in the archaeocetes was somewhat more primitive than
the skull in later whales. The bones of the facial region were not
telescoped into the back of the skull, as they were in the more advanced whales. There were forty-four teeth, as in primitive placentals, of which the incisors and the canines were simple, sharp
cones. The cheek teeth were cusped, but with the cusps arranged in
a single fore and aft line, and coming to a high point in the middle.
Teeth of this form are seen in other mammals, especially certain
seals that live on fish. The nostrils in the archaeocetes were placed
in a forward position, not on top of the skull as in the later whales.
In general this skull appears as if it might have been derived from
a creodont type, but there is little beyond superficial resemblances to
support such a relationship. It must be emphasized that the ancestry
of the whales is completely unknown at the present time.

ADAPTIVE RADIATION OF THE MODERN WHALES

During late Eocene or Oligocene times the modern whales arose
as descendants of the archaeocetes, and by Miocene times almost
all the families of modern whales had appeared. Two lines of
cetacean evolution developed from the archaeocete stem. One of
these was the toothed whales or odontocetes; the other was the
whalebone whales or mysticetes.

Most of the modern whales are odontocetes. In late Oligocene
times there appeared some comparatively small odontocetes, designated as the squalodonts, much like the modern porpoises in general appearance, but characterized by cusped, triangular cheek teeth
somewhat similar to the teeth in the early archaeocetes. Evidently
the squalodonts, of which the Miocene genus *Prosqualodon* is typical, were forms intermediate between the archaeocetes and the modern types of whales. In spite of their archaic teeth, the skull was
highly advanced, with the nostrils completely dorsal in position and
the skull bones modified accordingly. The squalodonts were impor-

tant whales during the Miocene epoch, but they did not survive long after the beginning of the Pliocene epoch.

Their place in Pliocene, Pleistocene, and Recent times was taken over by the small, toothed whales with which we are familiar, especially the porpoises and dolphins, collectively known as delphinids. These are compact, very swiftly swimming cetaceans that feed upon fish. The teeth are greatly multiplied in number and have the form of simple spikes. A common porpoise of Miocene times was *Kentriodon;* two of the most widely spread of the modern porpoises are *Delphinus,* the common dolphin, and *Phocaena,* the common porpoise of world-wide distribution. Related to these cetaceans are the fierce killer whales, the so-called blackfish, and some of the river dolphins. Other small to medium-sized odontocetes are the narwhals, the beaked whales, and the platanistids that live in the Amazon and the Ganges rivers.

There was an early trend toward giantism in the toothed whales, reaching its culmination in the physeterids or sperm whales. The modern sperm whale or cachalot (*Physeter*) is a giant odontocete with a great, square snout filled with gallons of sperm oil. Peg-like teeth are present on the lower jaw, and this whale feeds upon squids. In the great days of whaling the sperm whale was much sought for its oil, and incessant hunting has reduced it from its original vast numbers to the limited herds of the present day. Moby Dick was a white sperm whale.

The largest of the modern whales are the mysticetes or whalebone whales, of much lesser variety than the toothed whales, but none the less highly successful cetaceans. As mentioned above, these whales feed upon plankton, and it may have been the abundance of their food supply that led to the strong trend to giantism among these largest of all vertebrates. The primitive mysticetes were the cetotheres, in which the teeth had been lost and the skull had progressed toward the high degree of modification that is so characteristic of the modern whalebone whales. *Mesocetus,* of Miocene age, was typical of this group.

In the latter portion of Cenozoic times the evolution of the whalebone whales reached its ultimate stage with the development of the skull into a highly arched structure for bearing large plates of baleen, so that the eyes and brain case were limited to a very small posterior region. Some modern representatives of this evolutionary trend are the Greenland whales, the right whales (*Balaena*), the finbacks or rorquals (*Balaenoptera*), and the titanic blue whales. These last may reach lengths of one hundred feet and weights of one hundred and fifty tons. We are wont to look back at some of the giant dinosaurs with awe, yet such modern whales as the blue whale far exceed in size the largest dinosaurs. These are the ultimate extreme of giantism in the evolution of animals.

WHALES AND MAN

A few hundred years ago whales roamed the seas in vast herds. Then there was a demand for whale oil, and the large-scale systematic hunting of whales began, reaching a high point in the last century. Many species of large whales were drastically reduced in numbers. Whale oil is not used for lamps as it once was, but the hunting of whales continues on a vast scale, for the oil is used for soaps, the meat is processed for food, and the bone is ground up for fertilizer. Factory ships go out to hunt whales with airplanes, radar, modern whale guns, and other refined apparatus. Consequently some whales are in danger of extermination, and it is only through strict adherence to international treaties that these large mammals can be preserved for posterity. It is to be hoped that they will not disappear from the seas, for the giant whales together with their smaller cetacean cousins are marvelous animals that should never be allowed to vanish at the hand of man. There is still much to be learned about these wonderful mammals.

Pseudocynodictis

Fox

24 · Carnivores

ADAPTATIONS OF THE CARNIVORES

The early mammals that arose from primitive insectivore ancestors evolved along varied lines of adaptive radiation, to occupy the numerous ecological niches that had been vacated by the wide extinctions of reptiles at the end of the Cretaceous period. Several orders of mammals became adapted for feeding upon plants, whereas one order of land-living mammals, the carnivores, became dominantly specialized for eating other animals. Why was not the killing and eating of prey more widely followed among the orders of mammals? Perhaps the answer to this question is that the carnivores specialized as efficient predators at such an early date, and became so widely distributed, that no other mammals were able to compete with them on their own terms. It is an interesting fact that the successful predators outside the order Carnivora are those mammals that have lived in regions or in habitats where they have been free from carnivore competition, for instance, the carnivorous marsupials in Australia (and in past ages in South America), the insectivores, the bats, and the predatory whales and porpoises.

Adaptations for a predatory mode of life are on the one hand generally less extreme than those required for a life of plant-feeding, yet on the other hand they involve more "evolutionary risks" in the long battle for survival. The plant-eater must needs possess complicated teeth and digestive organs to gather and convert bulky plant food into energy, but in general the source of food for animals of this type is abundant and readily available. The meat-eaters, on the other hand, depend largely upon their ability to catch animals. This ability may not require advanced specializations, although often it has resulted in the evolution of highly modified animals, but it does make the carnivore dependent upon a very uncertain and variable source of food. Consequently there has been intense competition among carnivorous mammals through the ages, either on the level of species or of individuals.

The adaptations that have been characteristic of the carnivores from the beginning of the Cenozoic era to present times may be outlined briefly. These mammals usually have strong incisor teeth for nipping, and enlarged, dagger-like canine teeth for stabbing. In most carnivores the canines are the principal weapons with which they kill their prey. Certain cheek teeth in the carnivores are commonly transformed into blades that act against each other like the blades of a pair of scissors, for cutting and slicing meat into small pieces that can be swallowed easily and assimilated by the digestive system. These cutting teeth in the carnivores are called the *carnassials*. Naturally the carnivores have strong jaws, and strong crests and zygomatic arches on the skull for the attachment of powerful jaw muscles.

The carnivores are usually very intelligent animals, because a great deal of mental alertness and coordinated action are required if other animals are to be overcome and killed. The sense of smell is usually highly developed as an aid to hunting, and in many carnivores the eyesight is very keen. The body and limbs are generally strong and capable of lithe, powerful movements. There is little reduction of the toes, which have sharp claws. These animals are frequently fast runners over short distances, or adept climbers.

BEGINNINGS OF THE CARNIVORES

Fortunately there is a good fossil record for the carnivores, so that we can follow their evolutionary history in considerable detail from the beginning of the Tertiary period to Recent times. The first carnivores, known as creodonts and characterized by such genera as *Oxyclaenus* or *Tricentes* of Paleocene age, were primitive predators, generally small and archaic in structure. In these animals the skull was long and low, all the teeth were present, and the molars retained much of the original tribosphenic pattern. In these earliest creodonts there were no specialized carnassial teeth for cutting meat. The body was slender and long, something like that of a modern Oriental civet or a weasel, and the slender limbs terminated in sharp-clawed feet. Evidently these little carnivores were denizens of the forests or of low underbrush, and they probably climbed among trees, not only in search of food but also for protection.

From such ancestral forms the carnivores evolved through the wide range of adaptive types that was to characterize their development during Cenozoic times. The initial phase of their evolution was marked by the broad radiation of the creodonts that took place in Paleocene and Eocene times. Near the end of the Eocene epoch another group of carnivores, the Fissipedia, multiplied, and soon after the rise of the fissipeds the creodonts became virtually extinct. Indeed, only one family of creodonts survived beyond the close of Eocene times.

The fissipeds are the modern and familiar land-living beasts of prey that have been dominant from late Eocene and early Oligocene times to the present day. They are the dogs and their relatives, the bears, the raccoons and pandas, the varied mustelids such as the weasels, minks, badgers, wolverines, skunks and otters, the Old World civets, the hyenas and the cats. It is probable that at the time the early fissipeds appeared as descendants of advanced creodont ancestors, or soon after, the aquatic pinnipeds, the sea-lions, seals, and walruses, originated. However, the fossil record of these carnivores does not extend back beyond the Miocene epoch.

Having in mind this outline of the first carnivores and the general range of carnivore radiation through Cenozoic times, let us now turn to a consideration of carnivore evolution, beginning of course with the creodonts.

EVOLUTION OF THE CREODONTS

The basal Tertiary creodonts, like *Oxyclaenus*, have been designated as the Arctocyonoidea or Procreodi. These creodonts reached the zenith of their phylogenetic development during the Paleocene epoch, after which they rapidly declined, although they did persist through Eocene times. Many of them remained small during the extent of Paleocene times, maintaining in effect the form and primitive adaptations of the ancestral carnivores. *Tricentes* of middle Paleocene age, and *Chriacus*, extending through the final phases of Paleocene history, represent such persistent primitive types.

However, some arctocyonoids evolved into large carnivores during the Paleocene epoch. Among them were *Claenodon*, from the middle Paleocene sediments of North America, and *Arctocyon*, from the upper Paleocene of Europe, creodonts as large as small bears, with blunt teeth, possibly as an adaptation to an omnivorous diet. It

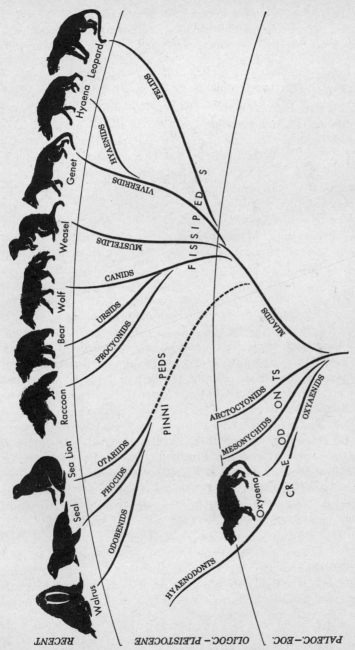

FIGURE 90. Evolution and relationships of the major groups of carnivores.

might be said that *Claenodon* and *Arctocyon* were the "bears" of
the Paleocene epoch, for they evidently fulfilled the ecological rôle
at that time that the true bears were to take over many millions
of years later, during late Tertiary history. Of course this does not
imply that these creodonts were in any way ancestral to the bears;
the resemblances are those of function rather than of relationships.

From certain Paleocene arctocyonoids there arose a second group
of creodonts, the Mesonychoidea or Acreodi, that flourished during
the Eocene epoch. There was a strong trend toward great size among
these creodonts, and the dentition was characterized by the blunt-
cusped, crushing cheek teeth. The feet were provided with flattened
nails, rather than with claws as in most other carnivores. These large
creodonts may have been giant carrion-feeders, comparable in a
general way to the hyenas of modern times. One of the last of
the mesonychoids, the Mongolian Eocene genus *Andrewsarchus,* was
a veritable giant among carnivorous mammals, with a skull three feet
or more in length.

There was a third branch of creodont evolution that arose from
arctocyonoid ancestors during Paleocene times. This branch com-
prised the Oxyaenoidea or Pseudocreodi, highly specialized creodonts
adapted for predatory activities. At an early stage in their evolutionary history the oxyaenoids branched into two phylogenetic lines,
the Oxyaenidae, in which the first upper molar and the second lower
molar were the carnassials, or cutting teeth, and the Hyaenodontidae,
in which the second upper and third lower molars were the carnassials. Adaptations were varied among these creodonts. Some were
small and slender like the Eocene hyaenodont, *Sinopa.* Others were
large and powerfully built, like the Eocene oxyaenids, *Oxyaena* and
Patriofelis, or the Oligocene hyaenodont, *Hyaenodon.* It is obvious
that these creodonts were the arch predators of lower Tertiary times
and anticipated the divergent evolution that was to take place among
the fissiped carnivores in later Tertiary times, after the creodonts
had become extinct.

After the extinction of all other creodonts at the end of the Eocene
epoch the hyaenodonts continued into the Oligocene epoch, and
from then through the Miocene and into the early phases of the
Pliocene epoch. Evidently these particular creodonts were sufficiently well adapted as beasts of prey so that they could compete
successfully with the progressive fissiped carnivores that arose at
the end of the Eocene times, to blossom into abundance and great
variety during subsequent geologic ages.

THE MIACIDS

The various creodonts that have so far been described shared their function of early Tertiary predators with still another group of carnivores, the miacids. These carnivores appeared in Paleocene times, and like many of the creodonts they continued through the Eocene epoch to become extinct at the close of that phase of geologic history. They had certain creodont characters, such as the general archaic structure, with a low skull, elongated body and tail, and short limbs, and because of these characters the miacids have been associated with the creodonts by many students of carnivore evolution, being designated as a superfamily, the Miacoidea or Eucreodi.

The miacids, however, were progressive in some very important features. For one thing, they seem to have had a proportionately larger and more highly developed brain than the typical creodonts, a feature that would have been of great advantage to them as beasts of prey. Of particular importance is the fact that in these carnivores the carnassial teeth were more anteriorly placed than in any of the other early Tertiary carnivores, for they consisted of the fourth upper premolar and the first lower molar. The molar teeth were tribosphenic in form, and the last upper molar was absent. These are exactly the conditions typical of the fissipeds, and for this reason the miacids are regarded by many authorities as the most primitive Fissipedia.

The miacids were small carnivores of weasel-like form. They were probably forest dwellers, preying upon small animals that lived in the dense undergrowth or in trees. *Viverravus* and *Miacis* were characteristic Eocene genera. These animals and their relatives were the direct ancestors of the modern carnivores.

FISSIPED CARNIVORES

If the miacids are regarded as outside the limits of the creodonts, the fissiped carnivores may be divided into three major categories of superfamily rank. These, with their constituent families, are:

Superfamily: Miacoidea.
    Family: Miacidae: the miacids of Paleocene and Eocene age.
Superfamily: Canoidea (or Arctoidea).
    Family: Canidae: dogs, wolves, foxes and their relatives.
           Ursidae: bears.
           Procyonidae: raccoons, coatis, kinkajous, pandas.
           Mustelidae: weasels, martens, minks, wolverines, badgers, skunks, otters.

Superfamily: Feloidea (or Aeluroidea).
Family: Viverridae: Old World civets.
        Hyaenidae: hyenas.
        Felidae: cats.

The twofold division of modern fissipeds into canoids and feloids
is based upon various technical details of anatomy, especially the
structure of the tympanic bulla that surrounds the middle ear. When
fossils are taken into account the distinction between these two groups
of carnivores is not very sharp, since some of the primitive forms in
each superfamily approach each other closely in structure. On the
whole, however, this makes a good practical arrangement for grouping the fissiped carnivores beyond the miacids, and it probably
expresses their basic relationships with a fair degree of accuracy.

THE ARCTOID CARNIVORES

The early arctoid and aeluroid carnivores were, like the miacids,
probably forest-dwellers that preyed upon the small game they could
catch in the undergrowth and in trees. *Cynodictis,* a late Eocene
form, and *Pseudocynodictis* (properly known as *Hesperocyon*) of the
Oligocene were among the first canids, and although they retained
many characters of their miacid ancestors they showed certain features that were to characterize the evolutionary development among
the dogs or canids. There was some elongation of the limbs and
feet in these early dogs, and the carnassial teeth were more highly
specialized as shearing blades than they had been in the miacids.
Also, the brain case was expanded. Thus we see the early dogs
embarking along the evolutionary path of long feet and limbs for
running, sharp carnassial teeth for cutting meat, and a large brain,
an indication of a high degree of intelligence. In these ways the
dogs advanced; in other ways they have remained as comparatively
primitive carnivores. For instance, there has been little loss of teeth
or change in the form and function of the dentition beyond the stage
characteristic of the late Eocene or early Oligocene carnivores.

From the small Oligocene *Hesperocyon* the canids progressed
to the Miocene genus, *Cynodesmus,* from thence to the Pliocene
Tomarctus, and finally to the modern dogs like *Canis* of Pleistocene
and Recent times. This sequence represents the "main line" of canid
evolution, but as so often happens there were several side lines of
canids during Miocene and Pliocene times. *Amphicyon* was a very
large, heavy, rather clumsy dog with a long tail. *Borophagus* was
another large dog, with a very deep, heavy skull and robust teeth.

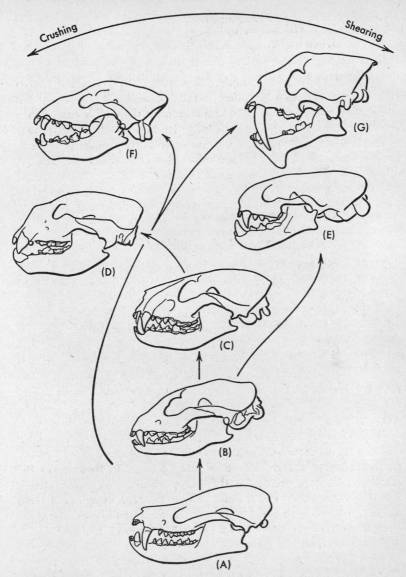

FIGURE 91. Carnivore skulls, showing evolutionary lines, and the dominance in later forms of crushing or shearing actions in the cheek teeth. Not to scale. (A) *Deltatherium*, a Paleocene creodont. (B) *Hesperocyon*, an Oligocene canid. (C) *Cynodesmus*, a Miocene canid. (D) *Arctodus*, a Pleistocene bear. (E) *Mustela*, a Pleistocene weasel. (F) *Hyaena*, a Pliocene hyena. (G) *Hoplophoneus*, an Oligocene saber-tooth cat.

Borophagus and various related genera constituted an important line of Miocene and Pliocene dogs.

In Pleistocene and Recent times the history of the dogs reached its culminating phases in the differentiation of our modern canids, the wild dogs and wolves, the foxes and fennecs of the northern hemisphere, and various highly specialized dogs of South America and Africa. These are intelligent animals that hunt and live in family groups and packs. For the most part they run down and kill their prey, often pursuing their victims for many hours over many miles of terrain. The foxes, however, are more solitary in habits and frequently hunt by stealth or by cunning stratagems, for which they are justly famous in folklore.

The social instincts of the wild dogs have made them ideal as companions, and they were certainly the first animals to be domesticated. Man and dog lived together and worked together as early as Neolithic times, and this relationship has continued ever since, through a period of many thousands of years. It is difficult to make positive statements as to the origin of the domestic dog, *Canis familiaris,* but these friends and companions of home and field are probably in the main of wolf ancestry. Since the dogs are structurally primitive in many respects, they are genetically plastic. The truly astonishing variety of modern breeds of dogs is a proof of this that needs no elaboration in words. Under the guiding hand of man, the domestic dog has indeed departed far from his wild, wolf-like ancestor in form and physical appearance, yet psychologically he is still a wolf—an intelligent, friendly canid that likes to run and hunt.

In Miocene times some dogs began to evolve as large, heavy carnivores. *Hemicyon,* a genus of late Miocene and early Pliocene times, was typical of this trend. From *Hemicyon* there arose the Pliocene *Hyaenarctos,* with a massive skull and robust teeth. In carnivores of this type the carnassial teeth lost their shearing function, and the molar teeth became square in outline, with blunt cusps. At the same time the legs and feet became heavy and the feet short, and the habit of pursuing the prey declined. The tail was reduced to a mere stub. Thus the bears evolved, geologically the youngest of all the carnivores. The trend of bear evolution reached its climax in the Pleistocene and recent bears, typified by *Ursus.* In the modern bears, some of them the largest of all land carnivores, the molar teeth are elongated and the crowns are complicated by a wrinkling of the enamel. This is obviously a specialization for an omnivorous diet and a great departure from the predominantly meat-eating habits of the dogs.

Bears are very adaptable animals, as are the dogs for that matter, and they are widely distributed throughout the world. The late Tertiary origin and evolution of the bears took place in the northern hemisphere. They entered South America during Pleistocene times, but curiously they never invaded Africa.

From the central canid stock there was another evolutionary trend that also led away from the chase and the kill, to adaptations for climbing and an omnivorous diet. This was the line of the procyonids —the raccoons, pandas, and their allies.

The procyonids probably diverged from the canids during the Oligocene epoch, for in Miocene times they were well established, as indicated by the genus *Phlaocyon*, a small, climbing carnivore with hand-like fore paws, flexible limbs, a dentition in which the carnassials had lost their shearing function, and molar teeth that were square with blunt cusps. The adaptations characteristic of *Phlaocyon* have been continued with little change in the modern *Bassariscus*, the ring-tailed "cat" or cacomistle of Mexico and the southwestern United States. Here we see in effect the structural ancestor of the procyonids, a small carnivore that lives among rocks or in trees, where it eats almost anything it can catch or gather. It is partly a meat-eater, partly a vegetarian.

From *Phlaocyon* the advanced procyonids evolved during late Tertiary times. Many of them have remained relatively small and have been confined to North America, where they originated, or to South America, a region that they invaded. These are the familiar raccoons, *Procyon* and its relatives, the coatis, *Nasua*, and the kinkajou, *Potos*, of South and Central America, and some other forms. All of them are forest-living animals that spend much of their time in the trees or along the banks of streams, where they feed upon a great variety of foods. The catholic diet of the common raccoon of North America is well known to many farmers and fishermen, who have had their fields, their chicken coops, or their fishing grounds raided by these intelligent little carnivores.

One branch of the procyonids would seem to have invaded Eurasia, probably during the Pliocene epoch. They were the pandas. The lesser panda, *Ailurus*, now lives in the Himalayan region, but fossils show that it once extended as far west as England. It looks very much like an enlarged raccoon, even to the ringed tail and the mask on the face. The giant panda, *Ailuropoda*, was rather widely distributed in Asia during Pleistocene times, but is now confined to a comparatively small area in western China. This animal is as large as a bear, and like a bear is heavily built, with a very short tail.

Because of these external resemblances the giant panda has been widely confused with the bears, but modern studies suggest it is a large procyonid that has paralleled the bears. The giant panda is interesting because it is a carnivore that has turned completely herbivorous. The molar teeth are low crowned, with blunt cusps, and the enamel is wrinkled, making a broad grinding surface. These decorative and popular animals live exclusively upon green bamboo shoots.

Although the dogs, bears, and procyonids are closely related, the mustelids, on the other hand, are set apart from the other arctoids, and have been a separate phylogenetic line since the time of their origin, at the beginning of the Oligocene epoch. *Plesictis,* one of the first of the mustelids, was a small carnivore of generalized structure, with tribosphenic molars. However, the carnassial teeth were well developed, and the posterior molars were suppressed. The face was short and the brain case long and expanded, characters quite typical of the mustelids. From this ancestry the mustelids evolved with bewildering variety during middle and late Cenozoic times. Their evolution was characterized by the development of several short-lived lines of adaptive radiation, now extinct, which add to the complexity of mustelid phylogeny and make an interpretation of their history particularly difficult. It is not possible at this place to go into the details of mustelid development, but perhaps it may be useful to discuss briefly the modern mustelids, the persisting groups that have emerged from the complex melange of middle and late Tertiary mustelid history.

Generally speaking, there are about five groups of modern mustelids, all of subfamily rank. In the first place there are the primitive mustelids, the mustelines, many of them retaining the characters of their middle Tertiary ancestors. In this group are the weasels, the martens, the minks and their relatives, and the wolverines. These are very active, highly carnivorous animals, living in trees and on the ground in the forests. Some of them, especially the weasels (*Mustela*), are savage out of all proportion to their size.

The second mustelid group is the mellivorines, now represented by the ratel or honey badger (*Mellivora*) of Africa. Specializations here have been toward a ground life and a varied diet. A third group is the melines, the badgers of Eurasia (*Meles*) and North America (*Taxidea*). They are large, heavy mustelids that live in burrows. They are aggressive, but not highly carnivorous.

The fourth modern group of mustelids is the mephitines, the skunks (*Mephitis* and other genera) of North America. These small mustelids are ground-dwellers that burrow, and feed upon a great variety of things—small animals, insects, worms, berries, plants, carrion, and garbage. The skunks are protected by special scent glands that emit

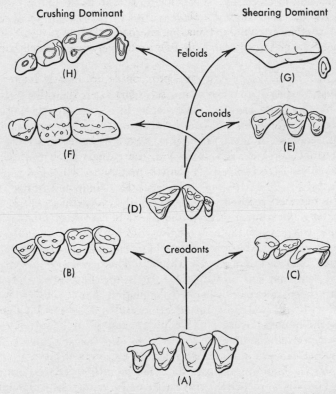

FIGURE 92. Crown views of left upper premolar and molar teeth of carnivores, showing evolutionary lines, and the dominance of crushing or shearing actions. Not to scale. (A) *Deltatherium*, a Paleocene arctocyonid, fourth premolar and three molars. (B) *Mesonyx*, an Eocene mesonychid, fourth premolar and three molars. (C) *Dissopsalis*, a Pliocene hyaenodont, fourth premolar and three molars. (D) *Vulpavus*, an Eocene miacid, fourth premolar and two molars. (E) *Hesperocyon*, an Oligocene canid, fourth premolar and two molars. (F) *Arctotherium*, a Pleistocene bear, fourth premolar and two molars. (G) *Smilodon*, a Pleistocene saber-tooth cat, fourth premolar and first molar. (H) *Hyaena*, a Pliocene hyena, last three premolars and first molar.

a strongly scented liquid, the smell and effects of which need no description for American readers.

Finally there are the lutrines, *Lutra*, and its relatives, the otters. They are aquatic mustelids specialized for catching fish, or even for feeding upon shellfish. Many of them live along the banks of streams, but the sea otters of the Pacific Ocean spend their life almost entirely in the shallow waters along the coasts.

From this brief review it can be seen that the evolution of the mustelids has been highly divergent, and of all the carnivores they certainly show the widest range of adaptive radiation.

THE AELUROID CARNIVORES

The most primitive of modern carnivores are some of the Old World civets, little modified descendants of the progressive miacids, that may be regarded as essentially late Eocene carnivores living on into modern times. The genet, *Genetta,* now inhabiting the Mediterranean region, is very near to the central stock from which all the civets have evolved. This is a small, forest-living carnivore, with a long body and a very long tail. The limbs are rather short and the feet are provided with claws that can be withdrawn to some extent, like the retractile claws of a cat. The skull is elongated and low, and narrow, the carnassial teeth are sharp, to form efficient shearing blades, and the molars retain the primitive tribosphenic pattern. The last molars are absent. The modern genet has a spotted coat, and it is probable that this is a primitive color pattern that has been retained through the ages. It has specialized scent glands with which it can spray its attackers, a characteristic adaptation in the modern civets.

The civets are abundantly represented in considerable variety among the modern faunas of Asia and Africa. From a central, conservative stem, approximated by the genet and its relatives, the viverrids have branched along varied lines of adaptive radiation. One branch is composed of the various African and Oriental palm civets and the binturong or bearcat of Asia, this last one of the largest of the civets. An extreme offshoot of this general line of adaptation is *Eupleres,* the falanouc of Madagascar, in which the teeth have been reduced to relatively simple pegs, as an adaptation to eating ants and insects. Another evolutionary branch is represented by *Cryptoprocta,* the fossa of Madagascar, a very cat-like civet. The position of this carnivore, whether a cat-like civet or a civet-like cat, has long been debated. It is very possible that the fossa arose from a primitive civet, but near the ancestry of the cats, so that it shares cat-like as well as civet characters. Finally, one large branch of the civets is the group of mongooses, small active civets that are famous as predators upon snakes and upon various small mammals.

Civets first appear in sediments of upper Eocene and lower Oligocene age, and are represented by such genera as *Stenoplesictis* and *Palaeoprionodon*. The subsequent epochs of the Cenozoic era reveal very little of the past history of the viverrids, probably because these predominantly tropical, forest-living carnivores were rarely preserved as fossils. The few genera known from Miocene and Pliocene sediments in Eurasia indicate that the viverrids continued as very primitive carnivores during much of Tertiary times. Thus the sequence from *Palaeoprionodon* through middle and late Tertiary forms, of which the Mongolian genus *Tungurictis* is an example, to the generalized modern civets, indicates only a minor amount of evolutionary progress.

In Miocene times one evolutionary branch split from the central civet stock and followed a trend toward increase in size and particularly the development of a heavy skull and very robust teeth. This was the line of hyenas, which share with the bears the distinction of being the youngest among the families of carnivores. Simply stated, the hyenas are very large, heavy descendants of the civets, in which the legs have been elongated for running and the teeth and jaws usually enlarged for cracking bones. The enlargement of the teeth is concentrated especially on the last two cone-shaped premolars, which are used for breaking the bones of large carcasses on which the carrion-eating hyenas feed. The jaws and the jaw muscles are necessarily very strong. The carnassials are highly specialized shearing blades in the hyenas, and the molars behind the carnassials are reduced to mere remnants.

Ictitherium, of late Miocene and early Pliocene age, was the first hyena. This carnivore was truly intermediate between the civets and the hyenas, larger and heavier than the former but much lighter and smaller than the latter. The step from *Ictitherium* to advanced and fully modern hyenas was a quick one, and we find fossil hyenas very similar to the modern animals in sediments of early Pliocene age. In effect the hyenas quickly reached the peak of their adaptational perfection soon after they split from the civets, and they have maintained their specialized form with little change since it was first attained. Hyenas live in Asia and Africa at the present time; but during the Pleistocene epoch they were widely distributed through northern Europe. One modern hyena, *Proteles*, the aardwolf of South Africa, is curiously specialized for eating termites, and the cheek teeth are reduced to small pegs, although the canines remain large.

The cats had an evolutionary history something like that of the hyenas, but it began at an earlier date. This is, the cats split from a viverrid ancestry, and, once having departed from the civet stem, they very rapidly evolved into fully specialized cats. They have maintained their high degree of specialization without much change for millions of years. The separation of the first members of the cat family from their civet ancestors took place during late Eocene times, and the upper Eocene genus, *Proailurus*, may represent an early step in the evolution of the cats. By early Oligocene times the cats were highly evolved cats, not very different from their modern relatives.

Of all land-living carnivores, the cats are among the most completely specialized for a life of killing, and for eating meat. They are very muscular, alert, supple carnivores, fully equipped for springing upon and destroying animals as large or larger than themselves. They generally hunt by stealth, and catch their prey with a long bound or a short rush of great speed. The limbs are heavy and strong, and the feet are provided with sharp, retractile claws that are used for catching and holding their victims. The neck is very heavy to take up the severe shocks imposed by the violent action of the head and the teeth. The teeth are highly specialized for just two functions—stabbing and cutting. The canine teeth are therefore long and strong, and the carnassials are large, perfected shearing blades; the other teeth are reduced or completely suppressed. The smaller cats are adept tree-climbers, but the larger cats spend most of their time upon the ground.

All cats are constructed pretty much to the pattern that was established by the cats of early Oligocene times. However, there seems to have been a dichotomy in the evolutionary history of the cats that went back to the time of their definition and continued until the end of the Pleistocene epoch. On the one hand, the cats evolved as active, fast-moving predators, the normal cats with which we are familiar; on the other hand, they developed as the comparatively heavy and slower saber-tooth cats. The ancestry of the normal or "feline" cats is exemplified by *Dinictis* of Oligocene age; that of the saber-tooth cats by *Hoplophoneus*, also of Oligocene age.

Both of them were medium-sized cats with long tails. In *Dinictis* the upper canine teeth were large and heavy, and the carnassials were well-developed shearing blades. There were premolar teeth in front of the carnassials, but the molars behind the shearing teeth were greatly reduced. In *Hoplophoneus* the upper canine teeth were elongated sabers, and there was a flange on the lower jaw to protect these down-pointing swords when the mouth was closed. The carnassials were specialized cutting blades, and the other cheek teeth were greatly reduced or suppressed.

As the feline cats evolved, the canine teeth became relatively smaller than they had been in *Dinictis;* but otherwise the dentition changed very little. As the saber-tooth cats evolved, the canine teeth remained large, as they had been in *Hoplophoneus.* Such trends indicate that the feline cats became increasingly perfected for catching and killing agile animals, while the saber-tooth cats became specialized for killing large, heavy animals.

The culmination of saber-tooth evolution was reached during the Pleistocene epoch, in the large saber-tooth cat, *Smilodon.* This cat was as large as a modern lion, and the upper canines were huge daggers of impressive proportions. Anatomical studies indicate that *Smilodon* was able to open the mouth very wide, thus clearing the way for the large canine sabers to function. In attacking its prey, *Smilodon* evidently struck down very hard with the sabers, using the force of the strong neck and the weight of the shoulders and body to give power to the thrust. This was an effective method of hunting, as long as there were large, comparatively slow animals available. But as the Pleistocene drew to a close, the large animals on which the saber-tooth cats had preyed became extinct, and so did the saber-tooths. They were unable to compete with their agile feline cousins in the chase of speedy animals.

The feline cats, on the other hand, have continued into modern times with great success. As said above, cats are cut pretty much to one pattern, yet there is a great variety of modern cats, differing mainly in size and in the habitats that they frequent. The modern cats show a distinct division into the typical cats, *Felis,* on the one hand, and the swift-running cheetah or hunting leopard, *Acinonyx,* on the other. As for the typical cats, they are found throughout the world except in Australia and on remote islands. There are many small cats, and from some of these, probably from a mixture of the ancient Egyptian wild cat and the European wild cat, our modern domestic cat has descended. The large cats are so familiar as to need no particular description—lions and leopards in Africa, leopards and tigers in Asia, jaguars and cougars in the Americas.

Cats did not enter South America until Pleistocene times, when both feline and saber-tooth cats invaded that continent. The invasions of South America by the cougar or puma from the north established one of the widest known ranges for a single species of mammal, except man, for this cat extends from the snows of Canada to the southern tip of South America. A comparable distribution is typical of the Old World leopard, which ranges from the southern portion of Africa into northern Asia.

THE PINNIPED CARNIVORES

The pinnipeds, the sea lions, walruses, and seals, do not appear in the geologic record until Miocene times, but it seems probable that they arose at an earlier stage of earth history, perhaps during late Eocene or early Oligocene times. Because of the complete absence of any pre-Miocene fossils, it is not possible to indicate the actual ancestors of the pinnipeds; however, it is likely that these carnivores arose either from advanced miacids, or more probably from early arctoid fissipeds, possibly from mustelid progenitors.

In making the transition from life on the land to life in the water, the pinnipeds became streamlined for swimming. However, their adaptations along this line have never been as complete as in some of the totally marine tetrapods, like the ichthyosaurs or the whales, for they have retained a flexible neck and have failed to evolve a dorsal fin or a propulsive tail. Perhaps the tail had been reduced to such a point in the ancestors of the pinnipeds that it was, so to speak, never available for transformation into a propeller. Consequently, the pinnipeds have had to rely upon the limbs in combination with body movements for propulsion through the water. In these carnivores all four feet are transformed into paddles, with webbing between the toes. The front paddles are used for balancing and steering, as well as for making propulsive thrusts. The back paddles are turned back and function like a sort of caudal fin when these animals are in the water. In the sea lions (*Zalophus*) and walruses (*Odobenus*) the back flippers can be turned forward or back at will, and are used when on land as aids to locomotion. In the seals (*Phoca*) the back flippers are permanently fixed in the backward direction, so that when seals are on land or on ice floes they have to move along on their bellies by a "humping" motion of the body.

The teeth are greatly modified in all the pinnipeds. The incisors are commonly reduced or suppressed, whereas in most pinnipeds the premolars and molars are secondarily simplified to the form of pointed, cone-shaped teeth, all much alike. Such a dentition is useful for catching fish. The walruses, probably derived from sea lion ancestors, have large canine tusks, and the cheek teeth, reduced in numbers, are broadened into crushing mills, with which these carnivores grind up the oysters and clams on which they feed. The sea lions have small external ears; in the other pinnipeds the external ear lobes or pinnae are completely suppressed.

Fossils of sea lions are found along the Pacific coast, which would make it appear that this was the region in which these carnivores evolved. Walruses are found in both the Pacific and the Atlantic oceans. Seals are of very wide distribution.

RATES OF EVOLUTION IN THE CARNIVORES

The carnivores are interesting not only because of the wide range of their adaptive radiation, but also because of the varying evolutionary rates displayed among the several families of these mammals. This is especially well exemplified by the fissipeds. For instance, the civets have remained on the whole very primitive through the extent of their history, so that their evolutionary rate may be regarded as having been relatively low. Broadly, the mustelids may be carnivores showing low or medium rates of evolutionary development. The dogs, though generalized fissipeds in many respects, have nevertheless shown a moderate rate of evolutionary development since the Oligocene epoch. Higher evolutionary rates are seen in the procyonids, which branched from canid ancestors, and even higher rates in the bears, a very late family to evolve. The hyenas and the cats show very high rates of evolutionary development at the beginnings of their histories, when they went through all the steps from viverrid to specialized hyenas and cats in remarkably short periods of time. Then the development of the hyenas and cats remained stationary— the hyenas since lower Pliocene times and the cats since Oligocene times.

As a result of these differing evolutionary rates the carnivores have attained the wide diversity of forms that inhabit our modern world. They have been truly successful mammals during middle and late Cenozoic times, and if they are not unduly persecuted by man they will extend their success far into the future.

Phenacodus

25 · Ancient Hoofed Mammals

THE UNGULATES

The term ungulate is a very broad and loosely defined word, used to indicate the hoofed mammals that feed upon plants. Beyond these generalizations it is difficult to find common characters for all the ungulates. In fact, the word ungulate describes ecological adaptations among several lines of parallel evolution rather than close zoological relationships, a fact that should be kept in mind when the term is used.

Adaptations in the ungulates have been most conspicuously developed in the teeth, which have been modified for cropping and grinding plants, in the digestive tract, which has been modified for converting bulky plant material into nourishment, and in the limbs and feet, which have been generally modified for running over hard ground. In addition, many ungulates have defensive weapons on the skull in the form of horns or antlers, or show modifications of some teeth for fighting and defense.

It is common but not universal for these mammals to have closely appressed incisor teeth that bite together along a slightly curved transverse line at the front of the skull. These teeth make an efficient nipping or cropping mechanism for gathering into the mouth leaves of trees and bushes, or grass. Although functional canine teeth are present in some ungulates, it is very common for these mammals to lack canines, or for such teeth, if present, to have lost their caniniform shape and function. In some ungulates the canine teeth join the incisor series, to increase the efficiency of the cropping function. However, the most remarkable adaptations in the dentitions of ungulates are to be seen in the cheek teeth, which in various ways act like grinding mills. Generally the crowns of the molar teeth become square or rectangular, by the strong development of the hypocone or of some other cusp near it in the upper teeth, and by the suppression of the paraconid and the growth of the talonid, so that it is equal in height and area to the trigonid in the lower molars. These modifications increase the area of the tooth crowns. Many ungulates feed upon hard grasses, and in them there has been an increase in height of the crowns of the cheek teeth—the development of hypsodont teeth, as they are called. By the increase in area of the molar crowns and by the increase in their height, the amount of tooth surface available for grinding plants during the life of the animal is enormously multiplied. In addition, the crowns of the teeth may be complicated by cross crests or by folded enamel. Finally many ungulates show a "molarization" of the premolar teeth, a process of enlargement and modification whereby the normally small premolars become as large as the molars, to increase the cumulative area of the dental grinding mills.

Naturally it is not possible for us to derive any information on the digestive tract in the extinct ungulates. In the living hoofed mammals, however, there is usually a chamber in the digestive tract within which bacterial action can break down plant cellulose.

A few ungulates have enlarged incisor or canine teeth with which they can defend themselves, but a more general means of defense is by the development of weapons upon the skull. These may be antlers, which are bony outgrowths from the top of the skull that are shed and replaced each year, or horns, which are permanent bony outgrowths covered or capped with horn and thus protected.

By far the commonest means of defense among the ungulates is flight by fast running. Therefore the hoofed mammals show dominant trends toward elongation of the limbs and feet. This lengthening of the legs increases the stride, enabling these animals to get over the ground rapidly. This adaptation is useful for flight from enemies; it also allows the ungulates to wander widely in search of food.

The ungulates commonly walk on the tips of their toes, a manner of locomotion that is designated as unguligrade. In feet of this sort the wrist and the ankle are far off the ground, as seen in the "knee" of the horse's fore limb and the "hock" of its hind limb. The toes are usually covered with hoofs that protect the feet and take up the shock of running over hard ground. In many progressive ungulates most of the function of walking and running is carried by the middle toes, so that there is a strong trend toward the reduction of the lateral toes. But in some of the ungulates, especially the large, heavy types, the feet remain short and broad, and there is little or no reduction of the toes. Thus the feet are wide, spreading structures that give broad bases for the support of great weight.

CLASSIFICATION OF THE UNGULATES

No ungulates are known from the Cretaceous period, but it is probable that these mammals, like so many of the other mammalian orders, evolved rapidly during the Cretaceous-Tertiary transition. Their most primitive representatives appear in sediments of early Paleocene age. Having arisen from insectivore ancestors, the ungulates evolved as about sixteen orders during Cenozoic times. Of these some are now extinct, and others continue as prominent members of modern faunas. Some of these orders had a very ancient ancestry, and it may be that there were several independent origins of ungulates from the insectivores. On the other hand, it is quite possible that all the ungulates were derived from a common ferungulate base of late Cretaceous age, and that they diverged widely to evolve along parallel lines during the Cenozoic era.

On the basis of their broad relationships, the orders of ungulates may with good reason be grouped into four categories that can be called superorders, as was pointed out in Chapter 19. One of these superorders, the Protungulata, contains for the most part the very primitive ungulates of early Tertiary times, and represents in essence the initial adaptive radiation of hoofed mammals. The Paenungulata contains a series of ungulate orders, most of which have been composed of large, heavy animals with strong limbs and broad, padded feet. The two remaining superorders of ungulates are the modern hoofed mammals with which we are familiar, the Mesaxonia or odd-toed ungulates, and the Paraxonia or even-toed ungulates.

The evolutionary history of the ungulates, like that of the land-living carnivores, shows two general phases of development. There was an early phase during Paleocene and Eocene times, when primitive ungulates in great variety spread over the face of the earth. The ancient ungulates began to decline during Eocene times, although a few of them persisted briefly into the Oligocene epoch.

At the same time the modern ungulates were arising, to evolve in ever-increasing diversity and complexity from about the beginning of the Eocene epoch to present times. However, this two-phase history of the ungulates was complicated by the fact that in South America there was a long continuation of peculiar ungulates descended from the primitive protungulates and unlike any hoofed mammals in the other continents. These South American ungulates lasted until that continent was reunited with North America at the end of the Tertiary period, at which time they quickly disappeared before the influx of invading mammals from the north.

On zoological grounds it would be logical to discuss in turn each of the four superorders of ungulates, but because of their evolutionary histories and some of the peculiarities of their distribution they will be considered on a somewhat different basis. The early Tertiary ungulates of protungulate and paenungulate relationships will first be described and discussed. Then all the South American ungulates will be considered together. Finally, the persisting ungulates will be taken up, those that had their beginnings during the Eocene epoch and continue in our modern faunas.

THE CONDYLARTHS

The most primitive of the ungulates, the condylarths, appear in sediments of early Paleocene age, and thus provide proof of the very early differentiation of the herbivorous mammals. Some of these ancient condylarths may not have been far removed from their insectivore ancestors, for they were small and had comparatively primitive teeth, and clawed feet.

From such early beginnings the condylarths radiated in various directions during the Paleocene epoch. In some, like *Meniscotherium*, of late Paleocene and Eocene age, there was a distinct advance in the teeth, which became almost selenodont with crescentic rather than cone-shaped cusps, yet the feet remained primitive. In others, like the Paleocene genus *Periptychus*, there was a great increase in size, and peculiar specializations in some of the premolar teeth, which became very large. However in middle Paleocene times there appeared *Tetraclaenodon*, with low-crowned but "squared" cheek teeth and with very broad claws on the ends of the toes. This type was probably directly ancestral to *Phenacodus*, one of the most completely known of the primitive ungulates, an animal that lived during the latter portion of the Paleocene and the early part of the Eocene epochs.

Phenacodus, known from complete skeletons, gives us a very good idea of what an ancestral ungulate was like. It was a fair-sized animal as large as a sheep, or even larger. In many ways it did not look as much like an ungulate as like some sort of primitive carnivore, for the skull was long and low, the tail was very long, the limbs were comparatively short and heavy, and the feet were short with all the toes present. The canine teeth were rather large. However the cheek teeth formed an almost continuous series, and the molars had square crowns, with a well-developed hypocone in the upper molars and a high talonid in the lower molars. The clavicle or collar bone was absent, as it is generally in the hoofed mammals, and the toes terminated in hoofs rather than claws. Evidently *Phenacodus* was a plant-eater that lived in forests or savannas, where it may have wandered widely in search of food. It was probably a clumsy runner.

LARGE UNGULATES OF EARLY TERTIARY TIMES

At an early stage in their evolutionary history certain lines of ungulates evolved toward large size. Two of the early orders of large ungulates were the Pantodonta, often known as amblypods, and the Dinocerata, often designated as uintatheres. Both these orders belong to the paenungulate division of the hoofed mammals, and, although neither is abundantly represented by genera and species, they none the less constitute very important segments of the mammalian faunas of Paleocene and Eocene times.

One of the earliest of the large hoofed mammals was *Pantolambda,* of middle Paleocene age, a pantodont about as large as a sheep. It had a rather long, low skull, in which the canines were large and the upper molars were triangular, with crescentic-shaped cusps. The limbs were rather heavy, and the feet were comparatively short, with all the toes present. Evidently these toes terminated in small hoofs. *Pantolambda* must have been a slow-moving ungulate that probably browsed upon the leaves of trees.

The evolution of the pantodonts to large size progressed rapidly through late Paleocene times, as illustrated by the genus *Barylambda.* This was a large animal, standing four feet or more in height at the shoulder. The entire skeleton of this pantodont was extraordinarily heavy, giving the impression of great stolidity and strength, obviously a difficult beast for the early creodonts to pull down and kill. In spite of its large size *Barylambda* had a comparatively small skull and a primitive ungulate dentition.

Perhaps the best known of the pantodonts is the lower Eocene form, *Coryphodon,* an animal as large as a tapir, having a heavy

Uintatherium

Coryphodon

FIGURE 93. Two ancient hoofed mammals of Eocene age, both drawn to the same scale. *Uintatherium,* one of the Dinocerata, was as large as the modern white rhinoceros of Africa. *Coryphodon* was a pantodont.

skeleton, with strong limbs and broad, spreading feet. In this early ungulate, as in many large hoofed mammals, the upper limb elements were long as compared with the lower limb elements and the feet. This type of limb gives great strength for the support of a heavy body but is not adapted for fast running. The tail was short, as is common in the hoofed mammals. The skull of *Coryphodon* was large, and the jaws were armed with elongated, saber-like canine teeth, which seems strange in a plant-eating mammal, but nevertheless was not uncommon in some of the early ungulates. The molar teeth had advanced beyond the primitive condition seen in *Pantolambda*, and on each molar crown were two prominent cross-crests, indicating that *Coryphodon* was an advanced browser, like the tapirs of modern times.

The pantodonts continued through the Eocene epoch, and in Asia at least survived into Oligocene times, after which they became extinct.

While the pantodonts were evolving, there was a parallel development of the Dinocerata or uintatheres, perhaps the largest of all early mammals. These animals, known at the present time from North America and Asia, had their beginnings during Paleocene times in such genera as *Bathyopsoides* and *Prodinoceras*. As in other large, heavy ungulates, the bones were massive, the limbs were heavy, the upper limb elements were long, and the lower limb elements and feet were short. The feet were broad and spreading. *Bathyopsoides* had a low skull, provided with a tremendously elongated canine tooth on either side. The front of the lower jaw was deeply flanged, making a protection for the canine saber when the mouth was closed.

The culmination of this line of ungulate development was reached in the upper Eocene genus, *Uintatherium*, an animal as large as a big rhinoceros, with an elongated skull grotesquely provided with six horns on top—two small ones on the nose, two above the canine teeth, and two at the back of the head. In this animal the upper canine teeth were very large, and on the molar crowns were cross ridges. The large uintatheres of late Eocene times were the last of the Dinocerata; by the advent of the Oligocene epoch these queer giants of early Tertiary times had become extinct.

AARDVARKS

The aardvark, *Orycteropus*, is a sturdy animal, about the size of a small pig, and it lives in Africa. It is almost hairless, and its skin is a dull-gray color. It has a compact body and very strong legs, terminating in long toes equipped with sharp, flat nails. It has a long head with a tubular snout, and ears that are very long and slender. The tail is heavy. The aardvark burrows in the ground (hence the name, which means "earth-pig" in Afrikans), and it feeds upon termites, tearing open their nests with its strong clawed feet, and licking up the insects with a long, protrusible tongue.

As in so many ant-eating or termite-eating mammals, the teeth of the aardvark are greatly reduced and modified. There are no incisors or canines, only some columnar-shaped cheek teeth, which when viewed under a microscope are seen to consist of closely appressed tubes of dentine. This character has given the name Tubulidentata to the mammalian order of which the aardvark is the single living representative.

Aardvark

FIGURE 94. The aardvark, *Orycteropus*, is a modern African mammal, highly specialized for feeding upon termites and for burrowing in the ground. This animal, about the size of a pig, is the sole living representative of the order Tubulidentata. It may have descended from condylarth ancestors.

The fossil history of the tubulidentates does not extend with certainty beyond the beginning of the Pliocene epoch. In sediments of lower Pliocene age fossil aardvarks, similar to the modern form, except for minor differences in size and proportions, are found in India and on islands at the eastern end of the Mediterranean Sea. Evidently the aardvarks were more widely distributed in late Tertiary times than they now are, and obviously they and their ancestors must have been living somewhere in pre-Pliocene times. Yet to date nothing is known of their early fossil history.

It has been common practice to regard these animals as related to the edentates, a conclusion drawn from their diet of termites and from the reduction of their teeth. We now realize, however, that various mammals have turned to an ant-eating diet and as a consequence have suffered a loss of teeth. If the skeleton of the aardvark is compared with the skeleton of the condylarths, a rather interesting series of similarities are apparent, which would suggest that perhaps the aardvark is of condylarth ancestry. If we think of this peculiar mammal as a condylarth in which the head and the feet have been highly modified as adaptations to a very special diet and to burrowing in the ground, the aardvark can be fitted in very logically among the protungulates. And if it is a protungulate, it is the only surviving representative of this group of early ungulates, so widely distributed and prominent in the faunas of Paleocene and Eocene times.

Macrauchenia

26 · South American Ungulates

THE INVASION OF SOUTH AMERICA BY PRIMITIVE UNGULATES

Some of the first placental mammals to reach South America were primitive condylarths, obviously derived from the ancient condylarths of North America. These early ungulates, known as didolodonts, arrived in South America during the Paleocene epoch, after which they continued in the southern continent during Eocene times. Although these South American condylarths became extinct, the evolution of hoofed mammals was carried on in South America by five ungulate orders that developed through a remarkably wide range of adaptive radiation.

Of the five orders of South American ungulates, three, the Notoungulata, the Litopterna, and the Astrapotheria, were of protungulate affinities and were probably all of condylarth ancestry; the other two, the Pyrotheria and Xenungulata, were orders of paenungulate relationships. By far the most numerous of the South American hoofed mammals were the notoungulates, which are represented in the known fossil record by about twice as many genera as are contained within the other four orders. It is interesting to see how these five orders of hoofed mammals divided the South American island con-

tinent between them, and how they paralleled the hoofed mammals
in other parts of the world, from which they were completely isolated

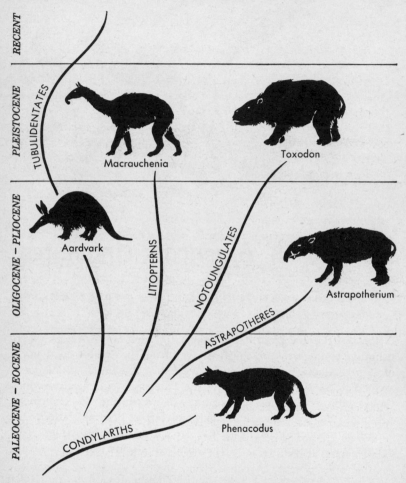

FIGURE 95.   Origin and radiation from a phenacodont ancestry of some South
American ungulates, and of the aardvark.

during the long interval between very early and very late Tertiary
times. The comparison of South American ungulates with hoofed
mammals in other parts of the world illustrates very nicely the close
correlation between animals and their environments, and indicates
how similar environmental conditions will lead, by genetic processes,

to the evolution of remarkably similar animals, quite unrelated except through their very remote ancestors.

THE NOTOUNGULATES

One of the oldest known notoungulates, *Palaeostylops,* of late Paleocene age, is from Mongolia and not South America. A related genus, *Arctostylops,* is known from the lower Eocene of North America. These are the only notoungulates recorded from beyond the limits of the South American continent, and they may indicate that this particular order had an Asiatic origin, that it spread during early Tertiary times from Asia across the Bering region into North America, and from there across the isthmus into South America. This concept may or may not be valid, but whatever their center of origin, the notoungulates were certainly abundantly established in the southern part of South America by early Eocene times.

These first notoungulates were small, primitive, hoofed mammals, with triangular-shaped upper molars characterized by two diagonal crests, the protoloph and the metaloph. The lower molars were likewise crested. *Notostylops* was typical of the early notoungulates, and the comparative abundance of fossils of this animal indicate that it must have lived in large populations throughout Patagonia during early Eocene times.

From the primitive members of the order, designated as notioprogonians, the notoungulates expanded along several lines during Tertiary times. As was common among the hoofed mammals, there was a general trend toward increase in size, reaching its climax in late Tertiary times, when some of these animals became as large as rhinoceroses. From the first, the notoungulates had crested or *lophodont* molar teeth, and as they evolved many of them developed high-crowned, rather prismatic molars, obviously well suited to eating hard grasses and other vegetation that cause a great amount of wear of the tooth crowns. A very common feature of dental evolution in the notoungulates was the development of rather uniform-sized teeth from front to back, without any appreciable gaps or diastemata between them. In many of these hoofed mammals the canine tooth lost its primitive shape, to become one in the continuous series of teeth that extended from the incisors to the last molars. The skull and the jaws were frequently rather deep, and the cheek-bone or zygomatic arch was commonly very heavy. There was never a bony bar or postorbital process, separating the eye from the temporal region in which the jaw muscles were lodged. In primitive noto-ungulates there were five toes on each foot, whereas in some of the advanced types these were reduced to three. The toes terminated in hoofs in most notoungulates, but in some there were claws on the feet.

Thomashuxleya was a lower Eocene notoungulate, belonging to the suborder of these mammals known as the toxodonts. In this animal, as large as a sheep, the skeleton was rather robust, the limbs were strong, the feet were comparatively short and retained all the toes, and the tail was reduced in length. The long, low skull, large in comparison with the size of the body, was provided with a rela-tively unspecialized dentition, in which the heavy incisor teeth re-tained their primitive form. *Thomashuxleya* may be compared in a general way with some of the slow, clumsy amblypods that were evolving at the same time in North America.

The toxodonts evolved in great profusion during late Eocene, Oligocene, and Miocene times, after which they began to decline, although they continued into the Pleistocene epoch before they be-came extinct. By the Oligocene epoch some toxodonts had become quite large, like *Scarrittia*, for example, an animal about the size of a horse, with a continuous dentition, heavy limbs, short feet, and a very short tail.

One line of toxodont evolution developed in a manner broadly paralleling the rhinoceroses of other continental areas. *Nesodon* of Miocene age, had a deep skull, tall, prismatic cheek teeth, and feet that were short and broad with three functional toes, the axis of the foot being through the middle toe. This arrangement is similar in function but of course not in origin to the feet in rhinoceroses. The culmination of this evolutionary line was attained in the Pleistocene genus, *Toxodon*, a very large, heavy mammal, standing five or six feet high at the shoulder, with a large and capacious body evidently as an adaptation for feeding upon and storing quantities of plant food. In this late notoungulate there had been a departure from the continuous series of teeth so characteristic of the middle Tertiary forms, and the large, nipping incisors were separated by a consider-able gap from the high-crowned grinding cheek teeth. It is inci-dentally a matter of some interest that *Toxodon* was discovered by Charles Darwin, when as a young man he went to South America as Naturalist on the survey ship, the "Beagle." Darwin excavated a partial skeleton of this animal from the bank of a creek in the Argen-tine pampas, and took it to England, where it was described by Sir Richard Owen.

In one group of toxodonts, the homalodotheres, the feet were provided with claws rather than with hoofs. *Homalodotherium*, of Mio-

Toxodon

Protypotherium

Thomashuxleya

FIGURE 96. Notoungulates, drawn to the same scale. *Protypotherium* was a small, middle Tertiary typothere. *Thomashuxleya* was an Eocene toxodont. *Toxodon*, an animal as large as a rhinoceros, was the last of the toxodonts, and lived well into Pleistocene times.

cene age, was a heavy animal some six feet in length, and it may be compared with the chalicotheres, which as we shall see were clawed ungulates living in the northern hemisphere during Cenozoic times.

As contrasted with the toxodonts, which developed many parallels to the large hoofed mammals of North America, Eurasia, and

Africa, the typotheres and hegetotheres were small notoungulates that have been compared in a very general way with the rabbits or rodents of the north. Many of these notoungulates had lightly constructed skeletons, long limbs, and rather long feet, and evidently were rapid runners. In primitive forms, like *Protypotherium* of Miocene age, the teeth formed a continuous series as in many other notoungulates; but in the specialized types, such as the Oligocene to Pliocene hegetothere *Pachyrukhos,* there were enlarged central incisor teeth, obviously adapted for gnawing, while the canines and premolars were reduced so that there was a gap between the front teeth and the grinding cheek teeth. The typotheres and the hegetotheres, like the toxodonts, reached their greatest diversity and abundance in middle Tertiary times, but some of them continued into the Pleistocene epoch.

This incomplete and very abbreviated summary of notoungulate evolution does scant justice to the most numerous and varied of the South American ungulates. Perhaps it does give some inkling of the wide degree of adaptive radiation in these interesting mammals, which if properly described would require a book to themselves. In brief it might be said that the notoungulates during their evolution ranged from small to very large mammals and that in their ecological adaptations they varied from rodent-like animals through sheep-like animals to large, rhinoceros-like animals. It is really difficult to make any valid comparison of adaptations and probable habits between these South American ungulates and the mammals with which we are familiar, and the approximate resemblances that must be cited are likely to be misleading. Suffice it to say that the notoungulates were highly successful mammals as long as South America remained disconnected from the rest of the world, but when the isthmian link was re-established near the close of the Tertiary period they soon disappeared before the impact of progressive invaders from the north. Even so, a few notoungulates were able to hold on well into the Pleistocene, as relics in the modernized fauna of South America.

THE LITOPTERNS

The litopterns, though never as numerous or as varied as the notoungulates, were nevertheless an important group of South American ungulates, first appearing in that region in sediments of Paleocene age, and continuing into the Pleistocene epoch. There are no known early litopterns outside South America, in which respect this order of mammals differs from the notoungulates; and it is probable that these animals arose on the southern continent as descendants of early condylarths. Indeed, the gap is small between the didolodonts, the early South American condylarths, and some of the primitive litopterns, an indication of the indigenous ancestry of the group now under consideration.

In a way the litopterns are easier for us to comprehend than are the notoungulates for they are more directly comparable to the hoofed mammals with which we are familiar. To put it another way, there were close parallelisms between the litopterns and some of the northern ungulates, parallelisms that make the litopterns seem to us like reasonably orthodox hoofed mammals. The litopterns evolved along two distinct lines of adaptive radiation, each beginning in the Paleocene epoch and continuing through the Tertiary period—one line, the proterotheres, to become extinct during the Pliocene epoch, the other, the macrauchenids, to continue into Pleistocene times.

The proterotheres were the "horses" among the South American ungulates. They never became very large, but some of them evolved in ways that were remarkably similar to horses, especially in the adaptations of the feet for running. This evolutionary trend reached its culmination in Miocene and Pliocene times, as exemplified by such genera as *Diadiaphorus* and *Thoatherium*. In these litopterns the skull was elongated and rather low, and there was a bony postorbital bar separating the eye from the temporal region, just as in the horses. The incisor teeth were rather chisel-like, and the cheek teeth were *selenodont,* with crescentic cusps, in which respect they paralleled to some degree the cheek teeth in horses of the same age. It is interesting that in these litopterns there was a molarization of the premolars as in the horses, thereby increasing the grinding area of the dentition.

The backbone was straight and the limbs were slender, an indication of rapid running. The feet were elongated, and the hind feet were especially horse-like. In *Diadiaphorus,* a three-toed form, the middle toe was greatly enlarged, terminating in a strong hoof, and the lateral toes were reduced to very small appendages. The upper articulating surface of the astragalus or ankle bone was shaped like a pulley, an adaptation similar to that seen in the astragalus of horses. In *Thoatherium* the evolution of the hind foot had progressed so far that the side toes were reduced to a greater degree than in any of the horses. It seems reasonable to suppose, therefore, that the habits and the mode of life of these litopterns were similar to those of middle Tertiary horses in North America. The proterotheres con-

tinued into Pliocene times and then became extinct, at about the time
that true horses invaded South America.

The other line of litoptern evolution, the macrauchenids, can be
compared in a general way with the camels of North America. In

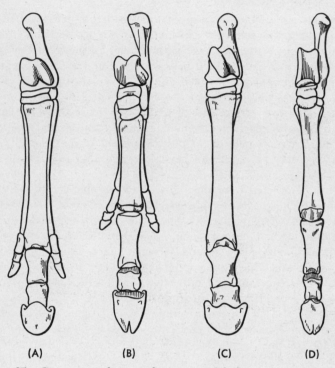

(A)   (B)   (C)   (D)

FIGURE 97. Convergence between litopterns and horses in the adaptations of
the feet for fast, sustained running over hard ground. The total length of the
foot is drawn to a unit scale, for the sake of easy comparison. (A) *Protohippus*,
a three-toed horse. (B) *Diadiaphorus*, a three-toed litoptern. (C) *Equus*, a
single-toed horse. (D). *Thoatherium*, a single-toed litoptern.

these litopterns the skeleton was rather lightly constructed, the back
was straight, and the neck and limbs were long. The feet had three
functional toes terminating in hoofs, and the axis of the foot passed
through the middle toe. The long skull and jaws were provided with
a continuous series of teeth that were rather high-crowned in comparison with the teeth in other litopterns. An interesting adaptation
in the macrauchenids was the recession of the nasal opening far back
on the face, and in the advanced forms even to the top of the skull.
In this respect the skull in these litopterns may be compared with the

skull in modern tapirs, and it is reasonable to think that the macrauchenids, like the tapirs, had a short proboscis, a flexible extension of the nose. *Theosodon* was a characteristic Miocene macrauchenid. *Promacrauchenia* continued the line into Pliocene times, and *Macrauchenia* lived in the Pleistocene epoch.

Macrauchenia, like *Toxodon*, lived alongside the northern invaders of South America after most of the indigenous hoofed mammals had become extinct. Its final demise during Pleistocene times may have been the result of competition from the new mammals from the north, but, in view of its considerable success after the invasion of South America, we are justified in thinking that this litoptern had become adjusted to the changed conditions so that it was able to hold its own among the immigrants from the north. However, like so many of the large mammals of the Pleistocene, it disappeared before the close of that geologic epoch—for what reason it is difficult to say.

THE ASTRAPOTHERES

Another South American order, probably arising on that continent from the ancient condylarths, is the Astrapotheria, a group that appeared in the Eocene epoch and continued into Miocene times. Among these mammals there was an early trend to gigantism, already apparent in lower Eocene members of the order. This trend toward large size was accompanied by a series of adaptations that are difficult to interpret.

The Oligocene and Miocene genus, *Astrapotherium,* was a heavy mammal that stood five feet or more in height at the shoulders. This was quite clearly an animal adapted for pushing through the forests or wandering boldly over the plains, as do the modern elephants.

The skull and jaws in *Astrapotherium,* however, were strangely modified. The front of the skull was much abbreviated, with the nasal bones small and retracted in position, and the upper incisor teeth had been lost. On the other hand, the upper canines were greatly enlarged, to form downwardly directed daggers of considerable length and strength. Instead of being shortened to match the skull, the lower jaw was long, with well-developed incisors and with enlarged canines. Very probably a long, tough upper lip extended forward from the retracted front portion of the skull, to meet the front of the lower jaw and cover it. Perhaps this constituted some sort of a cropping mechanism. Perhaps the nose extended beyond this upper lip as a sort of flexible proboscis. The posterior premolar teeth were very small, but the last two molar teeth were enormously enlarged to form long, high-crowned grinding mills.

The parallelisms to mammals in other parts of the world are not clear. Perhaps the astrapotheres may be compared after a fashion

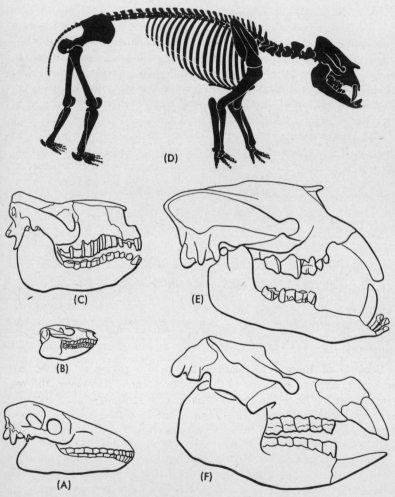

FIGURE 98. South American ungulates. (A) *Macrauchenia*, a Pliocene and Pleistocene litoptern. (B) *Protypotherium*, a Miocene typothere. (C) *Nesodon*, a Miocene toxodont. (D) *Astrapotherium*, an Oligocene astrapothere, an animal about nine feet in length. (E) *Astrapotherium*. (F) *Pyrotherium*, an Oligocene pyrothere. All skulls about one-twelfth natural size, except B, which is one-sixth natural size.

with the large uintatheres of North America that lived in late Eocene times. Perhaps they may be compared with some of the ancient proboscideans, the early mastodonts, in which the trunk was short, the upper tusks downturned, and the lower tusks protruded forward.

THE PYROTHERES

The pyrotheres, named from the Oligocene genus *Pyrotherium*, a small and isolated group of South American ungulates confined to early Tertiary sediments, may be regarded, as mentioned above, as of possible paenungulate relationships. If this is so, the pyrotheres entered South America at a very early date, and likewise at a very early date became distinctively specialized.

These mammals were like the proboscideans, the elephants and their relatives, in showing a very early growth to gigantic size. Also the pyrotheres showed various specializations in the skull and dentition that were remarkably similar to those of some proboscideans. For instance, the skull was very large, and the nasal opening was retracted, which would indicate the presence of a proboscis or a trunk of sorts. The zygomatic arches or cheek bones were very heavy, and the back portion of the lower jaw, the ascending ramus, was large, as in the proboscideans. Two of the upper incisors on each side were greatly enlarged to form tusks, and in the lower jaw there was a single enlarged, tusk-like incisor on either side. The cheek teeth, separated from the incisors by a gap, were low crowned, and each tooth crown consisted of two sharp cross-crests, very similar in general appearance to the crested teeth in the dinotheres, a group of proboscideans.

Because of these resemblances the pyrotheres were placed by earlier students as relatives of the proboscideans. However, the resemblances to the proboscideans that are so strikingly developed in the pyrotheres are probably all the result of convergent evolution. Modern opinion regards these as representing a quite independent order of mammals.

THE XENUNGULATES

The order Xenungulata has only recently been established, and at the present time it is based upon the single genus *Carodnia*, from Paleocene sediments in Brazil and Patagonia. This is indeed a restricted order of mammals, with a very narrow base for its definition, yet the evidence would seem to indicate that recognition of the

Xenungulata as distinct from all other orders of mammals is fully justified.

Carodnia was a large mammal, with a broad, five-toed foot and with rather short limbs. There was a complete set of teeth, of which the incisors were chisel shaped, the canines strong, the premolars generally rather pointed, and the molars strongly cross-crested. At the present time the fossils of this interesting animal are not sufficiently complete to give us information on the shape of the skull or other points about the anatomy. However, upon the basis of the materials at hand it would seem that *Carodnia* may have been related in a very broad sense to the uintatheres of North America, and, if this is true, we see, in the Xenungulata and Dinocerata, an interesting example of parallelism among animals that were geographically isolated but descended from an ultimate common ancestor.

END OF THE SOUTH AMERICAN UNGULATES

The history of the South American ungulates is an interesting and instructive story of parallelism and convergence, of long success under favorable conditions and of sudden extinction when those conditions changed.

The astrapotheres, Xenungulates, and pyrotheres, restricted to early and middle Tertiary times, filled certain ecological positions for a while but failed to continue, even though protected by the isolation of South America from the rest of the world. The notoungulates and the litopterns, on the other hand, had long evolutionary histories that ran from very early Tertiary times through most of the Cenozoic era. These must be considered as very successful mammals, flourishing along many lines of evolutionary development, the constituent members of which showed adaptations to an astonishing range of ecological habitats. As long as South America remained an island continent the notoungulates and the litopterns prospered, with broad plains and extensive forests in which to browse and graze, and with no enemies except the carnivorous marsupials. It is true that the carnivorous marsupials became adapted in many ways as predators, but still they were marsupials. They certainly lacked the intelligence and the cunning that have made our placental carnivores such efficient hunters.

When, toward the end of the Pliocene epoch, the isthmian link between North and South America emerged from the ocean, and the great influx of mammals from the north began, most of the notoungulates and the litopterns quickly disappeared. Only a few large, specialized forms, such as *Toxodon* and *Macrauchenia*, were able to continue as competitors of the mammals from the north. The disappearance of the notoungulates and the litopterns before the wave of immigrant northern mammals was brought about by two factors of importance.

In the first place the indigenous hoofed mammals suffered from direct onslaughts by the intelligent, progressive predators that came in from North America. It was one thing for them to defend themselves against the attacks from carnivorous marsupials; it was something else to become the prey of large wild dogs, foxes, bears, and various cats, including mountain lions and jaguars. This in itself was a major factor in hastening the end of many notoungulates and litopterns.

The other factor was competition for living space and food from the invading northern ungulates. With the emergence of the isthmus there came into South America tapirs, horses, deer, llamas, and mastodonts. It seems likely that these animals were more efficient browsers and grazers than the notoungulates and the litopterns, and consequently they literally took the land away from its original inhabitants. This second factor of competition, added to the other factor of direct attack from aggressive predators, was the final blow that terminated the long reign of the South American ungulates.

Eohippus

27 · Perissodactyls

PERISSODACTYL CHARACTERS

The perissodactyls are those hoofed mammals, persisting at the present time as the horses, zebras, and asses, the tapirs, and the rhinoceroses, in which there is usually an odd number of toes, and in which the axis of the foot passes through the middle toe. In all the perissodactyls the inner toe, the thumb in the fore foot, and the large toe in the hind foot, has been suppressed, and the same is true of the fifth digit in the hind foot. In most perissodactyls the fifth digit in the fore foot also has been suppressed, but in some of the more primitive forms this finger has remained. Thus in the hands and feet of perissodactyls there are generally three functional toes, or, as in the progressive horses, one.

In the perissodactyl ankle the astragalus has a doubly keeled, pulley-shaped surface for articulation with the tibia, whereas its distal surface that articulates with the other bones of the ankle is flat. The femur, the upper bone of the leg, is characterized by having a prominent process, the third trochanter, on the outer side of its shaft.

In the perissodactyls a full set of incisor teeth is commonly present, both above and below, to form an efficient cropping mechanism for biting plants. There is usually a gap between these teeth and the cheek teeth, and canines may or may not be present in this gap, frequently (if present) separated from the incisors in front and from the premolars behind. But perhaps the most characteristic feature of the perissodactyl dentition is the molarization of the premolar teeth. In the primitive perissodactyls this process has not progressed far, but in the more advanced members of the order it reaches such a degree of perfection that all the premolar teeth except the first of the series are completely molariform. This development has greatly added to the grinding surface of the dentition, thus increasing the efficiency of the teeth as mills for crushing hard plants.

Other striking perissodactyl characters, such as elongation of the limbs, growth to large size, the development of horns on the skull, and the like, are typical of the various families within the order and need not be discussed here.

THE FIRST PERISSODACTYLS

The first known perissodactyls appear in sediments of early Eocene age. The ancestry of the earliest perissodactyls is not indicated by the fossil record, but it is very possible that these odd-toed ungulates were derived from condylarths of Paleocene age, although there are no connecting links to indicate such a derivation.

Hyracotherium (commonly designated as *Eohippus*), although classified as the earliest primitive horse, is as characteristically primitive as any of the early perissodactyls, and can be used as a good example of the prototype for this order of mammals. This was a small animal, about the size of a fox. It was lightly built, with limbs clearly adapted for running, a moderately curved back, a somewhat

shortened tail and a long, low skull. *Hyracotherium* had nineteen
ribs, and behind these about five vertebrae free of ribs, as was
common among the perissodactyls. The spines of the vertebrae in

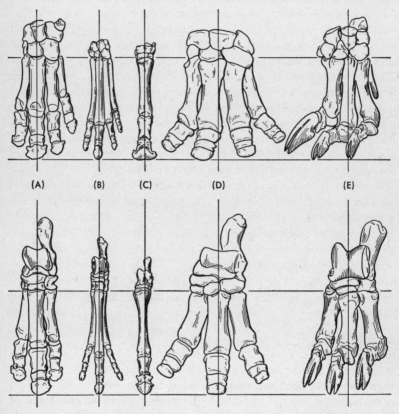

(A)   (B)   (C)   (D)   (E)

FIGURE 99. Left fore feet above, and hind feet below, of perissodactyls. The
digits are drawn to approximate unit lengths, to facilitate a comparison of
proportions of the feet in the several groups of odd-toed ungulates. The vertical lines pass through the axes of the feet. (A) *Tapirus*, a Pleistocene and
Recent tapir. (B) *Hyracotherium*, an Eocene horse, a generalized perissodactyl.
(C) *Equus*, a Pleistocene and Recent horse. (D) *Brontotherium*, an Oligocene
titanothere. (E) *Moropus*, a Miocene chalicothere, with clawed feet.

the shoulder region were somewhat elongated, for the attachment
of strong back muscles. The limbs were slender, and the feet were
elongated, with the wrist and ankle raised far off the ground so that
the digits were approximately vertical in position. There were four
toes in the front foot of this primitive perissodactyl and three toes

in the hind foot. In a functional sense all the feet were three toed, and each toe terminated in a small hoof.

The elongated skull had a comparatively small brain case, and the orbit was open behind, there being no bony bar separating the eye opening from the temporal opening as in later horses. The incisors were small, with rather chisel-shaped crowns, and small canine teeth were present. The cheek teeth were bunodont, which means that they had very low crowns, with rounded, cone-like cusps. The premolar teeth were not as yet molariform, and the last two upper premolars were triangular in shape. However, the upper molars were quadrangular, with four large cusps, protocone, paracone, metacone, and hypocone. There were also two small accessory cusps, the protoconule and the metaconule, between the main outer and inner cusps. In the lower molars the heel, or talonid, was as high as the fore part of the tooth. The anterior internal cusp, the paraconid, was much reduced, and the two anterior cusps, protoconid and metaconid, and the two posterior cusps, hypoconid and entoconid, were connected by transverse cross-crests or ridges. Such was the dental development and tooth pattern from which evolved the complex and varied teeth of the several lines of perissodactyls through Cenozoic time.

BASIC CLASSIFICATION OF THE PERISSODACTYLS

From an ancestral form approximated by *Hyracotherium* the perissodactyls developed along various paths of adaptive radiation, reaching the height of their evolutionary history in middle Tertiary times when they were the dominant ungulates in most of the world. Since then they have declined, and now must be regarded as an order of mammals that, in spite of the high specializations among some of its members, is on its way toward extinction.

From their primitive beginning the perissodactyls evolved in two distinct lines. One of these, the suborder Hippomorpha, contained the extinct palaeotheres, titanotheres and chalicotheres, and the horses. The other line, the Ceratomorpha, contained the tapirs and the rhinoceroses.

EVOLUTION OF THE TITANOTHERES

Among the largest of the perissodactyls were the titanotheres or brontotheres, which first appeared during early Eocene times as small, eohippus-like animals, and which attained the peak of their evolutionary development in middle Oligocene times as massive, gigantic beasts seven or eight feet in height at the shoulder. The titanotheres grew up quickly into giants, and once having become

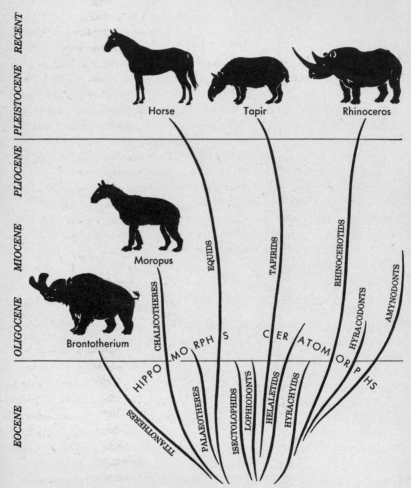

FIGURE 100. Evolution of the perissodactyls or odd-toed ungulates.

giants they soon died out. Theirs was a short, but dramatic phylogenetic history.

One of the first of the titanotheres was a lower Eocene genus known as *Lambdotherium*. In its general aspects *Lambdotherium* was like *Hyracotherium*, and indeed this first titanothere must have been rather closely related to the first horse. It was similar to *Hyraco-therium* in size, perhaps a little larger, and like the ancestral horse it was lightly constructed, with a back that was somewhat curved, with slender limbs and elongated feet for running, with a shortened tail and with a long, low skull. There were four toes on the front foot, of which the outer digit was not reduced, and the hind foot had three toes and the characteristic perissodactyl ankle structure. The skull was primitive and the opening for the eye was confluent with the temporal opening. There were small incisors, separated by a short gap from sharp canines; they in turn were separated by a rather long gap from the cheek teeth. The cheek teeth were low crowned, and there was little molarization of the premolars. The upper molar teeth were square and had four prominent cusps. The two outer cusps were joined by a W-shaped outer wall or ectoloph. In the lower molars the outer and inner cusps were alternately arranged, and joined by ridges that made a W-shaped pattern.

Two dominant trends marked the evolutionary history of the titan-otheres—a quick phylogenetic growth to large and even huge size, and the development of large horns on the skull. The increase in size preceded the development of horns. While these two evolution-ary advancements were taking place the titanotheres remained com-paratively primitive in other respects, particularly in the dentition and the feet.

Of course as they grew into large animals and then into veritable giants, the titanotheres showed those modifications of the skeleton that we have seen in other large, heavy ungulates. The elongated legs became very heavy, with the upper limb elements, the humerus and the femur, long in comparison with the lower limb elements. The feet developed as short, broad structures, well suited to support the great weight they had to bear. The body grew very capacious, partly as an adaptation for storing large amounts of plant food, with heavy ribs to enclose the thorax and the abdomen. The tail was comparatively short. In the shoulder region there were long spines on the vertebrae, to afford attachments for strong muscles that held up the heavy head.

The changes that took place in the feet during this process of growing large were mainly of proportion. Even in the latest titan-otheres there were still four toes in the front foot as in the first members of the group, and in all of the feet the lateral toes were large. The molars in the later titanotheres became very large as contrasted with the relatively small premolars, and the teeth in front of the premolars were reduced or often suppressed. These changes in proportions of the teeth were correlated with the changes in skull proportions as the titanotheres evolved, because as the titanotheres increased in size through time, that portion of the skull behind the eye became ever longer, while the facial region in front of the eye

Brontotherium

Eotitanops

FIGURE 101. A small Eocene titanothere, similar to other generalized perissodactyls, and a gigantic specialized Oligocene titanothere that stood about eight feet in height.

became shorter. In the last titanotheres, of early Oligocene age, the face was remarkably short, so that the eyes were located far forward in the skull.

The various evolutionary changes that have been outlined above began in early Eocene times. *Eotitanops,* not much later in age than *Lambdotherium,* already showed a considerable increase in size over its predecessor, although in most respects it retained the ancestral perissodactyl characters. Growth in size with consequent changes in the skeleton and the accompanying proportional changes in the skull and teeth can be traced through middle and upper Eocene titanotheres, such as *Palaeosyops* and *Manteoceras.*

Several lines of titanotheres were evolving parallel to each other during middle and late Eocene times. *Manteoceras* represents what might be called the "main line" of titanothere development that led to the gigantic horned titanotheres of Oligocene times. A lateral branch of middle and late Eocene age was that of the dolichorhines, characterized by *Dolichorhinus,* in which the skull was very long but never developed horns. Another side branch was the telmatheres, hornless titanotheres in which the canine teeth became rather large, perhaps as a compensation for the lack of defensive horns.

In *Manteoceras* there were small outgrowths on the frontal and nasal bones, side by side. They increased greatly in the Oligocene titanotheres, such as the gigantic *Brontops,* to form large, heavy horn cores, which in life probably were covered with tough skin or with horn.

During most of their history the titanotheres were restricted to North America, but in late Eocene and early Oligocene times they migrated into Asia, and some of them pushed as far west as eastern Europe. Most of them were advanced, horned titanotheres. *Embolotherium,* a Mongolian form of Oligocene age, had a pair of huge, conjoined horns on the front of the skull that made a sort of battering ram with which this big titanothere could hammer its adversaries.

Why did the titanotheres become extinct during the middle of the Oligocene epoch, after having successfully evolved at such a rapid rate to huge animals, much larger than modern rhinoceroses? It is very probable that their failure was in part because of the lack of progressive development in the teeth. The cheek teeth of titanotheres were always low crowned, adequate for the soft vegetation that grew in very early Tertiary times, but not suited for the harder grasses that were spreading during the middle reaches of the Cenozoic era. Their food supply was changing, and they seem to have been unable to adapt themselves to this change. This factor, together with a comparatively primitive brain, probably had much to do with bringing an end to the titanotheres.

THE CHALICOTHERES

The chalicotheres, closely related to the titanotheres, were successful perissodactyls in that their phylogenetic life extended from Eocene times into the Pleistocene epoch; yet these seemingly were never very

numerous animals. They were unique among the perissodactyls in
having large claws on the feet, rather than hoofs, and it is possible
that these beasts lived in small groups along streams, where they
could dig up roots on which to feed, instead of browsing or grazing
across the plains in large herds.

The first chalicotheres, typified by the upper Eocene genera,
Eomoropus of North America and *Grangeria* of Asia, were generally
similar to other primitive members of this order of ungulates. From

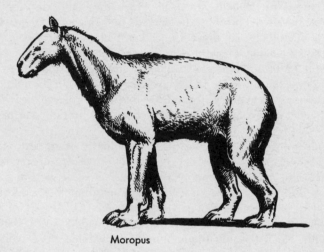

Moropus

FIGURE 102. A Miocene chalicothere, a perissodactyl as large as a modern horse,
with large claws on its feet.

these ancestors the chalicotheres evolved rapidly through the Oligocene epoch, reaching the full stature of their phylogenetic development by early Miocene times. From the Miocene into the Pleistocene
epoch the chalicotheres continued without much evolutionary advancement.

The chalicotheres followed the general perissodactyl trend of size
increase, so that the Miocene and later chalicotheres, like *Moropus*
in North America and *Macrotherium* in Eurasia, were as large as
large horses. In some respects the later chalicotheres had a horse-like
appearance, for the skull had a long, deep face, the body was
compact, and the limbs were elongated. But here the similarity ends.
The teeth were essentially similar to those of the titanotheres, with
low crowns, large molars, and small premolars. In these chalicotheres
the front legs were longer than the hind limbs, so that there was a
slope back from the shoulders to the hips, somewhat as in modern

giraffes. The feet were short, with three functional toes in each foot, and as already mentioned there were claws on all the toes, these claws being larger in the front feet than in the hind feet. Of the claws on the front feet, the inner one was the largest.

The chalicotheres managed very well with their strange way of life until sometime during the Pleistocene epoch, and then they became extinct. Their disappearance, however, probably cannot be blamed upon any inadequacies in their adaptations; their continuation during most of Cenozoic times shows that they were well suited for a very particular mode of life. They finally vanished during the wide extinction of large mammals that took place in late Pleistocene times, when many spectacular animals disappeared that had graced the Ice Age landscapes of the world.

THE PALAEOTHERES

During Eocene and early Oligocene times the palaeotheres were evolving in Europe in a manner somewhat parallel to the way the horses were evolving at the same time in North America. In the palaeotheres, of which *Palaeotherium* was typical, there was a rapid increase in size, so that by late Eocene times these animals were as large as small rhinoceroses. The legs were rather heavy, and all the feet had three toes. The skull was tapir-like in that the nasal bones were retracted, an indication that *Palaeotherium* may have had a short proboscis. The teeth were low crowned, and the premolars became molariform at an early stage in the evolution of these perisso-dactyls. Palaeotheres, like titanotheres, continued into the Oligocene epoch, and then became extinct.

EVOLUTION OF THE HORSES

Of all evolutionary histories, none is so widely known as that of the horses. There are several reasons for this, but perhaps the most cogent one is that the fossil record of the horses is remarkably com-plete and well understood. Because of their grazing habits, their life on savannas and plains, and their tendency to live in large herds, horses have been buried and fossilized in great numbers since the early stages of their phylogenetic history. It so happens that in North America, where the entire evolutionary sequence of horse history is recorded, there is an almost complete series of sedimentary deposits from early Eocene times to the present, containing the fossils of horses. Naturally this excellent array of fossil horizons gives a remarkable record through time of the progressive evolution of the horses.

The first horses belonged to the lower Eocene genus *Hyracotherium* (less correctly designated as *Eohippus*), an animal, as we have seen, that closely approximates the stem perissodactyl. *Hyracotherium* has already been described, and that description need not be repeated here. It is enough to say that this was a small animal, with a primitive skull, a generalized perissodactyl dentition in which the cheek teeth were low crowned and bunodont, and slender limbs and feet, with four toes on the front foot and three on the hind. This early Eocene horse was widely spread throughout North America and Europe, and very probably it lived in Asia as well. With the close of early Eocene times *Hyracotherium* became extinct in the Old World, and from then on the evolution of horses was limited to the North American continent. All the horses that appeared subsequently in other regions, in Eurasia, Africa and South America, were emigrants from North America.

The progressive trends that characterized the evolution of horses through the Cenozoic era may be listed as follows:

1. Increase in size.
2. Lengthening of legs and feet.
3. Reduction of lateral toes, with emphasis on the middle toe.
4. Straightening and stiffening of the back.
5. Widening of the incisor teeth.
6. Molarization of the premolars.
7. Increase in height of the crowns of the cheek teeth.
8. Progressive complication of the crown patterns.
9. Deepening of the front portion of the skull and of the lower jaws, to accommodate the high-crowned cheek teeth.
10. Lengthening of the face in front of the eye, also to accommodate the high-crowned cheek teeth.
11. Increase in size and complexity of the brain.

These changes, initiated in Eocene times, continued to the end of the Cenozoic era, so that in some horses there was a fairly consistent increase in size from the beginning to the end of their phylogenetic history, accompanied by the progressive molarization of the premolars, the deepening of the cheek teeth, the reduction of the lateral toes, and so on. However, when the horses are considered in their entirety no such picture of uniform evolution emerges. The horses are often cited as an outstanding example of "straight-line evolution" or of "orthogenesis," and it is frequently maintained that these animals evolved with little deviation, along a straight path from the little Eocene *Hyracotherium* or eohippus to the modern horse, *Equus*. It is true that most of the progressive changes listed above can be followed through time from *Hyracotherium* to the modern horses, but in middle and late Tertiary times there were various lateral branches of horses that were progressive in some features and conservative in others. When all fossils are taken into account the history of horses in North America is seen to be anything but a simple progression along a single line of development.

At the beginning of their history, however, the horses were confined to a single line of progressive development, as follows:

Middle and upper Oligocene	*Miohippus*
	↑
Lower Oligocene	*Mesohippus*
	↑
Upper Eocene	*Epihippus*
	↑
Middle Eocene	*Orohippus*
	↑
Lower Eocene	*Hyracotherium*

During their evolution from *Hyracotherium* to *Miohippus* the horses increased from small, terrier-sized animals to animals as large as sheep. The legs increased in length, as did the feet. The fifth digit on the hand was suppressed, so that all the feet became three-toed, with the middle toe much larger than the side toes. However, all the toes were functional. The back became progressively straighter and stiffer. The last three premolar teeth became molariform, and the crowns of all the cheek teeth became strongly crested. In the upper cheek teeth an outer W-shaped wall or crest developed, the ectoloph, and from it two oblique crests extended to the inner side of each tooth, an anterior protoloph and a posterior metaloph. On the crowns of the lower cheek teeth were two V-shaped crests with their points directed outward. These crested upper and lower cheek teeth were evidently very efficient choppers for cutting up leaves. However, they were still low crowned. In general the skull remained rather primitive, although there was some lengthening of the facial portion.

By the end of the Oligocene epoch the horses had through these changes attained the status of advanced browsers, capable of eating leaves and soft plants and able to run fairly rapidly and for sustained periods over hard ground. With the advent of Miocene times there was a branching out of horses along several lines of development, probably as a response to an increase in the variety of environments available to them, and especially because of the spread of early grasses and other flowering ground plants.

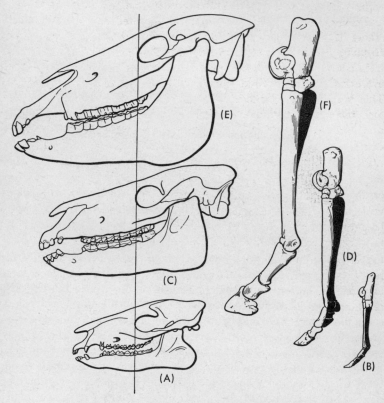

FIGURE 103.   Three stages in the evolution of the skull and feet in horses.   (*A* and *B*), skull and hind foot of *Hyracotherium,* a primitive Eocene horse.   (*C* and *D*), skull of *Parahippus* and hind foot of *Merychippus* of Miocene age. (*E* and *F*), skull and hind foot of *Equus,* a Pleistocene and Recent horse. This figure shows the progressive increase in the length of the facial or pre-orbital portion of the skull, the deepening of the skull and lower jaw to accommodate the increasingly higher cheek teeth, and the reduction of the side toes. (*C* and *E*), one-eighth natural size, the other figures one-fourth natural size.

Archaeohippus, of Miocene age, remained conservative and showed very little increase in size or progressive development of the skull, teeth, and feet beyond the *Miohippus* stage.   Another line of horses, the Miocene and Pliocene anchitheres, increased in size so that in the end they were as large as modern horses, but they retained the conservative *Miohippus*-like teeth and functional three-toed feet. These were probably forest-living horses that browsed in the deep woodlands, much as deer do at the present time. During late Miocene and early Pliocene times *Anchitherium* migrated into the Old World, where it spread widely, while in North America a large genus, *Hypohippus,* evolved from an *Anchitherium* ancestry.

As contrasted with these conservative horses, the main line of horse evolution was continued during Miocene times by *Merychippus*. This horse was as large as a small pony. The feet retained three toes, but the lateral toes were now reduced so that they were of little use, and the animal walked on the single middle toe, the end of which was clad in a rounded hoof. The face was elongated and rather deep, and the lower jaw was also deepened. In *Merychippus* the teeth were definitely high crowned and covered with *cement,* the crests had become variously conjoined, and the enamel of these crests was folded, so that when the tooth was worn the complex enamel bands projected slightly above the softer dentine and cement. These tooth crowns, so difficult to describe, were efficient grinding mills for breaking down hard plant fibers and seeds, in order that they might be more readily digested. In *Merychippus* there was a postorbital bar behind the eye opening, separating the orbit from the temporal region—a character typical of the later horses.

At the close of Miocene times two groups of horses arose from a *Merychippus* ancestry. One of them was an assemblage of closely related genera, of which *Hipparion* was typical; the other was centered around the genus *Pliohippus*. The hipparions were lightly built horses, progressive in the development of the skull and the very high-crowned teeth with complexly folded enamel, but conservative in the retention of three-toed feet. These horses, like the anchitheres, erupted from their North American center of origin at the beginning of Pliocene times, to spread into all the continents except South America. In fact, *Hipparion* was so characteristic of lower Pliocene mammalian faunas that they are often called the "*Hipparion* faunas." These horses continued through the Pliocene epoch, and a few stragglers held on into the Pleistocene epoch, when they became extinct.

Pliohippus was also a progressive horse, not only in the development of the skull and the teeth but also in the feet, for this horse became a single-toed equid. The side toes were reduced to mere splints that were concealed beneath the skin of the upper portion of the foot, a condition that continues in the feet of modern horses.

From *Pliohippus* two groups of horses arose at the end of the Pliocene epoch. One of them was embodied in the genus *Hippidium,* which originated in South America from *Pliohippus* ancestors that entered the southern continent when the isthmian bridge was re-established. *Hippidium* was a large horse, with rather short legs and feet. It inhabited South America during Pleistocene times, but became extinct before the close of the Ice Age.

The other descendant from *Pliohippus* was our modern group of horses belonging to the genus *Equus*, horses in which the *Pliohippus* trends were carried to a logical conclusion. *Equus* arose in North America and lived in this continent through the Pleistocene epoch, to become extinct a few thousand years ago. In the meantime, at the beginning of Pleistocene times, *Equus* had migrated into the other continents to become a horse of world-wide distribution. It has survived into modern times in the Old World, where it is found as a number of species that we designate as horses, zebras, and asses. These animals are so familiar as to need no description at this place.

This account, brief as it is, may give some idea of the rather involved history of the horses during Cenozoic times. Perhaps it may be summarized by the following diagram.

RECENT	Equus
PLEISTOCENE	Equus — Hippidium
PLIOCENE	Hipparion (and related genera) — Pliohippus — Hypohippus
MIOCENE	Merychippus — Anchitherium (and related genera) — Archaeohippus
OLIGOCENE	Parahippus — Miohippus — Mesohippus
EOCENE	Epihippus — Orohippus — Hyracotherium (Eohippus)

HORSES AND MEN

The history of man has been closely linked with the late history of the horses through many thousands of years. From paintings that were made by Stone Age men in the caves of Europe we know that our ancestors were hunters of horses. As man grew out of his Stone Age culture into the metal ages, he learned that horses were useful beasts of burden. Therefore, he gave up eating horses and adopted them as riding animals and as work animals that pulled his wagons and his plows.

The history of ancient civilizations in the Old World is a story of man's use of horses and of asses. (Zebras were never successfully domesticated.) Armies traveled and fought on horseback, and with horses whole populations moved from one region to another. Much of man's progress to his modern state has depended upon horses, and it is only within the last few decades that these useful ungulates have at last been supplanted by something new—the internal-combustion engine, attached to wheels and implements.

EVQLUTION OF THE RHINOCEROSES

Having reviewed those perissodactyls that may be grouped in the suborder Hippomorpha, we may now turn our attention to the other suborder of perissodactyls, the Ceratomorpha, containing the rhinoceroses and tapirs.

At the present time rhinoceroses are a very restricted group of ungulates, represented by two species in Africa and three in Asia, these last being among the rarest of modern mammals. It can safely be said that the rhinoceroses are well on their way toward extinction, and it is possible that one or two species of rhinoceroses, thanks in large part to the activities of modern man, will become extinct within the next few decades. In Tertiary times, however, the rhinoceroses were numerous and varied, belonging to several lines that were evolving parallel to each other. Such parallelism makes the past history of the rhinoceroses difficult to interpret.

The first known rhinoceroses appear in sediments of early Eocene age, and like so many other very early odd-toed ungulates they show the primitive characters of the stem perissodactyls that have already been described. *Hyrachyus*, the earliest rhinoceros, was a small perissodactyl, though not so small as the first horses. It was rather gracefully built, and it had slender limbs and long feet, adapted for running. There were four toes on the front feet and three on the hind feet. The skull was low, the eye was centrally located, and the orbit was confluent with the temporal opening. This early rhinoceros was hornless. All the incisor teeth were present, and immediately behind them were rather large canines. The canines

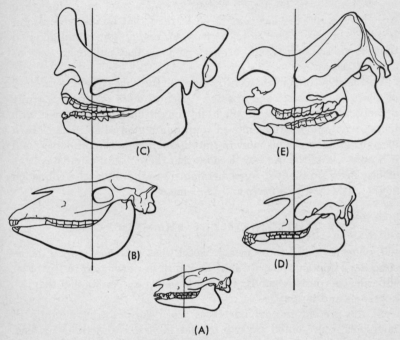

FIGURE 104. Skulls of perissodactyls. (A) *Hyracotherium,* an Eocene horse that in many respects is a typical primitive perissodactyl, one-sixth natural size. (B) *Equus,* a Pleistocene horse, one-twelfth natural size. (C) *Brontotherium,* an Oligocene titanothere, one-twentieth natural size. (D) *Miotapirus,* a Miocene tapir, one-tenth natural size. (E) *Rhinoceros,* a Pleistocene rhinoceros, one-twelfth natural size. Notice the central position of the orbit, the front border of which is indicated by a vertical line, in the ancestral type A, and the different proportions of facial or preorbital length to cranial or postorbital length in the specialized perissodactyls.

in turn were separated from the low-crowned cheek teeth by a considerable gap. There was little molarization of the premolars; yet these teeth were far from primitive, for they were strongly crested. The molars likewise were crested in the manner that was to be characteristic for rhinoceroses throughout their evolutionary history. These crested teeth indicate an early specialization for browsing.

At the end of the Eocene epoch there arose from primitive running rhinoceroses like *Hyrachyus* another group of running rhinoceroses, the hyracodonts, that continued through Oligocene times. *Hyracodon* was somewhat more specialized for running than its ancestors had been, and it may have paralleled in its habits the early horses with which it lived. It was larger than the Eocene running rhinoceroses, and the last premolars had become molariform. With the close of Oligocene history the hyracodonts and the running rhinoceroses in general became extinct.

However, a second branch of rhinoceros evolution had arisen during late Eocene times, probably from a hyrachyid ancestry. This was the group known as the amynodonts, represented in the upper Eocene by *Amynodon*, in the Oligocene by *Metamynodon*. From the first the amynodonts were large, heavy rhinoceroses, with strong limbs and short, broad feet. They are frequently found in stream-channel deposits, and it seems logical to think that they may have been water-lovers with hippopotamus-like habits. The skull was heavy, the incisor teeth and the anterior premolars were greatly reduced, and the canines and the molars were greatly enlarged, the former as large daggers, possibly for fighting, and the latter as long, cutting teeth. For a time the amynodonts were successful, spreading from North America, which would seem to have been the center of origin, into Asia and Europe. They became extinct soon after the close of the Oligocene epoch.

We now come to the central stock of rhinoceros evolution. *Caenopus*, an Oligocene member of the evolutionary line, probably arose from some of the running rhinoceroses. *Caenopus* was a large rhinoceros, standing some four or five feet in height at the shoulders, and it illustrates the early growth to large size that was so typical of most lines of rhinoceros evolution. It was a fairly heavy rhinoceros, seemingly hornless, and it showed some molarization of the premolars. From this point on, the later rhinoceroses evolved in several different directions. Their adaptive radiation included a general increase in size (although the members of a few lines remained comparatively small), the development of broad, three-toed feet for supporting the weight of the strong limbs and the heavy body, the molarization of the premolars, the lengthening of the crowns in the cheek teeth and the continuation of the pattern of strong crests established in the primitive rhinoceroses, and finally the development of horns on the skull.

The horns of rhinoceroses, known mainly from the modern forms, are unique among mammals in that they are formed completely of coalesced hair and have no bony cores. As might be expected, horns such as these were rarely fossilized, but their presence is clearly indicated by roughened areas on the skull, where the bases of the horns were attached.

The baluchitheres were the largest of the rhinoceroses, and the largest of all land mammals, past or present. *Baluchitherium,* which lived during Oligocene and early Miocene times, was an animal that stood sixteen or eighteen feet in height at the shoulders, and in life it must have weighed many tons. This giant rhinoceros was hornless. It probably browsed upon the leaves of trees.

The Miocene diceratheres were small rhinoceroses with a pair of horns, side by side, on the nose.

The Miocene and Pliocene teleocerines, as typified by *Teleoceras,* were heavy rhinoceroses with remarkably short limbs and feet. They carried a single horn on the nose.

The rhinocerines appeared in late Miocene times and have continued to the present day as the one-horned rhinoceroses, *Rhinoceros,* of India and Java.

Various two-horned rhinoceroses, with one horn in front of the other, appeared during late Cenozoic times. One of these survives as the modern two-horned Sumatran rhinoceros. The well-known woolly rhinoceros of the Ice Age, depicted in many European caves by Stone Age men, was probably related to this modern two-horned type. On a somewhat separate branch are the modern two-horned rhinoceroses of Africa, *Diceros,* the black rhinoceros, and *Ceratotherium,* the white rhinoceros.

The elasmotheres were giant rhinoceroses that lived in Eurasia during Pleistocene times. They had a single large horn on the forehead, not on the nose as in modern one-horned rhinoceroses, and were characterized by tall cheek teeth with very complicated enamel patterns.

From the above it can be seen that the rhinoceroses were numerous in most continental regions during late Cenozoic times. Many evolutionary lines coexisted side by side, but as the Cenozoic era came to a close most of these lines disappeared, one by one. Rhinoceroses became extinct in North America during the Pliocene epoch. At the same time various lines of rhinoceroses died out in Eurasia, but other Old World lines continued into the Pleistocene. Finally, at the close of Pleistocene times some of these disappeared, to leave the five species of rhinoceroses known to us as living animals. And as said above, they represent a vanishing group of ungulates. The heyday of rhinoceroses is long since past.

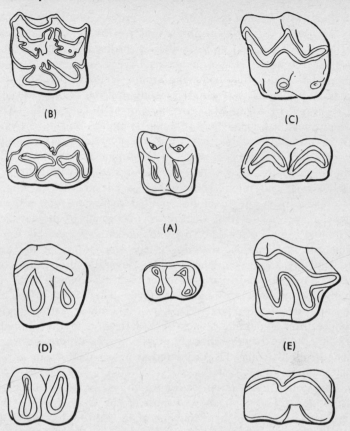

FIGURE 105. Crown views of left upper and right lower molars of perisso-dactyls, not to scale. (A) *Hyracotherium*, an Eocene horse and- a generalized perissodactyl. (B) *Equus*, a Pleistocene and Recent horse. (C) *Brontotherium*, an Oligocene titanothere. (D) *Miotapirus*, a Miocene tapir. (E) *Caenopus*, a Miocene rhinoceros. From the ancestral type (A), perissodactyl molars evolved as (B) high-crowned teeth with complexly folded enamel, adapted for grazing on hard grasses; as (C) low-crowned teeth with simple crescents and cones, for feeding upon comparatively soft vegetation; as (D) cross-crested teeth, for browsing in jungles; and as (E) medium to high-crowned crested teeth, for a combination of browsing and grazing.

THE TAPIRS

The modern tapirs of South America and Malaya are in some respects the most primitive of living perissodactyls. They retain the four toes on the front feet and the three toes on the hind feet, seen in various early Eocene members of the order. The body is heavy, the back is curved, and the limbs and feet are stocky and short. On the other hand, the tapir skull is specialized, in that the nasal bones are retracted. These mammals have a very flexible nose, a short proboscis that they can wrap around stems of plants or other objects. All the incisor teeth are present, and the canines are sharp and separated by a gap from the low-crowned cheek teeth. There is strong molarization of the last three premolars, and all the cheek teeth have crested crowns that are obviously related to the crested cheek teeth of the rhinoceroses. In the tapirs, however, the cheek teeth are perhaps more strongly cross-crested than in any other perissodactyls. The modern tapirs have a curious distribution, but it is obvious from the fossil history that these are remnants of a group that was once widely distributed over much of the earth.

Primitive tapirs, often known as lophiodonts, appear in Eocene sediments. It is evident that during the Eocene epoch the tapirs were evolving rather complexly, along several parallel lines. In general, however, these early tapirs may be compared with other primitive perissodactyls, already described. They were for the most part small, and were characterized by the usual primitive perisso-dactyl features, including a lack of molarization in the premolars. However, the teeth were strongly cross-crested. *Heptodon* was an Eocene genus that may be considered as approximately ancestral to the later tapirs.

In Oligocene times *Protapirus* appeared as a probable descendant of *Heptodon*. This tapir showed most of the characters that have been outlined above in the discussion of modern tapirs, except that there was less retraction of the nasal bones and therefore probably not so much of a flexible nose or proboscis as is seen in living tapirs. From here on, the evolution of the tapirs was comparatively simple, and involved mainly a certain degree of size increase. *Miotapirus* of the Miocene had strongly retracted nasals, as in modern tapirs, of which it was without much doubt the direct ancestor. *Tapirus* appeared in the Pliocene epoch and has continued to the present day. In Pleistocene times there was a giant tapir living in China that has been recognized as a separate genus, *Megatapirus,* but except for size this tapir was little different from the surviving tapirs.

Tapirs roamed widely during Pleistocene times, and were promi-nent in the Ice Age faunas of North America and Eurasia. But as the Pleistocene epoch came to a close the tapirs disappeared in northern continental regions, and have continued only in the East Indies and in Central and South America, a region they invaded after the isthmian link between the two Americas had emerged above the sea.

In looking at modern tapirs we get in some ways a glimpse of the primitive perissodactyls of early Tertiary times. We are carried back in our minds to a time when the perissodactyls were beginning the long and varied evolutionary history that carried them through the Cenozoic era. It is a history that has passed its culminating point. Several million years ago the decline of the perissodactyls began, as these hoofed mammals gave way to the dominant ungulates of modern times, the artiodactyls.

Mountain Sheep

28 · Artiodactyls

ARTIODACTYLS IN THE MODERN WORLD

Most of the hoofed mammals of the present day are artiodactyls. They are the ungulates having an even number of toes (except for the three-toed anoplotheres), either four or two on each foot, with the axis of the foot passing between the third and fourth toes. The modern artiodactyls are the pigs and peccaries, the hippopotamuses, the camels and llamas, the small tragulids, the deer, the giraffes, the pronghorns of North America, and the sheep, goats, muskoxen, antelopes, and cattle. This roster is in itself some indication of the great variety of artiodactyls that now inhabit the world, and we need think only of the white-tailed deer in eastern North America, the bison on the western plains before the coming of white men, or the vast herds of antelopes on the African veldt, to realize to what extent the artiodactyls are the dominant plant-eating mammals of our modern world. Of course artiodactyls are now threatened by the spread of modern civilization, but this is a very recent phenomenon and the restriction of the even-toed hoofed mammals under the impact of firearms, automobiles, airplanes, and tractors cannot be regarded as evidence of any lack of vitality on the part of the harassed ungulates.

It must be remembered that certain species of artiodactyls have been much utilized by man for many thousands of years, and they will continue to be used in the future, as food, as sources of wool or hair, and the like. These are the pigs, the camels and llamas, certain deer and various sheep, goats, and cattle. Moreover, man has been a hunter of artiodactyls of all sizes for thousands of years. So it can be said that the artiodactyls have been very important animals to ourselves and to our ancestors for a long time.

ARTIODACTYL CHARACTERS

In spite of their varied adaptations, the artiodactyls can be united by numerous common characters throughout the skeleton and the soft anatomy. The basic arrangement of the toes, which gives to the order its name, has already been mentioned. To repeat, there are generally two or four toes in each foot, with the axis of the foot passing between the third and the fourth digits. The first digits are almost never present, even in the most primitive artiodactyls. In the ankle the astragalus is distinctive, consisting of two pulleys, one above to articulate with the tibia and one below for articulation with the other bones of the ankle, quite different from the single pulley astragalus of the perissodactyls, described in the preceding chapter. In addition to these points of difference that distinguish the artiodactyls from the perissodactyls, the ungulate order now under consideration also is characterized by absence of a third trochanter on the shaft of the femur. In the more advanced artiodactyls the radius and ulna may be fused and the fibula may be reduced to a splint, coalesced with the tibia. Fusion also commonly unites the long bones or metapodials of the third and fourth digits into a single bone, often designated as the "cannon bone."

As in the perissodactyls, the artiodactyls generally have a capacious body, for accommodating the complex digestive tract and the large lungs. The back is strong, and most artiodactyls have strong back muscles that work with the muscles of the hind limbs, to give power to the propulsive thrust of the legs.

The primitive artiodactyls have a full complement of teeth, but during the evolution of these ungulates there has been a strong trend toward reduction of the upper incisors. This has resulted in their complete suppression in many artiodactyls, to be replaced by a horny pad against which the lower incisor teeth bite, making a very efficient cropping mechanism. In these artiodactyls the lower canine commonly assumes the shape of an incisor and takes a position in series with the incisor teeth, so that there are eight lower cropping teeth. In other artiodactyls the canines are large, dagger-like teeth, used for fighting and for defense, whereas in many artiodactyls the canines may be variously reduced or suppressed.

The cheek teeth of artiodactyls, usually separated by a gap from the anterior teeth, rarely show much molarization of the premolars. In the primitive artiodactyls the cheek teeth are bunodont and low

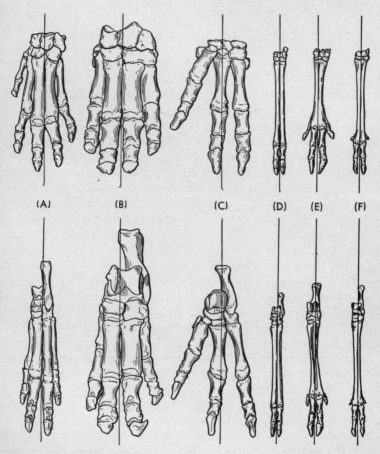

FIGURE 106. Left fore feet above, and hind feet below, of artiodactyls. The digits are drawn to approximate unit lengths, to facilitate the comparison of proportions of the feet in several types of even-toed ungulates. The vertical lines pass through the axes of the feet. (A) *Bothriodon*, an Oligocene anthracothere. (B) *Hippopotamus*, a Pleistocene and Recent hippopotamus. (C) *Diplobune*, an Oligocene anoplothere in which the second digit was reduced so that the foot was functionally three-toed. (D) *Oxydactylus*, a Miocene camel. (E) *Hippocamelus*, a Pleistocene deer. (F) *Merycodus*, a Pliocene antilo-caprid.

crowned, but in many advanced forms they become selenodont, with crescentic cusps, and are high crowned. The upper molars in all

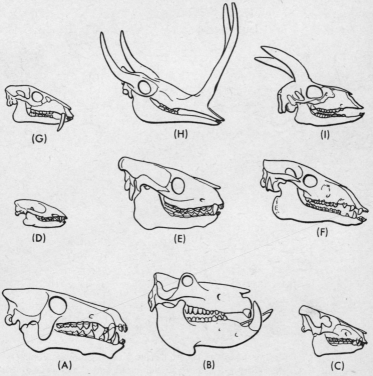

FIGURE 107. Skulls of artiodactyls. (A) *Archaeotherium*, an Oligocene entelodont, one-twelfth natural size. (B) *Hippopotamus*, a Pleistocene hippopotamus, one-twentieth natural size. (C) *Perchoerus*, an Oligocene peccary, one-twelfth natural size. (D) *Homacodon*, an Eocene dichobunoid, one of earliest and most generalized of artiodactyls, one-fifth natural size. (E) *Merycoidodon*, an Oligocene oreodont, one-fifth natural size. (F) *Oxydactylus*, a Miocene camel, one-tenth natural size. (G) *Parablastomeryx*, a primitive Miocene deer, one-sixth natural size. (H) *Synthetoceras*, a Pliocene protoceratid, one-sixteenth natural size. (I) *Gazella*, a Pliocene antelope, one-sixth natural size. *Homacodon* (D) was an early artiodactyl with a generalized skull and dentition. From an ancestry approximated by this genus, the various groups of artiodactyls evolved along widely divergent paths, as indicated to some degree by the very different skulls of specialized types shown in this figure.

but the most primitive artiodactyls have square-shaped crowns; but instead of the back inner corner of the tooth's being formed by the hypocone, as in the perissodactyls, this section of the tooth is generally formed by an enlarged metaconule, the intermediate cusp commonly between the metacone and the hypocone. In the advanced artiodactyls that have this tooth structure there is no hypocone.

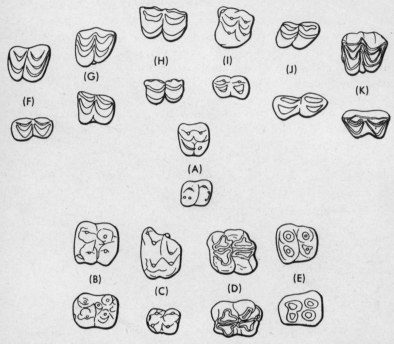

FIGURE 108.   Crown views of left upper and right lower molars of artiodactyls, not to scale. (A) *Diacodexis*, an Eocene dichobunoid and a generalized artiodactyl. (B) *Palaeochoerus*, a Miocene pig. (C) *Heptacodon*, an Oligocene anthracothere. (D) *Hippopotamus*, a Pleistocene hippopotamus. (E) *Dinohyus*, a Miocene entelodont. (F) *Cainotherium*, an Oligocene caenothere. (G) *Merycoidodon*, an Oligocene oreodont. (H) *Oxydactylus*, a Miocene camel. (I) *Archaeomeryx*, an Eocene hypertragulid. (J) *Odocoileus*, a Pleistocene deer. (K) *Selenoportax*, a Pliocene antelope. The teeth of *Diacodexis* (A) approximate the central type from which the varied teeth of more specialized artiodactyls evolved. In most of the Suina the teeth are bunodont, with low, conical cusps, or bunoselenodont, with low crescentic cusps. Such teeth are shown in the lower row of this figure. In some of the Suina and in the Tylopoda and the Ruminantia the teeth are selenodont, with highly developed crescentic cusps. These teeth are shown in the upper row of this figure.

As might be expected, the artiodactyl skull shows changes in proportions and adaptations that are correlative with the specializations of the teeth. In the advanced forms the face generally is long and deep, and the bones of the back portion of the skull are frequently much compressed. This is particularly true of the horned artio-dactyls.

Much of the success of the artiodactyls in late Cenozoic times can be attributed to the complex digestive system that characterizes a large section of this mammalian order. In the artiodactyls known as the ruminants the stomach is divided into four chambers. The plant food, after being cropped, passes into the first two chambers of the stomach, the rumen and the reticulum. Here it is broken down by bacterial action and reduced to a pulp. This pulpy mass is then regurgitated into the mouth in small masses and is thoroughly chewed; this is the chewing of the cud, so characteristic of the ruminants. The cud, after being chewed, is· swallowed and passes into the other two stomach chambers, the omasum and abomasum, for continued digestion. This complicated process enables ruminants to ingest large quantities of plant food in a hurry, after which the food can be thoroughly chewed and digested at leisure, when the animal is in a safe place, free from attack by enemies. The adaptation for eating in a hurry and digesting at leisure certainly gave the artiodactyls a great advantage over the perissodactyls in later Cenozoic times, when predatory carnivores were becoming ever larger and more efficient as hunters of big game.

BASIC CLASSIFICATION OF THE ARTIODACTYLS

The artiodactyls may be divided into three suborders, a scheme of classification that not only is logical but also serves the practical purpose of bringing some simplicity into what is otherwise a bewildering array of varied mammals. In the first place, the primitive artiodactyls of early and middle Tertiary times, as well as the pigs, peccaries, and hippopotamuses, can be combined in a single suborder, the Suina. A second suborder, the Tylopoda, is devoted to the camels. Finally, the largest suborder is the Ruminantia, the ruminants or advanced artiodactyls that chew the cud. These are the dominant artiodactyls of modern times—the tragulids, deer, giraffes, and the pronghorns, sheep, antelopes, and cattle.

THE FIRST ARTIODACTYLS

The first artiodactyls, like the first perissodactyls, appear in sediments of early Eocene age. Some of these early even-toed ungulates were indeed very archaic, perhaps not far removed from some of the primitive condylarths, and it is only the presence of an artiodactyl

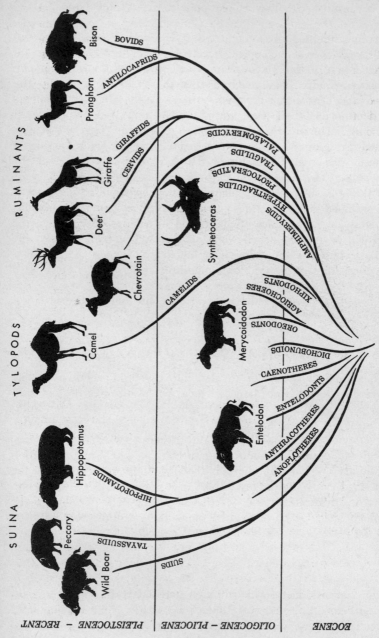

FIGURE 109. Evolution of the artiodactyls or even-toed ungulates.

type astragalus, with the characteristic double pulley arrangement, that justifies the inclusion of such types within the order of mammals now under consideration. *Diacodexis*, from the lower Eocene of North America, is a characteristic early artiodactyl. This was a small animal, as might be expected, with short limbs, having four functional toes on each foot. The skull was low, and the orbit was centrally placed and confluent with the temporal opening behind it. The full dentition was present, and the canine teeth were rather well developed. The cheek teeth were low crowned, and the upper molars retained the primitive triangular shape, with an essentially tricuspid crown.

An animal like *Diacodexis* might have been ancestral to almost any of the later artiodactyls. As a matter of fact, *Diacodexis* was an early member of the dichobunids, the most primitive of all the Suina. Dichobunids were widely distributed through North America, Asia, and Europe during the Eocene epoch, when they shared with the early perissodactyls the rôle of hoofed plant-eaters. It is interesting to see, however, that these Eocene artiodactyls were much less advanced than the perissodactyls of the same age; in fact *Diacodexis* and its relatives probably were not very much different in general appearance from some of the early creodonts that preyed upon them. In the latter part of the Eocene epoch some of the dichobunids became moderately specialized, and a few of them persisted into Oligocene times before they finally became extinct.

It is very probable that the early dichobunids were ancestral to other suiform groups that arose during Eocene or early Oligocene times. One of these groups was the entelodonts, showing definite relationships to the dichobunids, and ranging in geologic age from the late Eocene into the Miocene epoch.

The entelodonts showed an early growth toward large size, so that during Oligocene times some of these artiodactyls became as large as modern boars, whereas in early Miocene times they grew into giants, as large as bison. These animals were rather pig-like in some features, and for this reason they have often been called "giant pigs," but they were not pigs and such a designation is misleading. Two evolutionary trends especially characteristic of the entelodonts were the development of long legs and feet and a straight back for running, and the growth of the skull and teeth to truly enormous proportions. As the legs became elongated the side toes were reduced, so that at an early stage in their history the entelodonts became two-toed ungulates. These trends are exemplified by *Archaeotherium* of Oligocene age and by the giant *Dinohyus*, of early Miocene age, both found in North America.

The remarkable increase in the size of the head is illustrated by *Dinohyus*, an animal about the size of a bison, in which the skull was more than a yard in length. The brain case, however, remained relatively small. The face was elongated, and the posteriorly placed eye was completely circled by bone, so that it was set off from the temporal fossa in which the powerful jaw muscles were located. On

Archaeotherium

FIGURE 110.   An entelodont of Oligocene age.   More than three feet in height.

the cheek bone or zygomatic arch and on the border of the lower jaw were large flanges or knobs, possibly for muscle attachments. All the teeth were present, and the canines were of enormous size. The cheek teeth were bunodont, with conical cusps, and the molars above and below were quadrate, each with four cusps.

During Oligocene and early Miocene times the entelodonts were prominent members of the mammalian faunas of the northern hemisphere. Then they became extinct, perhaps because of competition from the more intelligent pigs and peccaries.

PIGS AND PECCARIES

The first pigs and peccaries were of early Oligocene age, the former appearing in the Old World, the latter in North America. Throughout their phylogenetic histories these artiodactyls, though clearly related to each other, retained separate ranges in the Old and New Worlds, and thus had parallel histories.

Propalaeochoerus, one of the first pigs, lived in Europe during early Oligocene times. This early pig, though considerably larger than the primitive Eocene dichobunids, was still a fairly small artiodactyl. It had legs of medium length, four-toed feet, and a moderately long, low skull. The canines were well developed, and the low-crowned teeth were bunodont, with conical cusps. The molar teeth were somewhat elongated, and in each tooth there were four main cusps.

The evolution of the pigs from this beginning was marked by a moderate increase in size, a great lengthening of the skull, especially of the face, and likewise of the teeth, the complication of the molar crowns by wrinkling of the enamel, the development of the canines as large, outwardly curved tusks, and the retention of the four-toed feet, with emphasis on the two middle toes. As the pigs evolved through middle and late Cenozoic times they branched along numerous lines of adaptive radiation that made theirs a varied group of artiodactyls. Yet in spite of their variety, it would seem that all the pigs have had similar habits, being primarily animals of the forests, where they spend much of their time rooting in the ground for all kinds of food. Pigs are very intelligent mammals, and for this reason have been able to hold their own very well in a highly competitive world.

Among modern swine *Sus* is the domestic pig with which we are familiar, in its wild state typified by the great wild boar of Europe, a rangy, belligerent pig with a very long skull and large, wicked, canine tusks. Other modern representatives of the pigs are the river hog, *Potamochoerus*, the giant forest hog, *Hylochoerus*, and the highly specialized wart hog, *Phacochoerus*, all of Africa. Pigs are common throughout Asia, and in Celebes is the strange babirusa, in which the upper tusks grow in long curves over the top of the skull.

Pigs were domesticated at an early date in the development of Old World civilizations, and during the last several thousand years these beasts have been taken by men to all parts of the world, even to some of the most remote Pacific islands. There is good reason to think that the progenitors of our domestic pigs were Asiatic pigs.

Perchoerus, one of the early peccaries of Oligocene age, lived in North America at the same time that *Propalaeochoerus* lived in Europe. Although the resemblances between the first known peccaries and the first known pigs are very striking, these North American animals followed evolutionary trends that were increasingly divergent from those that characterized the pigs. The peccaries showed a moderate increase in size, but not so much as did the pigs. In the peccaries there was a greater emphasis on running, so that these animals became long-legged, and the side toes were reduced to mere remnants. The skull in most of the peccaries never became so extremely elongated as it did in the pigs, but instead it was usually comparatively short and deep. The canine teeth were always directed straight down and up, to work against each other like sharp shears. Finally the molar teeth of peccaries have usually been simple as compared with the long, complexly wrinkled tooth crowns of pigs.

From *Perchoerus* the peccaries evolved in North America through the Miocene and Pliocene epochs along two lines of adaptive radiation. One line, typified by the Pliocene genus *Prosthennops* and the Pleistocene *Mylohyus*, was characterized by a certain amount of elongation of the face and the frequent development of large bony expansions on the cheek bones. This evolutionary line was successful for a time, but died out during the Pleistocene epoch. The other line, typified by the Miocene *Hesperhys*, the Pleistocene *Platygonus*, and the recent *Tayassu*, has been characterized by rather short, deep skulls and short molars, often strongly cross-crested. This line survives today as the peccaries that live from southern United States, through Mexico and Central America, into South America. The fossil evidence shows that peccaries entered South America in Pleistocene times, as did so many other northern mammals.

ANOPLOTHERES, ANTHRACOTHERES, AND HIPPOPOTAMUSES

In middle and late Eocene times there arose some artiodactyls known as anoplotheres and anthracotheres, of which the latter were to have a wide distribution, and a long history extending into Pleistocene times. The anoplotheres, on the other hand, were less successful, being confined in time to the Eocene and part of the Oligocene epoch and in space to Europe. The anoplotheres were about like pigs in size. The skull was generally primitive, long and low, and the dentition was superficially like that in some of the South American ungulates, in that there was a continuous row of teeth grading in form and function from the incisors to the last molars. The later anoplotheres were peculiar artiodactyls because the feet were three toed, a result of the retention of the second toe as a large digit and the suppression of the fifth toe.

The anthracotheres were widely spread throughout Eurasia during much of Tertiary times, and in the Oligocene epoch some of them invaded North America, where they continued briefly into Miocene times. These were in general pig-like animals, with legs of only moderate length, and with four-toed feet. The skull was long and low, and there was a full complement of teeth. In the early anthracotheres the cheek teeth were bunodont, with conical cusps, but as these animals evolved there was a strong trend toward the development of selenodont or crescentic-shaped tooth cusps. The earliest anthracotheres were very close indeed to some of the primitive dichobunids, an indication as to their ancestry, but as they evolved they evidently became specialized for life in streams and along river banks. Indeed, some of the last of the anthracotheres, such as *Merycopotamus* of Pleistocene age, were like hippopotamuses in the configuration of the skull and the development of the teeth.

Perhaps it is significant that there are no traces of hippopotamuses in the fossil record until late Pliocene times. Because of the resemblances between the hippopotamuses and certain advanced anthracotheres it is therefore reasonable to think that the "hippos" diverged from some of the late anthracotheres—that they are in a sense specialized surviving anthracotheres. Their characters are so well known as to need little elucidation at this place. Briefly, they are very large, heavy artiodactyls with short limbs and broad, four-toed feet. The skull is enormous, with elevated orbits, and the lower jaw is very deep. The incisor and canine teeth are enlarged; each molar crown has four trefoil-shaped cusps that may very well have been derived from the selenodont cusps of anthracothere teeth.

During Pleistocene times the hippopotamuses were widely spread throughout Eurasia and Africa; now they are much restricted in their distribution.

CAENOTHERES

The caenotheres were very small, highly specialized artiodactyls that lived in Europe during late Eocene and Oligocene times. They are so distinct in their adaptations that it is not easy to fit them into the larger artiodactyl categories. It is possible, however, that they can be regarded as broadly related to the anthracotheres and anoplotheres.

Cainotherium was no larger than a rabbit, and was remarkably like the hares in some of its adaptations. The back was strongly curved, and the hind limbs were long, an indication that this little artiodactyl ran with a bounding or hopping gait. The legs were slender; the side toes were short, and only the middle toes were functional. The large eye was closed behind by a bony bar. The teeth formed a nearly continuous series, and the canines were reduced and like the incisors in shape. These animals had inflated auditory bullae, possibly an indication of an acute sense of hearing.

Perhaps the caenotheres lived much as do the rabbits, and they may have competed with some of the early lagomorphs. If so, the caenotheres were not strikingly successful, in spite of the high perfection of their adaptations, for they had a short phylogenetic history, limited to a restricted part of one continent.

ADAPTIVE RADIATION OF THE OREODONTS

The oreodonts were strictly North American artiodactyls. They arose in late Eocene times and continued into the Pliocene epoch, when they became extinct. They were distinctive in their adaptations, and it has not been possible to relate them with certainty to any other artiodactyl groups. They have been considered as allied to the anthracotheres, to the camels or to the ruminants.

Certainly the oreodonts were anthracothere-like in general body form. They ranged in size from small animals to beasts comparable in size to very large pigs. The body was generally long and the legs short. The feet were four toed. In the primitive oreodonts the skull was low, but as these animals evolved the skull became fairly deep. The eye was centrally located, and was closed behind by a bony bar that separated it from the temporal fossa. The teeth formed an almost continuous series, with the upper canine enlarged as a sort of dagger-like tooth. The lower canine, however, was small and in series with the lower incisors, whereas the first lower premolar often took over the function of a lower canine. The molar teeth were selenodont, with crescentic cusps.

There was a dichotomy in the evolution of the oreodonts that began in late Eocene times, with the first appearance of these artiodactyls, and extended through their entire phylogenetic history. *Protagriochoerus* of the Eocene epoch was the direct ancestor of the agriochoeres, which flourished through the Oligocene, represented by the genus *Agriochoerus,* and into the beginning of Miocene times. These were aberrant oreodonts, in which the thumb was retained on the front foot while all the toes terminated in claws, rather than hoofs.

It has been suggested that the agriochoeres were able to scramble around in trees.

Protoreodon of the Eocene was the direct ancestor of the merycoidodonts, the most abundant and varied of the oreodonts. During Oligocene times these oreodonts were remarkably numerous, and

Agriochoerus

Merycoidodon

FIGURE 111. Oligocene oreodonts. These animals were about the size of sheep.

they must have roamed across the landscape in vast herds. Their fossils, especially those of *Merycoidodon,* are the commonest mammals found in the White River badlands of South Dakota, and in other Oligocene exposures. The merycoidodonts were rather sheeplike animals that continued into Pliocene times. *Leptauchenia* of the Oligocene epoch and its relatives were small, lightly built oreodonts. *Ticholeptus,* a Miocene oreodont, typifies a branch of the oreodonts in which the skull and jaws were deep and the teeth high crowned. *Merycochoerus* represents a line of oreodont evolution in which the animals became large and heavy, and in some of the more specialized genera seemingly evolved elongated noses or short trunks.

These were probably water-living forms, with hippopotamus-like habits.

As can be seen from this brief outline, the oreodonts were very successful artiodactyls in North America during middle and late Tertiary times. But as the Tertiary period drew to a close, the fortunes of the oreodonts declined. Perhaps they succumbed to competition from the more advanced artiodactyls, specifically the ruminants, that were evolving and spreading at rapid rates during late Tertiary times.

THE LLAMAS AND THE CAMELS

We think of camels as beasts of the Orient or of the great Sahara, but as a matter of fact these ungulates, like the horses, were of North American origin, and they went through the major part of their evolutionary development on this continent. The present distribution of camels in the Old World and of llamas in South America represents emigrations of these animals out of their homeland during the Pleistocene epoch, whereas their present absence in North America is the result of extinction at the very close of the Ice Age. Why the camels should have failed in North America at the end of Pleistocene times is one of those unaccountable evolutionary mysteries, comparable to the extinction of the horse on this continent.

Although camels chew the cud, like the ruminants, they may be conveniently kept apart from the other cud-chewing artiodactyls because of their long, separate history. The first camels appeared in late Eocene times as small artiodactyls, not unlike some of the early oreodonts. *Protylopus* had short limbs and four-toed front feet, and a full complement of teeth forming an almost continuous series. This animal was certainly distinct from the first ruminants, also of late Eocene age, and it had already begun to evolve along the lines that were typical of the camels.

As the camels evolved through Cenozoic times most of them increased in size to become medium sized or even very large artiodactyls. However, in a few lines of camelid evolution the animals remained small. There was a very rapid reduction and loss of the side toes in the early camels, so that even by Oligocene times the feet were two-toed, the lateral toes having completely disappeared. As the camels continued to evolve there was a fusion of the two long bones of the feet, the metacarpals and metatarsals, to form in each foot a single "cannon bone" having separate articulations at the lower end for the two toes. The legs became long in these animals as an adaptation for rapid running, and in the later camels the hoofed feet were transformed into spreading, padded feet, adapted for walking through soft sand. The neck increased in length.

Stenomylus

Alticamelus

FIGURE 112. A small Miocene camel, and a very large camel of Pliocene age, to the same scale. The head of *Alticamelus* was ten feet or more above the ground.

During evolution the camelid dentition underwent definite changes. In the advanced camels the first two upper incisors were repressed, leaving a single, pointed third incisor that bit down behind the lower incisors. In place of the upper front teeth was a horny pad, that opposed the spoon-shaped lower incisors, an excellent mechanism for cropping plants. The canines remained as pointed teeth and were separated by a gap from the cheek teeth, among which the anterior premolars were suppressed. The molar teeth became high-crowned and elongated, and each tooth had four crescentic cusps.

From *Protylopus* of the Eocene the central line of camel evolution proceeded through *Protomeryx* of Oligocene age into *Procamelus* and *Pliauchenia* of the Miocene and Pliocene epochs, to *Lama,* the llamas, and *Camelus,* the camels, of modern times. The llamas represent camels in essentially a Miocene stage of evolution, and the large camels represent the culminating phase of the central camelid line of development. These camels show certain specializations that probably developed within the latter portion of Cenozoic time—long hair in the llamas for protection against cold, and humps in the camels for the storage of fat for nourishment. The camels also have water-storage chambers in the rumen of the stomach.

During middle and late Tertiary times there were several lateral branches of camelid evolution that died out before the advent of the Pleistocene epoch. The stenomylines, exemplified by *Stenomylus,* were small, lightly built, long-legged camels of Miocene and Pliocene age. Evidently they were rapid-running animals, something like the modern gazelles in their habits. *Alticamelus* and its relatives of the Miocene and Pliocene epochs were very large camels with greatly elongated, stilt-like limbs and long necks. They were evidently adapted for browsing in tall trees, and because of these specializations they are often designated as the "giraffe-camels."

In late Eocene and early Oligocene times some artiodactyls related to the early camels lived in Europe. They were the xiphodonts, which in the Old World paralleled the early development of the camels in the New World. But they failed to live on, and thus are relatively unimportant in the history of the artiodactyls.

ADAPTIVE RADIATION OF THE TRAGULOIDS

We come now to a consideration of the ruminants, the most varied and numerous of modern-day artiodactyls. The ancestry of the ruminants is indicated by *Archaeomeryx,* an upper Eocene genus from Mongolia. This was a small animal about the size of a modern Oriental chevrotain or "mouse-deer," which means that it was hardly larger than a big jack rabbit. In *Archaeomeryx* the limbs were long and the back was curved. It had a long tail, a primitive feature that is lost in most of the ruminants. The feet were somewhat elongated, and, although the four long bones of the feet, the metapodials, were separate elements, emphasis was on the two middle toes in each foot, and the lateral toes were of secondary importance in locomotion. In the skull the eye was centrally located, about halfway between the front and the back of the head, as in so many primitive mammals, but it was closed behind by a bony bar. This character continued through all the ruminants. All the teeth were present, but the three upper incisors were small and obviously on the way to being suppressed. There was a small gap between the front teeth and the cheek teeth, and each molar had four selenodont or crescentic cusps.

Archaeomeryx was a traguloid, using this term in a very broad sense, and its general stage of development has been preserved in the modern tragulids or chevrotains, *Hyemoschus* of Africa and *Tragulus* of Asia. These are small, primitive ruminants, like *Archaeomeryx,* except for the reduction of the tail to a 'small appendage, the complete suppression of the upper incisors as in typical ruminants, the enlargement of the canines into large sabers for defense, and the fusion of the third and fourth metapodials or long bones of the feet into cannon bones. The chevrotains give us a very good impression of what the ancestral ruminants were like.

The main line of traguloid development leading to the modern Old World chevrotains was in Eurasia, but during middle and late Tertiary times there were some interesting side branches of traguloids that evolved in North America. One of these was the hypertragulid group (*Archaeomeryx* was actually an hypertragulid), which retained with some variations the primitive small size and general adaptations of the early traguloid ruminants. *Hypertragulus* was a common animal in the Oligocene faunas of this continent, and it evidently lived in large herds along with oreodonts, early camels and creodonts.

A particularly interesting line of North American traguloids were the protoceratids, represented by the Oligocene *Protoceras,* the Miocene *Syndyoceras* and the Pliocene *Synthetoceras.* There was some size growth in these ruminants so that their last representatives were as large as small deer. But the most spectacular development among the protoceratids was the growth of horns on the skull in the males. In *Protoceras* there were six horns, two on the nose, two above the eyes, and two on the back of the head. In *Syndyoceras* there was a pair of horns above the eyes and two long, diverging horns on the

nose.   In *Synthetoceras* the horns above the eyes were long and
directed backward, and on the nose there was a very long beam or
pedicle that diverged like a Y at its tip.   This front Y-shaped horn was
longer than the total length of the skull, and it must have been a
potent weapon for fighting.

FIGURE 113.   Traguloids.   *Archaeomeryx* was an Eocene hypertragulid and in
most respects a generalized ruminant.   *Tragulus* is the modern Oriental chevrotain that has retained many of the characters of the ancestral ruminants.   Both
these animals about a foot in height.   *Synthetoceras* was a Pliocene protoceratid,
with a skull about eighteen inches in length.

DEER

The traguloids are the primitive ruminants, continuing today as little-changed descendants from generalized early Tertiary types, or diverging during middle and late Tertiary times in a few branches that failed to survive. All the rest of the ruminants are frequently included in a single group known as the Pecora. They are the deer, the giraffes, and the bovoids, these last being pronghorns, sheep, goats, antelopes, and cattle. Of the pecorans, the deer are the most primitive.

The deer were obviously of traguloid ancestry, and it would seem likely that they arose during Oligocene times. *Eumeryx*, of Oligocene age, is an almost ideal progenitor for the deer, and its primitive characters are continued in certain Miocene forms, like *Palaeomeryx* in Europe or *Blastomeryx* in North America. These primitive deer were rather small, and they lacked antlers upon the skull. Usually the upper canine teeth were enlarged as long sabers. The skull was fairly long and low, the back was arched, the tail was very short, the legs and feet were elongated, the two central metapodials were fused into a cannon bone, and four toes were present, of which the lateral ones were much reduced so that only the middle toes functioned. The modern Asiatic musk deer, *Moschus*, is a persistent primitive type, very much like these early Miocene deer.

As the deer evolved there was a strong trend toward increase in size, as is so common in the artiodactyls. Many deer became very large, although some evolutionary lines have remained rather small. Because the deer have been browsers through the extent of their evolutionary history the selenodont cheek teeth have remained low crowned. But the striking specialization during the evolution of the advanced deer has been the development of antlers on the skull of the males. Antlers are outgrowths from the frontal bones, above the eyes. There are two cylindrical bony stumps on the skull that form the bases for the antlers. These are the pedicles, and in life they are covered with skin. From the pedicles new, skin-covered antlers grow each year, increasing in size year after year as the deer reaches the full stature of its maturity. This growth of bone takes several months. When the antlers have reached their full size the skin that has covered them dries, and is rubbed off by the deer. The antlers are now hard, bony spikes or branching, many-pointed weapons, with which the male deer fight each other during the mating season. After the mating season the antlers drop off, and new antlers begin

Muntjac

Wapiti

FIGURE 114. Two late Cenozoic and Recent deer. The muntjac, a small deer living in Asia, is in many respects similar to the primitive deer of Miocene time. The male has small antlers borne on long pedicles, and there are large canine teeth. The wapiti or stag, a large deer with magnificent antlers in the male, is an Eurasiatic deer that migrated into North America during Pleistocene times.

to grow, to replace them. This remarkable adaptation supplies the male deer with efficient weapons for part of the year, and at this time he is a belligerent animal. But during the time the new antlers are growing, the male deer are shy and timid, and very careful to protect the skin-covered antlers, which are said to be "in velvet."

Antlered deer began to evolve along many adaptive lines during the Miocene epoch, reaching the culmination of their development in Pleistocene times, to continue into our modern age. When the isthmus arose to connect South America with North America the deer pushed into the southern continent, as did so many other North American mammals. Deer, however, never invaded Africa below the Atlas Mountains, perhaps because of the competition from the host of antelopes that had already taken over the forests and plains of that continent.

As the primitive deer developed in Eurasia, a group of aberrant deer, the dromomerycines, evolved in North America. They did not survive beyond the Pliocene epoch. In the meantime the more familiar lines of deer that continue at the present time were evolving. They are:

The muntjacs. Asiatic deer with very long pedicles and very small antlers. *Muntiacus* is the characteristic genus.

The cervine deer or stags. Deer that evolved in the Old World, and invaded North America during Pleistocene times. The European stag and the American Wapiti or "elk" (*Cervus*) are superb examples of these noble deer.

The deer of the New World. Deer that evolved in North America and invaded South America during Pleistocene times. The common white-tailed and black-tailed deer (*Odocoileus*) represent this line in North America.

The alcine deer or moose. The true "elk" (*Alces*) of the Old World, which invaded North America in Pleistocene times.

The reindeer and caribou. Arctic deer (*Rangifer*), unusual in that the females have antlers.

The water deer of Asia.

The roebucks (*Capreolus*) of Eurasia.

GIRAFFES

The giraffes are closely allied to the deer, and it is apparent that these artiodactyls and the deer had a common ancestry. Indeed the giraffes can be considered as having branched from the deer during Miocene times, after which they diverged widely from their deer cousins.

Sivatherium

Giraffe

Palaeotragus

FIGURE 115. *Palaeotragus* was a Pliocene giraffe that represents the approximate stem from which later giraffes evolved. The modern okapi of the Belgian Congo is a little-changed descendant from a *Palaeotragus*-like ancestor. *Sivatherium* was an ox-like giraffe of Pleistocene age. The recent giraffe of Africa needs no introduction. All to the same scale.

The primitive giráffes are well exemplified by the modern okapi, a persistent Miocene type of giraffe that was living in the deep forests of the Belgian Congo, unknown to white men, until after the turn of the present century. The okapi is a rather large artiodactyl, standing five or six feet in height at the shoulder. The legs are long, and the front legs are somewhat longer than the hind legs, so that the back slopes from the shoulders to the pelvis. As in other pecorans, the feet are long, the metapodials are fused into a cannon bone, and the middle toes form the functional foot. The skull is elongated, and in the male there are two small outgrowths from the frontal bones, covered with skin. This type of skin-covered "horn" is characteristic of the modern giraffes. The teeth are rather low crowned, and the enamel of the cheek teeth is very much wrinkled, as it is in all the giraffes.

In Miocene and Pliocene times the first giraffes, such as *Palaeotragus*, were strikingly similar to the modern okapi. From them the modern giraffe (*Giraffa*) evolved, by tremendous elongation of the limbs and the neck, and bv the growth of large, skin-covered horns above the eyes.

However, there was another branch of the giraffes that developed during late Pliocene and Pleistocene times. This was the group of sivatheres, very large, massive giraffes, with normally proportioned limbs and ox-like bodies. They were characterized by large, strikingly ornate "horns" on the skull, bony outgrowths of such size that it seems possible they may have been covered with hard horn during life. *Sivatherium*, known from the Pleistocene of India, was one of the last of this line of girrafid evolution, a giant pecoran with two huge, flaring bony horns on the back of the skull and two smaller, conical horns in front of them, above the eyes. A tantalizing little bronze figure, made by an ancient Sumerian, several thousand years ago, indicates that sivatheres may still have been living when this early civilization flourished in the Middle East.

THE BOVOIDS, DOMINANT ARTIODACTYLS OF THE MODERN WORLD

The bovoids—the pronghorns, sheep, goats, muskoxen, antelopes, and cattle—form a bewildering array of ruminants widely distributed throughout the world. These artiodactyls, the most advanced of the ruminants, arose in Miocene times, but most of their evolutionary development has been confined to Pliocene and subsequent ages. They were pretty clearly of northern origin, but they invaded southern

Asia and Africa in late Pliocene and Pleistocene times, and in these continental regions they now live in the greatest abundance and variety. Bovoids never reached South America, until they were introduced by man.

These ruminants are characterized by powerful bodies and long limbs for running. The feet are even more progressive than in the deer, and the lateral digits are in an advanced stage of reduction. The cheek teeth are hypsodont or high crowned, often extremely so, and the enamel is generally folded to form rather complex surface patterns when the tooth crown is worn. However, the most characteristic feature of the bovoids is the presence of horns on the skull, almost always in both males and females. The horns are outgrowths of the frontal bones, covered with a very hard outer casing of horn. Except in the antilocaprids this horny cover is permanent, expanding as the bony pedicle or horn core grows during life. This is certainly a more efficient manner of providing a weapon than the yearly production of antlers in the deer, which necessarily places a great drain on the energy of the animal. The horns of the bovoids have been a large factor, together with the habit of ruminating or chewing the cud, in assuring the success of these artiodactyls in the modern world, for the horns are powerful and efficient weapons, and many bovoids are quite able to defend themselves against attack from predatory carnivores by fighting back. Indeed, some of the bovoids, particularly the large cattle, are themselves very aggressive animals, much more dangerous than the so-called lords of the jungles, the great cats, the lions, leopards, and tigers.

One group of bovoids, the antilocaprids, has been limited to North America. They appeared in the Miocene as small, deer-like animals, of which *Merycodus* was characteristic. *Merycodus* had branched horn cores, which look like the antlers of deer, but it is clear that they were never shed during life. Later antilocaprids had flattened or twisted horn cores, and lived in considerable variety during Pliocene and Pleistocene times. However, these varied ruminants became extinct except for one genus, *Antilocapra*, the "antelope" or pronghorn of our western plains, which until the arrival of white men inhabited the West in vast herds. The pronghorn is unique among bovoids in that the horn sheath is shed and renewed each year.

The remaining bovoids, all belonging to the family Bovidae, arose and evolved in northern Eurasia during the Pliocene and Pleistocene epochs, in which time they followed numerous and truly confusing lines of adaptive radiation that resulted in the great host of genera and species now living in many parts of the world. It would seem that in late Pliocene times the varied bovoids of Eurasia moved south into Africa to populate that continent. A few of them invaded North

Bison

Springbok

Stockoceros

LMD

FIGURE 116. Bovids, to the same scale. Here is shown one of the very large Pleistocene bison, which had enormous, sweeping horns. *Stockoceros* was a four-horned prongbuck of Pleistocene age. It was about the same size as the modern pronghorn antelope. The springbok is an African antelope.

America, where as species, such as the bison, they multiplied enormously to live in tremendous herds that were numbered in the millions. However, this continent was never the home of a numerous array of genera and species, as are Asia and Africa.

Some of the facets of bovoid evolution are difficult to understand. For instance, why should there be such a great variety of antelopes now living in Africa? On the face of it, we would think that a good pair of horns would enable a species of antelope to protect itself and spread widely. Yet in Africa there are literally dozens of antelope species with an astonishing variety of horns. There are the straight-horned oryx, the twisted-horned elands, the spiral-horned kudus, the

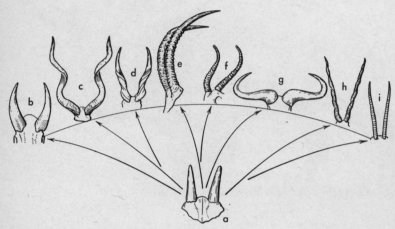

FIGURE 117. Adaptive radiation of horn shapes in some modern antelopes. Not to scale. (a) *Eotragus*, a primitive Miocene bovid that represents an ancestral type from which later bovids may have evolved. (b) *Boselaphus*, the nilgai. (c) *Strepsiceros*, the kudu. (d) *Taurotragus*, the eland. (e) *Hippotragus*, the sable antelope. (f) *Cobus*, the waterbuck. (g) *Connochaetes*, the gnu. (h) *Antilope*, the blackbuck. (i) *Oryx*, the oryx. The nilgai and the blackbuck live in India, the other modern forms in Africa.

curved-horned sable antelopes, the recurved-horned wildebeests, and so on. And many of these antelopes seemingly live in the same environment. What are the advantages of a kudu's horns over an eland's horns, or vice versa? These are questions still to be answered. Perhaps the modern African antelopes represent numerous popula-tions.that have evolved in genetic isolation from each other, and all have been successful.

No attempt will be made to describe the bovids. They can be listed, as follows:

Strepsicerine antelopes: such as the kudu and the eland.
Boselaphine antelopes: such as the nilgai of India.
Bovines: anoas, buffaloes, cattle, bison.
Cephalophines: the small duikers of Africa.

Reduncine antelopes: the puku and reedbuck and their relatives.
Hippotragine antelopes: the oryx, the sable antelope, and others.
Alcelaphine antelopes: the blesbok, hartebeest, and gnus.
Neotragine antelopes: klipspringers and dik-diks.
Antelopines or gazelles: gazelles, impala, and their relatives.
Saigines: the saiga antelope of Asia.
Rupicaprines: the goral, serow, Rocky Mountain "goat" and chamois.
Ovibovines: muskoxen and takin.
Ovines: sheep and goats.

A Cave Drawing

29 · Elephants and Their Kin

THE EARLY MAMMALS OF NORTH AFRICA

The Proboscidea, namely, the mastodonts, the elephants and their relatives, the Desmostyliformes, an extinct group, the Sirenia or sea cows, the Hyracoidea, which are the conies mentioned in the Bible, and the Embrithopoda, another extinct group, may be included within the superorder of paenungulates, but except for the very general relationships indicated by this grouping they have little in common. The proboscideans have been throughout their history large and even gigantic mammals of the forest and the plain. The sea cows have been aquatic herbivores, living in shallow waters along seacoasts, or venturing up rivers that flow into the sea, where they feed upon underwater plants. The desmostylids likewise were water-living herbivores. The conies are small ungulates that look more like rodents than hoofed mammals. The embrithopods were giant, horned ungulates, paralleling in some ways the Oligocene titanotheres of North America or the late Cenozoic rhinoceroses of the Old World. Yet, in spite of such obvious dissimilarities, it is possible that all these early mammals arose from protungulate ancestors, and followed very divergent lines of evolutionary development during the course of Cenozoic times. The earliest known fossils, which are found in Egypt, indicate that by late Eocene times they had already progressed far along their separate lines of adaptive radiation.

FIGURE 118. Evolution and relationships of the orders of paenungulates.

EMBRITHOPODA

Arsinoitherium, of Oligocene age, is the single genus of the Embrithopoda. This was a large ungulate, as big as a rhinoceros, with a heavy skeleton, strong, elephant-like limbs, and broad, spreading feet. The skull was large, and the teeth formed a continuous series from incisors to last molars. The cheek teeth were tall crowned, which is surprising in an ungulate as early as *Arsinoitherium,* and each molar crown was strongly cross-crested. The most striking character of *Arsinoitherium* was a pair of massive, bony horns, side by side, the confluent bases of which occupied the top of the skull from the nostrils back to the middle of the brain case.

Arsinoitherium

Saghatherium

FIGURE 119. Two Oligocene mammals of northern Africa, drawn to the same scale. *Arsinoitherium,* as large as a rhinoceros, is the only known genus belonging to the order Embrithopoda. *Saghatherium* was a large hyracoid or cony.

Arsinoitherium is something of a paleontological mystery. There are no known fossils that might represent its ancestors, and it apparently left no descendants. This animal stands alone in time and in its zoological position; it appears suddenly in the lower Oligocene sediments of Egypt, and that is the end of it. It is the solitary representative of an order of mammals about which we may learn more at some future date.

THE CONIES

The conies of Africa and the Middle East (not to be confused with certain lagomorphs known as conies) are small rabbit-like or rodent-like mammals that live among the rocks of steep hillsides, or in trees. Among ancient peoples, and even among the earlier of modern naturalists, these mammals were thought to be rabbits of some sort, but with the growth of modern systematic zoology the position of the conies has been clarified; these are small ungulates that constitute a separate order of mammals.

In several respects the conies, or dassies, or hyraxes, have paralleled the rabbits. This is apparent in their small size and in their habits. Conies are herbivorous. In the skull there is on each side a single rootless incisor tooth, very much like the large, chisel-shaped incisor teeth of rodents. This tooth is opposed by two incisors in the lower jaw. A gap separates the incisor teeth from the cheek teeth, which are high crowned, with the molars showing a pattern somewhat like that seen in the rhinoceroses. The feet are completely distinctive, there being four toes on the front feet, three on the hind, terminating in small, hoof-like nails. A single pad makes up the bottom of each foot.

Various genera and species of conies now live in Africa and adjacent regions along the Mediterranean Sea. The first members of the Hyracoidea appear in the Oligocene sediments of Egypt, and the history of these mammals can be traced in a limited way in the Mediterranean region through Tertiary times. There was a certain amount of evolutionary radiation of the Tertiary hyraxes, and some of them like *Megalohyrax* of the Oligocene epoch became as large as pigs. However, the larger hyraxes failed to survive, perhaps because of competition from other ungulates, and only the small, rabbit-like conies, represented by the modern *Procavia*, carried the line into recent times.

THE SEA COWS

Although they are classified as ungulates of a sort, the sea cows have become completely modified for an aquatic mode of life. Adaptations for life in the water took place at an early date among these mammals, because the earliest-known sea cows, of Eocene age, were already highly specialized sirenians. These early sea cows are well represented in the upper Eocene beds of Egypt, but they are also found in beds of similar age in Europe, and as far distant as the West Indies. It seems very probable, therefore, that the early sea cows were widely distributed through the world, as might be expected of animals able to swim along the shores of the continents.

Modern sea cows are large mammals, with strange, blunt-nosed heads, torpedo-shaped bodies, flipper-like front limbs, and a broad,

horizontal tail fin. The skin is naked and tough. The hind limbs
are suppressed, and the pelvis is reduced to a rod-like bone. The
ribs are very massive and heavy, making a sort of ballast for the
body in these mammals. The skull is rather long and low, and in
its back portion it resembles to some degree the skull in the very
primitive proboscideans, the ancestors of the elephants. The front
of the skull forms a narrow rostrum that in the modern sea cows
is sharply downturned. The cheek teeth may be doubly cross-crested
or they may have bunodont cusps, like the teeth in some of the
Tertiary proboscideans. Sea cows are of course adept swimmers, and

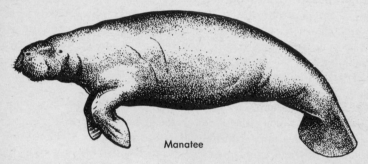

Manatee

FIGURE 120. A modern sea cow. A large manatee is ten feet or more in length.

as mentioned above they frequent rivers that flow into the sea, where
they feed upon aquatic vegetation.

The earliest sea cows were slightly more primitive than the modern
forms. For instance, in the Eocene genus *Protosiren* the front of the
skull or rostrum was not turned down, as it was in later sirenians like
Halitherium of the Miocene or the recent dugong. In *Eotheroides*,
another Eocene form, the pelvis was still a recognizable pelvis, not
a rod of bone as in the later sea cows. But these are differences
of degree, not of kind, and the first sirenians were completely aquatic
mammals.

As they evolved the sea cows followed two lines of development,
probably from Eocene times on. The manatees evolved on both
sides of the Atlantic basin, inhabiting the shores of Africa and
America. The dugongs evolved in the Pacific and Indian oceans.

THE DESMOSTYLIDS

Within recent years some very interesting mammals of Oligocene
and Miocene age have been discovered along both sides of the Pacific

Ocean. They are the desmostylids, typified by the Miocene *Desmostylus*, found in California and in Japan.

Desmostylus had a long, mastodont-like skull, with tusks. The nasal opening was retracted, and it seems likely that this mammal had a short trunk. The cheek teeth were peculiar; they consisted of vertical columns, arranged in pairs along the length of each tooth. The skeleton, recently discovered in Japan, is surprising to say the least, for it indicates an animal with a large body, very heavy limbs, and broad, elephant-like feet.

Desmostylus is found in sediments of marine origin. One is led to believe, therefore, that this mammal was a sort of "marine hippopotamus" wading and swimming in the shallow waters along the seacoasts. But the comparison with hippopotamuses is one of function only. In its anatomy *Desmostylus* shows resemblances to the sea cows on the one hand, and to the early proboscideans on the other. Perhaps this was a truly intermediate mammal. Only time, discoveries, and further researches will settle this point.

AN INTRODUCTION TO THE PROBOSCIDEANS

Elephants are familiar and fascinating creatures to all of us. These giant mammals, still living in considerable numbers in Asia and Africa, and widely domesticated by man, seem like permanent fixtures in our world. Yet the modern elephants are actually the last representatives of a dying group, and it is quite possible that even without the intervention of man as a destructive agent they may very well be on their way to extinction within the next few thousand years. Even though they are still numerous as individuals, elephants are limited at the present time to two genera, each with a single species, one in Asia and one in Africa. It would hardly be suspected from knowledge of modern elephants alone that their ancestors and collateral relatives inhabited the world in prodigious numbers and in a bewildering array of genera and species through the middle and later portions of the Cenozoic era. That they did we now know from the fossils.

Remains of these great beasts were among the relics of extinct animals first known to man. They were collected by the ancient Greeks and Romans as curious objects, worthy of preservation; and a leg bone of a fossil elephant was among the treasures of the Tlascalan Indians of Mexico, who were subdued by and then became the allies of stout Cortez. Many of the legends of giants, so popular among men of earlier ages, were based upon the discoveries of fossil elephant bones. The modern science of vertebrate paleontology had its beginnings with the study of these animals. Consequently there has been time for the accumulation of a great mass of data on the past history of the proboscideans.

The fossils show that at various times during the Cenozoic era the proboscideans lived on all the continents of the world, except Australia. During the later phases of the Tertiary period these great beasts evolved along numerous lines of adaptive radiation, some of which continued into Pleistocene times. Consequently the phylogenetic history of the proboscideans is very complex and not at all easy to interpret, especially since there was a great deal of parallel evolution within this order of mammals.

THE MOERITHERES

The first proboscideans known from the fossil record were the moeritheres, named from the typical genus, *Moeritherium,* that lived in Egypt during late Eocene times. They were heavily built animals about the size of pigs, with stout legs that terminated in broad, spreading feet, having flat hoofs on the end of the toes. The tail was short. All in all the body of *Moeritherium* was generalized and about what might be expected in a medium-sized paenungulate of Eocene age.

The skull, however, was specialized in a number of interesting ways. It was a long skull, with the eye set far forward in front of the most anterior premolars, thus making the cranial region of the skull very much elongated. Because of the forward position of the eye the zygomatic arch or cheek bone was also very long. The back surface of the skull, the occiput, was broad and forwardly sloped, to give a large area of attachment for strong neck muscles. The lower jaw was deep, and its back portion, the large ascending ramus, extended up so that the articulation between the jaw and the skull was placed high above the level of the teeth.

The second upper and lower incisors of *Moeritherium* were enlarged and were set in a transverse line across the front of the skull and the lower jaw. The first incisors were very small teeth, crowded between these rather tusk-like second incisors; and in the skull the third incisor and the canine were small teeth, separated by a gap from the large incisors in front. The third incisor and the canine had been completely suppressed in the lower jaw. The cheek teeth were separated by gaps from the anterior teeth, and the molars, both above and below, were doubly cross-crested, each crest being formed by two large cusps placed side by side.

The external nostrils were situated at the front of the skull, and it is obvious that although *Moeritherium* may have had a thick upper lip, it did not have a trunk or proboscis.

These were the basic proboscidean characters, and from such a base the proboscideans evolved along several lines of adaptive radiation during middle and late Cenozoic times. Although the evolution of these mammals was extraordinarily varied, it was marked by certain dominant trends running through the wide range of proboscidean forms. These trends were:

1. Increase in size. Almost all the proboscideans became giants.
2. Lengthening of the limb bones and the development of short, broad feet. This has been a common evolutionary trend among very large mammals.
3. Growth of the skull to extraordinarily large size.
4. The shortening of the neck. Since the skull and its associated structures became large and heavy, the neck was reduced in length to shorten the lever between the body and the head.
5. Elongation of the lower jaw. In many of the later proboscideans there was a *secondary* shortening of the lower jaw, but lengthening of the jaw was an early, primary trend.
6. Growth of a trunk. Elongation of the upper lip and the nose probably went along with elongation of the lower jaw. Subsequently the nose was further elongated to form a very mobile trunk or proboscis.
7. Hypertrophy of the second incisors to form tusks, used for defense and for fighting.
8. Limitation and specialization of the cheek teeth in various ways, as adaptations for chewing and grinding plant food.

THE LINES OF PROBOSCIDEAN EVOLUTION

Excluding the barytheres (a peculiar and little-known group, to be discussed briefly at the end of this chapter) there were two principal lines of proboscidean development after the moerithere stage, namely, the dinotheres and the elephantoids. The dinotheres were quite distinct from the beginning, and they evolved along a very narrow path of adaptations through most of Cenozoic times, becoming extinct during the Pleistocene epoch. The elephantoids, on the other hand, flowered into many diverging branches during middle and late

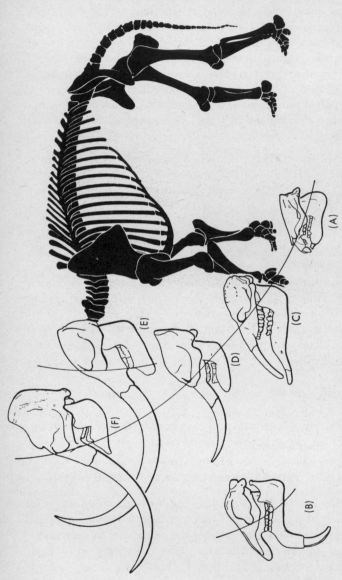

FIGURE 121. Proboscideans, to about the same scale. The mastodon skeleton is about nine feet high. (A) *Moeritherium*, a moeritheriid of late Eocene and early Oligocene age. (B) *Dinotherium*, a dinotheriid, of middle and late Cenozoic age. (C) *Serridentinus*, a Miocene mastodont. (D) *Stegomastodon*, a Pleistocene mastodont. (E) *Mastodon americanus*, the Pleistocene American mastodon. (F) *Parelephas*, a Pleistocene mammoth. The lines indicate broad relationships, from moeritheres through early mastodonts to late specialized mastodonts. Elephants were derived from moeritheres, from moeritheres through early mastodonts to late specialized mastodonts. The dinotheres were isolated from other proboscideans throughout their history.

Cenozoic times, to produce a great concourse of large, trunked, tusk-bearing giants that spread to almost all corners of the earth. Indeed the diversity among the elephantoids was so great that we might question the propriety of classifying all of them within a single large group. However, the various elephantoids have more in common with each other than any of them have with the moeritheres or with the dinotheres, and therefore such an arrangement is quite logical.

The divergence of the elephantoids was so marked during their evolutionary history that for practical purposes it is useful to think of them as being composed of three groups, rather than as a single entity. These groups, which may be given family rank, are the long-jawed mastodonts or gomphotheres (very generally known as the trilophodonts), the short-jawed mastodonts, and finally the elephants and their relatives. The two groups of mastodonts constitute parallel series, evolving side by side during Tertiary times and extending into the Pleistocene epoch. The elephants represent a group that arose at a late date from the long-jawed mastodont stem, to evolve with great rapidity and profusion during Pliocene and Pleistocene times.

With these general considerations of proboscidean evolution in mind, let us now turn to a more detailed discussion of the several lines of adaptive radiation in these large and interesting mammals.

THE DINOTHERES

The first dinotheres appear in Miocene sediments, fully specialized and showing no intermediate antecedents to connect them with their presumed moerithere ancestors. There is no record anywhere as to the Oligocene evolution of the dinotheres, but it must have been proceeding at a rapid rate to bridge the gap between *Moeritherium* and the first *Dinotherium*.

The history of the dinotheres from Miocene times until their extinction during the Pleistocene epoch was so stereotyped that all these proboscideans may be placed within the single genus *Dinotherium*. It is obvious that there was little progress in the dinotheres after their first appearance, and the changes that took place during the long lapse from early Miocene into Pleistocene times were those of details. Here is an interesting example of rapid initial evolutionary development (as yet unknown to us) followed by a long period of evolutionary stability at a high level of specialization.

The first dinotheres were modestly proportioned giants, but in late Cenozoic times they became some of the largest of the proboscideans, standing ten feet or more in height at the shoulder. These were long-legged proboscideans, comparable to the modern elephants in this respect. In the skull and dentition, however, the dinotheres were quite unlike any of the other proboscideans. The skull was rather flat, not high as usual among the advanced proboscideans, and it was quite tuskless. In the lower jaws there were two large tusks that curved down from the front of the jaws and then back toward the body. They formed a sort of huge hook on the front of the jaws. It is difficult to say just how such tusks might have been used; very likely they were employed for digging into the ground and pulling up roots or plants. (Incidentally one of the pioneers of paleontology thought that the dinotheres lived in rivers, and that they used the strange tusks to anchor themselves to the bank at night, where they slumbered in watery repose!) The cheek teeth of the dinotheres, like those of most mammals, were arranged in long rows in the skull and the lower jaw (a rather unproboscidean character as we shall see), and most of the teeth had two sharp cross-crests constituting each crown.

There was evidently a well-developed trunk, as in other proboscideans.

Dinotheres lived in Eurasia and Africa, but never entered the New World.

Even though they may seem strange to us, the dinotheres were nevertheless well-adapted mammals, for theirs was a long history. Indeed the persistence of the single genus *Dinotherium* through almost three geological epochs is an outstanding example of unusual mammalian stability in a changing world. The extinction of the dinotheres during Pleistocene times was probably part of the pattern of proboscidean extinction that so characterized the later phases of this last division of the Cenozoic era.

THE LONG-JAWED MASTODONTS

We now go back to early Tertiary times in Egypt. Not long after *Moeritherium* lived in what is now the valley of the Nile, some proboscideans appeared that showed definite advances beyond the ancestral moeritheres. They were the first of the mastodonts, the lower Oligocene genera *Palaeomastodon* and *Phiomia*. *Palaeomastodon* was considerably larger than any of the moeritheres, standing perhaps as much as seven or eight feet tall at the shoulder. It had an elephant-like skeleton, with comparatively long legs. The skull was greatly enlarged by the expansion of sinus cavities above and in front of the brain case, so that the back portion of the skull had increased in height. The nasal bones were retracted far back on this high, swollen skull, an indication that *Palaeomastodon* was provided with a well-formed trunk. And in front there were two tusks, projecting forward and down, tusks that had been derived from the enlarged second incisors of *Moeritherium*. The lower jaw was very long, and in front it carried two tusks that protruded horizontally. The cheek teeth were low crowned, and each molar was provided with three transverse pairs of bluntly conical cusps.

All in all *Palaeomastodon* probably looked something like a medium-sized elephant with a long lower jaw that was provided with straight, horizontally directed tusks. From an ancestor of which this is an approximation the numerous elephantoids evolved.

There is a strange gap of several million years comprising most of the Oligocene epoch and the early part of Miocene times, without any known record of mastodont evolution. It will be remembered that the same was true for the dinotheres. Where were the proboscideans during this phase of geologic history? This is an intriguing question, and some day we may discover the answer to it.

Gomphotherium, more commonly known as *Trilophodon,* was the central type of long-jawed mastodont, living during late Miocene and early Pliocene times. This mastodont was in effect a large edition of *Palaeomastodon* with certain refinements. The lower jaws were much elongated, and provided with two tusks. The first two molars had three pairs of transversely arranged, conical cusps, which became, when worn, three low cross-crests. The third molar was elongated by the development of a heel behind the last two of the paired cusps. There was evidently a long and flexible trunk.

In some of the long-jawed mastodonts accessory cusps were added to the sides of the main molar cones, giving to the tooth a complexly sinuous enamel pattern when it was worn. Naturally this increased the effectiveness of the teeth as grinding mills. This trend is seen in the Miocene-Pliocene genus *Serridentinus,* closely allied to the trilophodonts, and reaches its culmination in the upper Pliocene *Synconolophus* and the lower Pleistocene *Stegomastodon*. In these last two mastodonts the lower tusks were suppressed so that they disappeared, and the lower jaw was shortened. The upper tusks became large and curved strongly upward. Here we see a parallelism in some of the "long-jawed" mastodonts to other lines of advanced proboscideans. During Pleistocene times a branch of these mastodonts invaded South America, and became widely distributed on that continent.

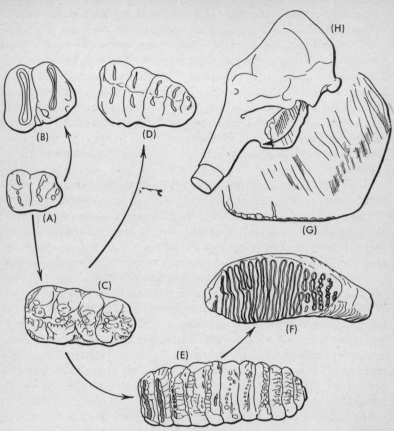

FIGURE 122. Form and relationships of left upper molar teeth in proboscideans. All crown views, except G and H, about one-fifth natural size. (A) *Moeritherium,* an Oligocene moerithere. (B) *Dinotherium,* a Miocene-Pleistocene dinothere. (C) *Serridentinus,* a Miocene-Pliocene mastodont. (D) *Mastodon,* a Pleistocene mastodont. (E) *Stegodon,* a Pleistocene stegodont. (F) *Parelephas,* a Pleistocene mammoth. (G) Side view of a large elephant molar. (H) Direction of eruption of an upper molar in the elephant skull. In the ancestral moeritheres (A), the crowns of the cheek teeth consisted of low cones arranged tranversely to form incipient crests. In the dinotheres the cheek teeth became sharply cross-crested, and changed little throughout the evolutionary history of this group. In the mastodonts the tooth crowns were composed either of cones or of crests. From certain crested-toothed mastodonts the Pliocene stegodonts arose, with long, cross-crested teeth. These in turn gave rise to the Pleistocene and Recent elephants, in which the cheek teeth are very tall and consist of parallel plates. These teeth are so large that there is room in each jaw for only one or parts of two teeth at a time. Consequently the teeth erupt one after another, the last molar coming into place when the animal has reached a fully adult stage of growth.

In another lateral branch of long-jawed mastodonts the front of the lower jaws and the tusks were strongly downturned. These were the Miocene and Pliocene rhynchotheres, of which *Rhynchotherium* was characteristic. Some of the most remarkable of the long-jawed mastodonts were the so-called shovel tuskers of Pliocene age, *Amebelodon* of North America and *Platybelodon* of Asia. In these mastodonts the lower tusks became very broad instead of having the primitive round cross-section, so that they literally formed huge scoops or shovels on the front of the jaws. Presumably these shovels were used for digging up plants, perhaps from the bottom of shallow waters.

While the long-jawed mastodonts were evolving there was a second and independent evolutionary line of short-jawed mastodonts, that from the outset of their history had virtually tuskless lower jaws. These mastodonts, perhaps arising from a *Palaeomastodon* type of ancestor, evolved as the Miocene *Miomastodon*, the Pliocene *Pliomastodon* and its relatives, and the Pleistocene *Mastodon* (which according to the rules of zoological nomenclature should be called *Mammut*, but almost never is). The American mastodon, *Mastodon americanus*, is one of the best known of fossil vertebrates, for its remains have been found in great abundance throughout most of North America. This was a large proboscidean, not as tall as a large modern elephant, but heavily built. It had sharply cross-crested molars, as did all members of this line of mastodont evolution, and the upper tusks were large and strongly curved. The American mastodon persisted until the very end of Pleistocene times, and skeletons that show virtually no alteration of the bones have been found in swamp deposits. From soft materials preserved with some of the skeletons we know that this mastodont was covered with long, reddish-brown hair, and that it browsed upon the leaves of trees. There seems little doubt now that early man in America was contemporaneous with the mastodon, and recent methods of dating by Carbon 14 give conclusive proof that mastodons were living on this continent about eight thousand years ago. Sometime after the entry of early man into North America, but several thousand years before the coming of white men, the mastodon became extinct. Why, we do not know.

THE ELEPHANTS

An evolutionary line derived from the Miocene trilophodonts was that of the stegolophodonts, named from the late Cenozoic genus *Stegolophodon*. These were proboscideans intermediate in structure and position between the long-jawed mastodonts on the one hand

and the primitive elephants on the other. In *Stegolophodon* the lower
jaw was shortened, the upper tusks were large, and the molar teeth
were cross-crested, the crests being formed by a sort of breaking up
of the original large mastodont cones into conelets, arranged in transverse rows across the tooth. Correlated with this development of
cross-crests was the lengthening of the molar teeth and the multiplication in the number of crests, to four in the intermediate molars
and as many as six in the third molars. These events took place in
Eurasia during late Miocene and early Pliocene times.

From the stegolophodonts it was but a short evolutionary step
to *Stegodon*, representative of the first elephants. The stegodonts,
appearing in the Old World in late Pliocene times and continuing
into the Pleistocene epoch, were large, very long-legged animals,
in which the skull was deep, the upper tusks very long and curved,
the lower jaw short and tuskless, and the molar teeth greatly elongated, with numerous low cross-crests on each molar crown. Indeed
there were as many as twelve or thirteen crests in the third molars
of some of the advanced stegodonts.

The elongation of the cheek teeth in *Stegodon* introduced a problem
with regard to the arrangement of the teeth within the skull and the
lower jaws, and the matter of tooth succession. In many of the
earlier mastodonts the teeth were arranged in longitudinal rows, with
all the premolars and all the molars in place at once. As proboscidean teeth became larger, two evolutionary alternatives were possible
for the accommodation of the teeth. Either the skull and the lower
jaw could become very long, to take care of a series of long teeth, one
behind the other, or the tooth succession could be altered so that
only a few teeth were in place at one time. The advanced mastodonts, the stegodonts, and the elephants developed in the second way.
In these highly specialized proboscideans the cheek teeth come into
use one or two at a time. The skull and the jaw are greatly deepened,
and the teeth are formed behind and above the tooth sockets in
the skull, and behind and somewhat below the sockets in the lower
jaw. Then the teeth push forward into place; as the back teeth push
ahead, the teeth in front of them are shoved forward in the jaws,
where they finally break away at the front and disappear. This
specialization reaches an extreme in the Pleistocene mammoths and
the modern elephants.

The step from *Stegodon* to the mammoths and recent elephants
included a remarkable growth in the height of the cheek-tooth crowns.
The ridges of the *Stegodon* teeth became increasingly higher, and
compressed together from front to back, until in the elephants they

took the form of tall, parallel plates, rather than V-shaped ridges. Thus the tall grinding teeth of the most advanced proboscideans came into being.

This process of transformation of the cheek teeth from low-crowned into very tall teeth was remarkably fast in the geologic sense. The stegodonts and the first true elephants of lower Pleistocene times had low teeth, and before the end of this geologic epoch, spanning a time lapse of perhaps less than a million years, the change had taken place. Elephants and men are mammals that show an appreciable amount of evolutionary development during Pleistocene times.

The Pleistocene or the great Ice Age was the age of mammoths (which is the name commonly applied to extinct elephants) on all the continents except South America. These giant mammals wandered far and wide across Eurasia, Africa, and North America, being immigrants into this continent from the Old World. There were various species of mammoths; one group was related to the modern Asiatic elephant, *Elephas,* another to the modern African elephant, *Loxodonta.*

One of the largest of the mammoths was the great imperial mammoth that lived in North America, and attained shoulder heights of fourteen feet or more. Perhaps the best known of the mammoths was the woolly mammoth, living until the very end of Pleistocene times in northern Eurasia and North America. This mammoth was well known to ancient Stone Age man in Europe, and he drew pictures of it on the walls of caves. Within the last century several carcasses of the woolly mammoth have been found frozen in the ice, in Siberia and Alaska. From this evidence we know that the woolly mammoth was covered by a dense coat of hair, enabling it to live in an arctic climate.

Man has lived with mammoths and elephants during the course of his evolutionary history. To the earliest men living in Eurasia and Africa the giant mammoths must have been truly fearsome beasts, against which there was little protection. But as man evolved and became a tool and weapon maker, he also became a hunter of mammoths. Numerous discoveries in Europe show that Stone Age man pursued the mammoths, prevailing against these giant beasts by the use of guile and well-conceived strategy. Mammoths were frequently trapped in deep pits, where they could be stoned to death, or killed with heavy deadfalls. And when man came from Asia into the New World he found mammoths on this continent, to be hunted and killed. There is definite evidence to show that early men in

America hunted mammoths, perhaps as recently as eight or ten thousand years ago.

Various species of mammoths lived until the very end of the Pleistocene epoch. Then they became extinct, and only two proboscideans, the African and Asiatic elephants, survived into modern times. Primitive men in our present-day world are still elephant hunters, but with the rise of Old World civilizations man became the master of the elephants instead of their foe. For several thousand years elephants have been caught and domesticated, and they have played no little part in the rise and spread of culture in Asia and the Middle East. These great mammals are remarkably docile, once they have been kept in captivity for a while, and because of their long life and their great strength they have been very useful servants of man. Elephants are now being displaced by the gasoline engine, and their use as work animals has been greatly restricted. However, modern man is a lover of elephants, and it is probable that he will do his best to see that these noble mammals do not disappear from the face of the earth.

Why did the mammoths become extinct? This question, like so many of the questions having to do with problems of extinction, is extremely difficult to answer. In fact, it is probable that we shall never know the real reason for the disappearance of mammoths a few thousand years ago, after their successful reign through Pleistocene time. Very likely the extinction of the mammoths was the result of complex causes. Man may have had something to do with it, but we can hardly believe that primitive men were of prime importance in bringing an end to these numerous, widely distributed, and gigantic mammals. It seems possible that factors of which we have little inkling at the present time brought about the disappearance of the mammoths, and that these or similar factors may be operating at the present time to cause the eventual extinction of the two remaining species of elephants.

THE BARYTHERES

Barytherium inhabited Egypt during late Eocene times. This animal, imperfectly known from the lower jaw and some limb bones, had a general proboscidean appearance, and for this reason it is tentatively placed in the Proboscidea. It is so poorly known at the present time, a single genus, based upon incomplete fossils and without antecedents or descendants, that it is of little paleontological significance.

Cenozoic
Landscape

30 · The Age of Mammals

THE ADVENT OF THE CENOZOIC ERA

With the transition from the Age of Reptiles into the Age of Mammals, the world entered the modern phase of its geologic history. The relationships of the continents to each other became essentially what they are today, with a trans-Bering connection between Asia and North America, an isthmian link between North and South America, and a Middle East connection between Eurasia and Africa. Australia, which had been a part of Asia during Mesozoic times, became completely isolated, to remain from then until now an island continent.

The establishment of modern continental connections was to a large degree the result of uplifts that began in late Cretaceous times. Continental areas, which had been low and partially inundated by shallow seas during middle and late Mesozoic times, were lifted to new heights during late Cretaceous and early Cenozoic history. There were broad recessions of the shallow seas, and, what is particularly important, the modern mountain systems were born. This was the time of the initial uplift of the Alps and of the Himalaya chains in the Old World, of the Rocky Mountain and of the Andean chains in the New World. It was the beginning of a long period of mountain-making that is actively continuing at the present day.

The delineation of modern continents, the uplift of great land masses, and the rise of mountain systems were accompanied by the beginning of world-wide climatic changes, of the utmost importance to the evolution of life during the last seventy million years. In middle and late Mesozoic times much of the world was tropical and subtropical. Uniform temperatures, with but slight seasonal changes, ranged from the equator into very high latitudes, so that tropical plants and dinosaurs lived from northern Eurasia and Canada to the tips of the southern continents and to Australia. As the continents were uplifted and the new mountain systems began to grow, there were gradual alterations of world environments in the direction of increased variety and differences. Climatic zones became established, and as time went on they became ever more sharply defined from each other. The alternation of seasons became more marked, especially in the higher latitudes, so that cold winters followed hot summers, year in and year out. These changes took place gradually during Cenozoic times, to culminate in the extreme climatic conditions of the great Ice Age, in one phase of which we are now living.

Of course such profound changes in world climates brought about changes in the plant life of the globe. Even before the close of the Cretaceous period the modern deciduous trees had made their appearance, to lend much botanical variety to landscapes. Forests, which in previous ages had consisted of ancient tree ferns and various conifers, were freshened by the variegated shapes and leaf patterns of oaks, willows, sassafras, and other trees quite familiar to us. And with the progression of the Cenozoic era flowering plants and grasses evolved, thereby introducing new habitats for the development of animal life. Green savannas and broad prairies spread across large continental areas, to provide the setting in which the many hoofed mammals of Cenozoic times lived, in a long succession of complex faunas.

Continental uplifts and the rise of new mountain systems, the diversification of climates, and the evolution and spread of the flowering plants were all factors that affected the evolution of animal life on the earth. These events together, probably with the interaction of other factors of which we have no knowledge, resulted in the extinction of the dominant reptiles, including the great dinosaurs, at the close of the Cretaceous period and cleared the way for the rise and the profuse radiation of the mammals. To the student of vertebrate evolution, the change from reptilian dominance in the Cretaceous period to mammalian dominance in the Tertiary period was one of the great events in the history of life on the earth.

The changes briefly outlined above affected continents and life on the continents. Parallel with these transformations that took place during the Mesozoic to Cenozoic transition there were changes in the waters as well. It follows that, as tropical conditions became restricted to the equatorial belt, there would be changes in the temperatures of the oceans. The warm seas, which we know lapped the shores of northern and southern lands during Mesozoic times, gradually contracted to the middle region of the earth, and cold seas spread through the latitudes toward the poles. Perhaps these changes had not set in at the close of the Cretaceous period, but it is significant that during the transition the numerous and widely distributed marine reptiles of late Mesozoic times disappeared from the waters of the earth, just as the dinosaurs became extinct on land. With the advent of the Tertiary period there were no more plesiosaurs, ichthyosaurs, or mosasaurs. The gaps created by their disappearance were filled by new animals, especially the whales.

Even before the close of Cretaceous history the bony fishes had enjoyed a long period of diverse adaptive radiation, during which time they became the most numerous and varied of the aquatic vertebrates. Their development continued into Tertiary times, and indeed has carried on to the present day. The bony fishes are supreme in the waters, and as has been pointed out earlier in this book, they far outnumber all other vertebrates in variety, in numbers of genera and species, and in numbers of individuals. We live in the Age of Bony Fishes, as well as the Age of Mammals.

THE DEVELOPMENT OF CENOZOIC FAUNAS

Our record of the succession of Cenozoic mammals is much more complete than the comparable records for late Paleozoic and Mesozoic amphibians and reptiles. There are several reasons why this should be so. Perhaps the most important one is that Cenozoic continental sediments have suffered less destruction and on the whole are more completely preserved than the continental deposits of Paleo-

zoic and Mesozoic age; therefore a larger proportion of the actual
fossil record of Cenozoic mammals has been preserved than of the
earlier land-living vertebrates. For instance, the sequence of mammalian faunas ranging from the lower Paleocene to the end of the
Pleistocene in North America gives a reasonably continuous story of
the changing assemblages of mammals through time on this continent. Compare this succession of faunas with the record of Jurassic
land-living vertebrates, a record so incomplete that most of our
knowledge about Jurassic dinosaurs and other land-living reptiles is
gained from faunas of late Jurassic age.

Another factor that contributes to our superior knowledge of Cenozoic mammal faunas, as compared with earlier tetrapod faunas, is
the nature of the fossils themselves. Because of the complexity of
their teeth, and because teeth are hard and more frequently preserved than other parts, fossil mammals may be studied from the
teeth alone (although of course every effort is always made to base
studies of mammals on as complete materials as can be obtained).
With reptiles, on the other hand, it is frequently impossible to make
any significant conclusions or to attempt comprehensive faunal studies without more complete material—at least partial skulls or fragmentary skeletons.

Again, the fossils of Cenozoic mammals are generally much more
abundant than the fossils of Paleozoic and Mesozoic amphibians and
reptiles.

In broad terms, the succession of Cenozoic mammalian faunas may
be grouped into four major events.

1. In the first place, there was the initial faunal radiation of Paleocene and Eocene times. This was the period of archaic faunas, and
of the dominance of mammalian groups that failed to survive into
later times.

2. Second, there was a replacement (except in South America) of
the archaic faunas of the Paleocene and Eocene epochs by the ancestors of the modern mammals. This was a phenomenon of late
Eocene and Oligocene times.

3. During later Cenozoic times there was a modernization of faunas, a process that extended over many millions of years to produce
the advanced, specialized mammals of the modern world.

4. Finally there was the establishment of present-day faunas, a
process taking place in Pleistocene and "post-Pleistocene" times. The
bases for our contemporary faunas were set by the emergence of
faunal assemblages during the Pleistocene period. But the final

event that gave a contemporary complexion to the mammalian faunas of the world, making them distinct from the strictly Pleistocene faunas, was a wave of extinction that took place within the last few thousand years. It brought an end to many of the larger Pleistocene mammals, so that our modern faunas are impoverished relics of the rich Pleistocene faunas.

The initial radiation of archaic mammals was the distinctive zoological phenomenon of early Tertiary times. Insectivores and early marsupials had already lived for millions of years in association with the dinosaurs. Now the niches occupied by the dinosaurs were vacated, and various mammals, derived from insectivore or marsupial ancestors, quickly grew up to occupy these vacancies. Archaic hoofed mammals, condylarths, amblypods, uintatheres, and the like took over the rôle of large plant-eaters, and the varied creodonts were the predators that hunted them. In South America the notoungulates, litopterns, and astrapotheres became the herbivores, and the function of predatory carnivores was taken over by the marsupials.

These last-named faunal relationships were maintained through much of Cenozoic times in South America. In the other continents, however, the archaic ungulates and the creodonts were replaced during late Eocene and Oligocene times by the perissodactyls, the artiodactyls, and the proboscideans, and by the fissiped carnivores, whereas the faunas were enriched by the development of the rodents, the primates,. and the bats. (The whales and sea cows, having returned to the water, are elements of a separate story.) Thus the bases for modern faunal groups were established.

As time passed during the latter portion of the Cenozoic era, the hoofed mammals and the carnivores, the rodents, primates, and other lesser groups became increasingly specialized toward their modern state. Three-toed horses gradually evolved into single-toed horses; ancient deer disappeared as they were replaced by their descendants, the modern deer; primitive dogs grew into modern wolves, foxes, and the like. The details have already been set forth in several chapters preceding this one.

So it was that with the advent of the Pleistocene epoch the mammalian faunas of the world were essentially modern in their aspect, but much richer than they now are. They contained numerous mammoths and mastodons, woolly rhinoceroses, giant ground sloths and glyptodonts, varied giraffes, and so on. If these mammals had continued into modern times this would indeed be an interesting world for explorers and for visitors to zoological parks. But they didn't.

And the domination of the land, that for ages had been shared by many large mammals, was taken over by a single species, man.

INTERCONTINENTAL MIGRATIONS IN CENOZOIC TIMES

As mammals evolved during Cenozoic times they frequently wandered back and forth from one continent to another. These intercontinental migrations, and in many cases the lack of such migrations, were of great importance in determining the composition of faunas in the several continental regions. For instance, various factors, particularly those of ecological relationships, prevented many mammals from migrating freely from one continental region to another, and these sedentary animals gave to the fauna of a particular region its distinctive characters. On the other hand, some mammals, especially the larger ungulates and carnivores, roamed widely, and their migrations led to faunal resemblances over wide expanses of land surface.

One of the striking features of Cenozoic mammalian faunas was the general unity of the animals living in the great circumpolar land mass of Europe, northern Asia and North America. Through much of Cenozoic times there was a land bridge in the Bering region, across which mammals migrated east and west. Therefore, it is not surprising that Tertiary and Pleistocene faunas of northern Eurasia and North America show many resemblances, a condition that is reflected in the modern faunas of this region. The north circumpolar land mass is recognized, on the basis of the distribution of modern mammals, as a major zoogeographical region, the great Holarctic Region, and it is probable that the faunal relationships characteristic of this region extended back through time to the beginning of the Tertiary period.

Primates appeared at an early date in the faunas of the Holarctic Region, but after a brief sojourn in this area they disappeared, to evolve in other parts of the world. However, many of the major groups of mammals did evolve through Cenozoic times in the Holarctic Region, particularly the creodonts, most of the fissiped carnivores, the proboscideans, the perissodactyls, and the artiodactyls. The wide distribution of most of these mammals gave to the Holarctic faunas their community of appearance.

At the present time the fauna of southeastern Asia is distinct from that of northern Asia, and is thereby designated as the Oriental fauna, characteristic of the Oriental Region of zoogeography. In the modern Oriental Region primates are prominent elements in the local faunas. Carnivores are well represented, and include viverrids and hyenas, which are now largely absent from the Holarctic Region. Likewise the Oriental Region is typified by elephants, tapirs, rhinoceroses, and many artiodactyls. The differences whereby the modern Oriental fauna is distinguished from the Holarctic fauna are in large part the result of mountain uplifts, of the raising of the Himalaya chain and of the mountains that separate northern and southern China, to form high barriers that have prevented animals from wandering north and south in Asia.

The Himalayan and related uplifts did not constitute the formidable barriers to migrations in the early and middle parts of the era that they do at the present time. Consequently there was a considerable flow of mammals in and out of the Oriental Region during much of Cenozoic history. Horses erupted from North America and made their way into India and China in great numbers. Bears, which arose in India, made the long trek into North America. The pandas, which we think of as Oriental mammals, wandered as far west as England. And many other similar cases of migrations into and out of the Orient might be cited.

Africa is still another major zoogeographic region in the modern system of classification. This, the Ethiopian Region, includes the continent south of the Atlas Mountains and the Sahara. During much of Cenozoic time the Mediterranean Sea was contracted as compared with its present extent, so that there were avenues for the migration of mammals north and south between Africa and Europe. Also mammals pushed back and forth between Africa and the Oriental Region. Indeed, much of the modern African fauna of artiodactyls represents an influx into that continent of animals that lived in southern Europe and the Orient during late Pliocene and Pleistocene times. In the Ethiopian Region primates were prominent during Cenozoic times, and it was here that some of the very advanced man-like apes arose. Creodonts were present in early Tertiary times, and most of the carnivores were prominent in later faunas. However, bears and deer never reached Africa. Proboscideans, perissodactyls, and artiodactyls were important in the development of African faunas, as they were in the Orient. The distinct characters of modern African faunas is the result in part of animals being present in the Ethiopian Region that have become extinct elsewhere, frequently within the last few thousand years. For instance, spotted hyenas, elephants, hippopotamuses, various antelopes, the aardvark, and other animals, now characteristically African, lived in Europe or Asia during very late Pleistocene times.

Two zoogeographic regions of continental extent were isolated from the rest of the world during much of the Cenozoic era. They are the Neotropical Region, consisting of South America and part of Central America, and the Australian Region, consisting of Australia, New Guinea, and certain other islands. The Neotropical Region, as we have seen, was connected to North America at the beginning of the Tertiary period, after which it was completely isolated until the end of Tertiary times. The Australian Region has been isolated from Asia since the close of Cretaceous times.

This isolation contributed to the very distinct faunas of these two regions. During much of Cenozoic history the Neotropical fauna consisted to a large degree of ungulates unique to that region, carnivorous marsupials, and edentates. Primates appeared in the Neotropical faunas during Tertiary times; just how it is difficult to say. Then at the close of the Tertiary period there was a great influx of Holarctic mammals into this region, to give the Neotropical fauna its modern cast—that of a mixture of ancient survivors and recent immigrants.

The isolation of Australia was complete, and Cenozoic history in that region was a period of marsupial radiation. The only placentals in the Australian Region before the coming of man were bats and rodents. Since his arrival, man has introduced various placental mammals into Australia, much to the detriment of the native marsupials.

THE DISTRIBUTION OF CENOZOIC VERTEBRATE FAUNAS

Most of our knowledge of the earliest Cenozoic faunas comes from the Paleocene of North America, the only region, in fact, where the continental Paleocene is reasonably well represented by fossil mammals. In New Mexico are the Puerco and Torrejon faunas, the classic mammalian assemblages of early and middle Paleocene age, respectively; in Utah is the Dragon fauna, intermediate in age between the New Mexican assemblages. In Wyoming and Colorado are the Clark Fork and Tiffany faunas, representing the upper Paleocene. Thus a sequence through the Paleocene can be established by the study of these faunas, and some idea as to the course of evolution during this phase of earth history may be obtained.

The Paleocene is poorly represented in other parts of the world. Mammals of late Paleocene age are found in the Cernay deposits of France, in the Gashato formation of Mongolia, and in the Rio Chico beds of Patagonia.

When we reach the Eocene, the record is much more abundant. Numerous Eocene faunas are now known from North America and Europe, and in Asia and South America certain portions of the Eocene are well represented by fossil faunas. In western North America the sequence runs from the so-called Wasatch faunas of early Eocene age through the Bridger faunas of middle Eocene age to the Uinta and Duchesne River faunas of the late Eocene. The Green River formation of middle Eocene age contains an abundant and very important fish fauna. The parallel series in Europe ranges from the London Clay of England and several lower Eocene faunas found in France, through the middle Eocene calcaire grossier and other contemporaneous faunas of France, to the gypsum beds of Montmartre and the lower portion of the Quercy phosphorites, of late Eocene age. In Italy there is an interesting fish fauna of middle Eocene age, the Monte Bolca fauna.

Only the upper portion of the Eocene record is known from Asia, but here are several faunas of great importance. They are the Irdin Manha and Shara Murun faunas discovered and collected by the Central Asiatic Expeditions of the American Museum of Natural History, and the Pondaung fauna of Burma. In northern Africa are the upper Eocene Birket-el-Qurun beds and Qasr-el-Sagha beds of the Fayûm district of Egypt that have yielded the most primitive known proboscideans and sirenians.

In South America the early stages in the history of the unique faunas of that continent are found in sediments of early and middle Eocene age, namely, the Casa Mayor beds below and the Musters beds above.

One of the most picturesque and best-known Oligocene series in the world is found in the famous White River badlands of South Dakota. Here the entire Oligocene sequence is represented by the Chadron formation or "titanothere beds" of early Oligocene age, and the Brulé formation or "oreodon beds" of middle and late Oligocene age. The lower portion of the Brulé, the Orella member, represents the middle Oligocene; the upper portion, the Whitney member, represents the upper Oligocene in the White River area.

In France the Quercy phosphorites continue from the upper Eocene into the Oligocene, the lower portion of which is especially well represented by the Ronzon fauna. In Asia the lower Oligocene is represented by the Ardyn Obo fauna, the middle Oligocene by the Houldjin fauna, and the upper Oligocene by the Hsanda Gol fauna, all of which are in Mongolia. The early Tertiary sediments of North Africa continue into the lower portion of the Oligocene period, where in the Fayûm the first long-jawed mastodonts are found. South America at present has a record of lower and upper Oligocene continental sediments, with a middle Oligocene break—perhaps an imperfection of the geologic record. In Patagonia the lower Oligocene sediments are the Deseado beds, and the upper Oligocene sediments are the Colhué Huapi beds. In these beds are found fossils that show the progressive development of the South American mammals along their particular lines of evolutionary development, so different from what is seen in faunas on other continents.

The Miocene and Pliocene of North America are abundantly represented by numerous rich faunas, many of which have been discovered during the last two or three decades and are as yet not completely studied or described. They give a hint as to the abundance of life on this continent during middle and late Tertiary times, when mammals were beginning to assume, through the long processes of evolution, their modern form. The lower Miocene faunas worthy of special notice are those of the Gering, Monroe Creek, and Lower Harrison formations, belonging to the Arikaree group, all found in western Nebraska and South Dakota, and of the John Day formation of Oregon. Of middle Miocene age are the Sheep Creek and Marsland faunas of Nebraska, and the Hawthorn formation of Florida; the upper Miocene is represented by the Pawnee Creek fauna of Colorado, the Mascall fauna of Oregon, and the Barstow fauna of California.

Europe is likewise rich in faunas of Miocene and Pliocene age. Here are found the St. Gerand-le-Puy fauna of lower Miocene relationships, the Sansan, Simorre, Grive St. Alban, St. Gaudens, Steinheim, and Oeningen faunas of middle Miocene age, and the upper Miocene Sebastopol fauna. In Baluchistan are the lower Miocene Bugti beds, in which are found the fossils of the giant rhinoceros *Baluchitherium*. The Loh formation represents the lower Miocene in Mongolia, and the Tung Gur formation is the upper Miocene horizon in this part of Asia. In India are the Kamlial beds, the initial sediments of the Siwalik series, which forms a most important and thick sequence of mammal-bearing sediments along the lower flanks of the Himalaya uplift.

One of the most famous mammalian faunas of the Miocene is the Santa Cruz assemblage of South America. This fauna, representing a high point in the development of the mammals in South America, can be regarded as of early Miocene age.

The history of mammalian evolution in North America is carried into the Pliocene by the Clarendon fauna of Texas, the Santa Fe fauna of New Mexico, and the Valentine fauna of Nebraska. Of middle Pliocene age are the Rattlesnake, Hemphill, and Ash Hollow faunas of various western states, whereas the Benson, Hagerman, and possibly the Blanco faunas bring the Pliocene to a close in western North America. (The Blanco fauna, regarded by many students as of late Pliocene affinities, may be more intimately related to Pleistocene history than to the close of the Pliocene sequence.) In Florida the middle Pliocene is represented by the fauna of the Alachua clays.

The lower Pliocene of Eurasia is the time of the Pontian fauna, when the horse *Hipparion*, having entered the Old World from North America, spread widely through the eastern part of the earth. Well-known Pontian faunas are those of Concud in Spain, Mt. Leberon in France, Eppelsheim in Germany, Pikermi in Greece, and the island of Samos in the eastern Mediterranean. The same faunal complex is continued in the Maragha beds of Persia and in the Chinji formation of the Siwalik series of India. The middle and upper Pliocene in France is continued by the Perpignan below and the Montpellier and Rousillon faunas above. In India the Nagri and the Dhok Pathan faunas, continuing the Siwalik sequence above the Chinji stage, represent part or perhaps all of the Pliocene above the Pontian.

The Pliocene is present in South America as a series of fossil-bearing formations known as the Mesopotamian beds of early Pliocene age, the Monte Hermosa beds of middle Pliocene age, and the Chapadmalal beds of late Pliocene age.

Finally we come to a consideration of the Pleistocene mammalian faunas. They usually can be identified as of Pleistocene age, but often it is not easy to determine to which portion of the Pleistocene epoch they should be assigned. The Pleistocene was a relatively short period of time, and for the most part the evolution of mammals was not very great during this phase of geologic history. Moreover, the deposition of Pleistocene sediments, frequently as river terraces or river gravels, makes their age determination difficult. Finally, some Pleistocene faunas are known from cave deposits, and many of these are almost impossible to date within the Pleistocene.

The Pleistocene epoch opened with the appearance of the Villafranchian fauna of Europe, a mammalian assemblage containing the horse *Equus* (an immigrant from North America), cattle of the *Bos* type, and mammoths of the *Elephas* type, these last two of Old

CORRELATION OF CENOZOIC VERTEBRATE-BEARING SEDIMENTS

Epoch		South America	North America			Europe	Asia		Africa
Pleistocene		Pampean		Rancho la Brea / Hay Springs / Broadwater		Caves, Terraces / Perrier / Val d'Arno (Villafranchian)	Caves, Terraces / Irrawaddy / Pinjor		Caves, Terraces / Oldoway
Pliocene	U	Chapadmalal	Blanco	Rexroad	Hagerman	Rousillon / Montpellier	Tatrot		
	M	Monte Hermosa / Tunuya	Hemphill	Ash Hollow / Rattlesnake	Santa Fe / Alachua	Perpignan	Dhok Pathan		Wadi Natrûn
	L	Huayqueria	Clarendon	Valentine / Ricardo	Goliad	Concud / Vallés-Penedés / Mt. Leberon / Eppelsheim / Pikermi, Samos	Nagri / Chinji	Maragha	
Miocene	U	Mesopotamia	Barstow	Pawnee Creek / Mascall		Sebastopol	Kamlial	Tung Gur	
	M	Chasico / Rio Frias	Hemingford	Sheep Creek / Marsland	Hawthorn	Vallés-Penedés / Sansan / Simorre / Grive St. Alban / Steinheim			Moghara
	L	Santa Cruz	Arikaree	Harrison / Monroe Creek / Gering	Oakville / Thomas Farm / John Day	Vallés-Penedés / St. Gerand-le-Puy / Orléans	Bugti	Loh	Namib

Epoch		South America	North America	North America	Europe	Asia	Africa
Oligocene	U	Colhué Huapi	Brulé	Whitney	La Rochette / Mainz	Hsanda Gol	
	M			Orella	Quercy	Houldjin	
	L	Deseado	Chadron		Aveyron / Weinheim	Ardyn Obo	Upper Fayûm
Eocene	U	Musters	Duchesne River / Uinta	Washakie	Ronzon / Hampstead; Montmartre gypsum / Isle of Wight	Shara Murun; Irdin Manha; Pondaung	Qasr-el-Sagha
	M		Bridger	Green River	Calcaire grossier / Issel / Monte Bolca		Birket-el-Qurun
	L	Casa Mayor	Wasatch	San José	London Clay		
Paleocene	U	Rio Chico	Clark Fork / Tiffany	Fort Union	Thanet / Cernay	Gashato	
	M		Torrejon				
	L		Dragon / Puerco				

World origin. The spread of these diagnostic mammals may be
accepted as indicating the advent of the Pleistocene in most parts of
the world, except South America and Australia. Other mammals of
North American origin invaded South America at the opening of the
Pleistocene epoch; Australia, of course, remained isolated as it had
been during Tertiary times.

A few of the particularly significant Pleistocene faunas might be
mentioned at this place. In addition to the lower Pleistocene Villafranchian fauna, there are found in Europe the Perrier fauna of
France, the Crag faunas of the North Sea coast of England, and
various cave and river terrace faunas. In Asia the Siwalik series is
continued by the Pinjor fauna, of early Pleistocene age, and the upper
Irrawaddy fauna of Burma is generally correlative with the Pinjor
assemblage. Various cave faunas from western and southern China
are of middle Pleistocene age. Africa is also characterized by cave
faunas, some of which have in recent years yielded important fossils
of primitive man-like primates. The Oldoway fauna of Africa is a
middle Pleistocene assemblage that can be related to contemporaneous faunas in Asia. In North America are the lower Pleistocene
faunas of Broadwater and Hay Springs, Nebraska. Of later age are
various cave and swamp deposits containing fossil mammals, and the
famous tar pits of Rancho la Brea, California. The abundant Pam-
pean fauna of South America is the last in the sequence of mammalian faunas on that continent, before the establishment of modern
faunas.

THE CORRELATION OF FAUNAS

The problem of correlation can be difficult, especially from one
continent to another. It is not always clear as to whether comparable faunas are exactly comparable in age, and many correlations
must be accepted as tentative and approximate rather than as abso-
lute. However, if these considerations are kept in mind, the various
faunas of the Cenozoic can be correlated rather satisfactorily.

Europe was a series of islands during much of Cenozoic times, so
that marine deposits containing the shells of invertebrates and continental deposits containing fossil mammals are frequently contigu-
ous or even interfingered with one another. Therefore, it has been
possible to build up a series of European age names, based on the
marine succession, and to tie the continental sediments into this
sequence.

Because of the unity of the Holarctic Region during the Cenozoic
era, the North American faunas can be related upon the basis of

many resemblances to the standard European succession. But since the North American sequence of mammalian faunas is unusually complete, American paleontologists have in recent years set up an age sequence for this continent, based upon the outstanding mammalian faunas. The Asiatic and African faunas are fitted into the Cenozoic sequence upon the basis of faunal resemblances, and there is good reason to believe that these faunas have been correlated with a fair degree of accuracy.

However, the problem of the South American faunas is separate and difficult, because these faunas evolved in isolation from the rest of the world and therefore cannot be directly related to the well-known faunas of North America and Eurasia. Correlations of the South American faunas consequently must be based upon varied lines of evidence, geologic as well as paleontologic, and at best many of them must be regarded as of a tentative nature.

The general aspect of the correlation of Cenozoic mammal faunas, as discussed in the foregoing pages, is set forth by the accompanying correlation chart. Perhaps this will help to make clear the relationships of the numerous faunas on which our knowledge of the Age of Mammals has been erected.

A Classification of the Chordates

This classification is intended to assist the reader in maintaining his orientation among the orders and lesser categories of the vertebrates. For this reason it is not a comprehensive classification, but rather a synoptic outline, in which the larger relationships are emphasized. With this in mind the classification is not carried down below the grade of families, and in many orders it is not carried down that far, for it is felt that such unequal emphasis will make the system of the greatest practical use to the reader of this book. As a further attempt to emphasize the larger relationships that are of particular importance in a book like this, genera have not been included in the classification. However, there is a list of genera at the end of the book, and each genus is designated by a letter and a number, or a series of letters and numbers that correspond to the letters and numbers given to orders and lesser categories in the classification. The reader can thereby refer back to the classification by use of these symbols, to place any particular genus in its proper position.

For more comprehensive classifications the reader is referred to certain textbooks listed in the bibliography of this book. Perhaps the best usable classification of the fishes is to be found in the book by Berg. For the amphibians and reptiles, the reader is referred to Romer's *Vertebrate Paleontology,* and for the reptiles alone to his new *Osteology of the Reptiles.* A modern classification of the birds is the paper by Mayr and Amadon. The mammals have been thoroughly treated by Simpson in his *Classification of the Mammals.* Finally, Romer's *Vertebrate Paleontology* gives what is perhaps the best comprehensive classification of all the vertebrates.

In the classification presented here, the classes of vertebrates are indicated by certain capital letters, thus:

A—Agnatha.
P—Placodermi.
C—Chondrichthyes.
O—Osteichthyes.
B—Amphibia.
R—Reptilia.

X—Aves.

M—Mammalia.

Letters and numbers are assigned to orders and lesser units down to families, as follows:

Order—Arabic numerals.

Suborder—capital letters.

Superfamily—small Roman numerals.

Family—lower-case letters.

PHYLUM CHORDATA

The Chordates

Subphylum Hemichordata: *Balanoglossus.*

Subphylum Cephalochordata: *Amphioxus.*

Subphylum Urochordata: sea squirts.

Subphylum Vertebrata: the vertebrates.

A. Class Agnatha: the jawless fishes.
   Subclass Cephalaspidomorpha: a dorsal nostril, between the eyes.
   1. Order Cyclostomata: secondarily cartilaginous—the modern lamprey and the hagfishes.
   2. Order Cephalaspida: armored ostracoderms, with a flattened head shield.
   3. Order Anaspida: small, armored, deep-bodied ostracoderms.
   Subclass Pteraspidomorpha: no dorsal nostril.
   4. Order Pteraspida: ostracoderms with a head shield of large plates.
   5. Order Coelolepida: ostracoderms without armor, denticles covering the body.
P. Class Placodermi: early jawed fishes, mostly heavily armored. All of these became extinct.
   1. Order Acanthodii: spiny fishes.
   2. Order Arthrodira: armored fishes with jointed necks.
   3. Order Macropetalichthyida: armored fishes related to arthrodires.
   4. Order Antiarchi: small, armored fishes, with jointed, movable pectoral spines.
   5. Order Stegoselachii: "skate-like" placoderms.
   6. Order Palaeospondyloidea: *Palaeospondylus,* an enigmatic form.
C. Class Chondrichthyes: cartilaginous fishes, the broad category of sharks.
   Subclass Elasmobranchii: the sharks.
   1. Order Cladoselachii: ancient sharks, ancestral to the later sharks.
   2. Order Pleuracanthodii: early fresh-water sharks.
   3. Order Selachii: the familiar marine sharks.
   4. Order Batoidea: skates and rays.
   Subclass Holocephali: shark-like fishes.
   5. Order Bradyodonti: late Paleozoic fishes with strong tooth-plates.
   6. Order Chimaerae: the chimaeras or ratfish.

O. **Class Osteichthyes:** the bony fishes.

Subclass Actinopterygii: the ray-finned fishes.

Superorder Chondrostei: primitive ray-finned fishes.

1. Order Palaeoniscoidea: ancestral ray-finned fishes.
2. Order Polypterini: surviving palaeoniscoid types living in Africa.
3. Order Acipenseroidei: represented today by the sturgeon and paddlefish.
4. Order Subholostei: varied, advanced chondrosteans.

Superorder Holostei: intermediate ray-finned fishes.

5. Order Semionotoidea: early holosteans.
6. Order Pycnodontoidea: deep-bodied holosteans.
7. Order Amioidea: the central holostean group; the surviving bowfin.
8. Order Aspidorhynchoidea: heavily scaled, elongated holosteans.
9. Order Pholidophoroidea: advanced holosteans, approaching the teleosts.

Superorder Teleostei: the culminating bony fishes.

10. Order Isospondyli: the most primitive teleosts. Salmon, etc.
11. Order Ostariophysi: characins, carp, catfishes.
12. Order Apodes: the true eels.
13. Order Heteromi: certain deep-sea fishes.
14. Order Mesichthys: intermediate teleosts; pike, needlefishes.
15. Order Acanthopterygii: the spiny teleosts; a majority of the teleosts.

Subclass Choanichthyes: the lobe-finned or air-breathing fishes.

16. Order Dipnoi: the lungfishes.
17. Order Crossopterygii: progressive air-breathing fishes.
   A. Suborder Rhipidistia: ancestors of the first amphibians.
   B. Suborder Coelacanthini: predominantly marine crossopts; the surviving *Latimeria*.

B. **Class Amphibia:** the amphibians; the earliest tetrapods, or land-living vertebrates.

Subclass Apsidospondyli: vertebrae preformed in cartilage.

Superorder Labyrinthodontia: large, solid-skulled amphibians.

1. Order Ichthyostegalia: the ancestral labyrinthodonts.
2. Order Embolomeri: early labyrinthodonts evolving toward reptiles.
3. Order Rhachitomi: the culmination of labyrinthodont evolution.
4. Order Trematosauria: long-jawed, fish-eating labyrinthodonts.
5. Order Stereospondyli: last of the labyrinthodonts.

Superorder Salientia: frogs, toads and their ancestors.

6. Order Proanura: ancestors of the frogs and toads.
7. Order Anura: the frogs and toads.

Subclass Lepospondyli: vertebrae not preformed in cartilage.

8. Order Aistopoda: ancient, limbless lepospondyls.
9. Order Nectridia: varied lepospondyls.
10. Order Microsauria: small, early lepospondyls.
11. Order Urodela: salamanders and newts.
12. Order Apoda: coecilians; limbless amphibians of the tropics.

R. Class Reptilia: the reptiles; "cold-blooded" tetrapods with scaly or armored skins.

Subclass Anapsida: reptiles with a solid skull roof.

    1. Order Cotylosauria: the stem reptiles.

       A. Suborder Seymouriamorpha: ancestral reptiles, derived from labyrinthodonts.

       B. Suborder Captorhinomorpha: generally small, carnivorous cotylosaurs.

       C. Suborder Diadectomorpha: small to large, herbivorous cotylosaurs.

    2. Order Chelonia: turtles.

       A. Suborder Eunotosauria: early reptiles, possibly ancestral to turtles.

       B. Suborder Amphichelydia: the primitive turtles.

       C. Suborder Pleurodira: side-neck turtles.

       B. Suborder Cryptodira: vertical-neck turtles.

Subclass Synapsida: the mammal-like reptiles.

    3. Order Pelycosauria: early mammal-like reptiles.

       A. Suborder Ophiacodontia: primitive pelycosaurs.

       B. Suborder Sphenacodontia: large, carnivorous pelycosaurs.

       C. Suborder Edaphosauria: small to large herbivorous pelycosaurs.

    4. Order Therapsida: varied mammal-like reptiles.

       A. Suborder Anomodontia: small to large, heavy herbivorous therapsids.

          i. Superfamily Tapinocephaloidea: large, massive herbivores.

          ii. Superfamily Dicynodontoidea: beaked therapsids, tusks in males.

       B. Suborder Theriodontia: advanced, carnivorous therapsids.

          i. Superfamily Titanosuchoidea: large, heavy theriodonts.

          ii. Superfamily Gorgonopsoidea: primitive theriodonts.

          iii. Superfamily Therocephaloidea: early advanced theriodonts.

          iv. Superfamily Cynodontoidea: late advanced theriodonts.

       C. Suborder Ictidosauria: advanced mammal-like reptiles, close to mammals.

Subclass Synapsida (?)

    5. Order Mesosauria: very ancient aquatic reptiles.

Subclass Parapsida: the ocean-living, fish-like reptiles.

    6. Order Ichthyosauria: the ichthyosaurs.

Subclass Euryapsida: generally marine reptiles with large paddles; early primitive types lived on land.

    7. Order Protorosauria: agile, land-living euryapsids.

    8. Order Sauropterygia: shore-dwelling and marine forms.

       A. Suborder Nothosauria: small, primitive sauropterygians.

       B. Suborder Plesiosauria: the plesiosaurs; large, marine reptiles.

          i. Superfamily Pistosauroidea: ancestral plesiosaurs.

          ii. Superfamily Pliosauroidea: short-necked plesiosaurs.

          iii. Superfamily Plesiosauroidea: long-necked plesiosaurs.

       C. Suborder Placodontia: mollusk-eating sauropterygians.

Subclass Diapsida: the ruling reptiles.
Superorder Lepidosauria: primitive diapsids and their immediate descendants.
  9. Order Eosuchia: ancestral and early lepidosaurs.
  10. Order Rhynchocephalia: rhynchocephalians; the modern tuatera.
  11. Order Squamata: lizards and snakes.
      A. Suborder Lacertilia: lizards.
      B. Suborder Ophidia: snakes.
Superorder Archosauria: advanced diapsids.
  12. Order Thecodontia: ancestral archosaurians.
      A. Suborder Pseudosuchia: varied thecodonts, including primitive types.
      B. Suborder Phytosauria: crocodile-like thecodonts; phytosaurs.
  13. Order Crocodilia: the crocodilians.
      A. Suborder Protosuchia: ancestral crocodilians.
      B. Suborder Mesosuchia: dominant crocodilians of Mesozoic times.
      C. Suborder Thalattosuchia: marine crocodiles.
      D. Suborder Sebecosuchia: aberrant crocodilians of South America.
      E. Suborder Eusuchia: modern crocodilians; gavials, crocodiles, alligators.
  14. Order Pterosauria: the flying reptiles.
      A. Suborder Rhamphorhynchoidea: primitive pterosaurs.
      B. Suborder Pterodactyloidea: advanced pterosaurs.
  15. Order Saurischia: the saurischian dinosaurs.
      A. Suborder Theropoda: small to gigantic carnivorous dinosaurs.
          i. Superfamily Coeluroidea: small to medium-sized carnivores.
          ii. Superfamily Megalosauroidea: giant carnivores.
          iii. Superfamily Plateosauroidea: ancestors of sauropods.
      B. Suborder Sauropoda: gigantic, swamp-dwelling dinosaurs.
  16. Order Ornithischia: the ornithischian dinosaurs.
      A. Suborder Ornithopoda: duck-billed and related dinosaurs.
      B. Suborder Stegosauria: plated dinosaurs.
      C. Suborder Ankylosauria: armored dinosaurs.
      D. Suborder Ceratopsia: horned dinosaurs.
X. Class Aves: the birds; "warm-blooded" tetrapods with feathers.
Subclass Archaeornithes: primitive, toothed birds of Jurassic age.
  1. Order Archaeopteryges: *Archaeopteryx.*
Subclass Neornithes: post-Jurassic birds.
  2. Order Hesperornithes: *Hesperornis* and related genera of toothed birds.
  3. Order Ichthyornithes: *Ichthyornis* and related genera.
  4. Order Struthiones: the ostrich.
  5. Order Apteryges: moas and kiwis.
  6. Order Aepyornithes: elephant birds.
  7. Order Casuarii: cassowaries and emus.
  8. Order Rheae: rheas.
  9. Order Crypturi: tinamous.

10. Order Sphenisci: penguins.
11. Order Tubinares: albatrosses, petrels.
12. Order Podicipedes: grebes.
13. Order Gaviae: loons.
14. Order Steganopodes: cormorants, gannets, pelicans.
15. Order Falcones: hawks, eagles, vultures.
16. Order Gressores: herons, ibises, storks.
17. Order Phoenicopteri: flamingoes.
18. Order Anseres: ducks, geese, swans.
19. Order Galli: pheasants, quail, grouse, turkeys, fowls.
20. Order Cuculi: cuckoos.
21. Order Grues: cranes, limpkins, bitterns, rails.
22. Order Diatrymae: *Diatryma* and related genera.
23. Order Laro-Limicolae: snipe, plovers, sandpipers, gulls, terns, auks.
24. Order Columbae: doves, pigeons, dodo.
25. Order Psittaci: parrots.
26. Order Striges: owls.
27. Order Caprimulgi: goatsuckers.
28. Order Trogones: trogons.
29. Order Coraciae: kingfishers, rollers, hoopoes, hornbills.
30. Order Colii: mousebirds.
31. Order Macrochires: swifts, hummingbirds.
32. Order Pici: woodpeckers, toucans, honey guides.
33. Order Passeres.
   A. Suborder Eurylaimi: broadbills.
   B. Suborder Tyranni: antbirds, ovenbirds, tyrant flycatchers.
   C. Suborder Menurae: lyrebirds.
   D. Suborder Oscines: songbirds, including bulbuls, babblers, warblers, thrushes, wagtails, shrikes, waxwings, creepers, nuthatches, titmice, nectar eaters, vireos, finches, tanagers, American blackbirds, weaverbirds, starlings, Old World orioles, drongos, crows, jays, magpies, wattlebirds, bowerbirds, birds of paradise.

M. Class Mammalia: the mammals; "warm-blooded" tetrapods with hair.
Subclass Prototheria: egg-laying mammals.
   1. Order Monotremata: the recent platypus and echidna.
Subclass Allotheria: a long line of early mammals.
   2. Order Multituberculata: multituberculates.
Subclass uncertain.
   3. Order Triconodonta: triconodonts.
Subclass Theria: most of the mammals.
Infraclass Pantotheria: the first therians.
   4. Order Pantotheria: pantotheres, ancestors of marsupials and placentals.
   5. Order Symmetrodonta: symmetrodonts.
Infraclass Metatheria: the marsupials or pouched mammals.
   6. Order Marsupialia: the marsupials.
     i. Superfamily Didelphoidea: opossums.

    ii. Superfamily Borhyaenoidea: carnivorous marsupials of South America.

    iii. Superfamily Dasyuroidea: Tasmanian wolf, pouched mice.

    iv. Superfamily Parameloidea: bandicoots.

    v. Superfamily Caenolestoidea: opossum-rat and related fossil forms.

    vi. Superfamily Phalangeroidea: phalangers, koala, kangaroos, diprotodonts.

Infraclass Eutheria: the placental mammals.

Cohort Unguiculata: the unguiculates, mammals with nails or claws.

  7. Order Insectivora: insectivores, the most primitive placentals.

    i. Superfamily Deltatheridioidea: ancestral insectivores.

    ii. Superfamily Tenrecoidea: tenrecs.

    iii. Superfamily Chrysochloroidea: golden moles.

    iv. Superfamily Erinaceoidea: hedgehogs.

    v. Superfamily Macroscelidoidea: elephant shrews.

    vi. Superfamily Soricoidea: shrews.

    vii. Superfamily Pantolestoidea: pantolestids.

    viii. Superfamily Mixodectoidea: mixodectids.

  8. Order Dermoptera: the colugos or "flying lemurs."

  9. Order Chiroptera: the bats.

    A. Suborder Megachiroptera: the fruit-eating bats.

    B. Suborder Microchiroptera: the common bats.

10. Order Primates: tupaioids, lemurs, tarsiers, monkeys, apes, men.

    A. Suborder Lemuroidea: the lemurs and their relatives.

      i. Superfamily Tupaioidea: tree shrews.

      ii. Superfamily Lemuroidea: lemurs.

      iii. Superfamily Daubentonioidea: the aye-aye of Madagascar.

      iv. Superfamily Lorisoidea: the lorises and bush-babies.

    B. Suborder Tarsioidea: the tarsiers.

      a. Family Anaptomorphidae: fossil tarsioids.

      b. Family Tarsiidae: the spectral tarsier of the Orient.

    C. Suborder Anthropoidea: monkeys, apes and men.

      i. Superfamily Ceboidea: New World monkeys.

        a. Family Cebidae: fossil and recent howlers, spider monkeys, etc.

        b. Family Callithricidae: marmosets.

      ii. Superfamily Cercopithecoidea: Old World monkeys.

        a. Family Cercopithecidae: macaques, baboons, guenons, langurs.

      iii. Superfamily Hominoidea: apes and men.

        a. Family Parapithecidae: *Parapithecus*, an ancestral ape.

        b. Family Pongidae: gibbons, dryopithecines, chimps, orangutans, gorillas.

        c. Family Hominidae: men.

11. Order Tillodontia: tillodonts.

12. Order Taeniodonta: taeniodonts.

13. Order Edentata: New World edentates.

    A. Suborder Palaeanodonta: ancestral and early edentates.

    B. Suborder Pilosa: sloths and anteaters.
      i. Superfamily Megalonychoidea: ground sloths.
      ii. Superfamily Bradypodoidea: tree sloths.
      iii. Superfamily Myrmecophagoidea: anteaters.
    C. Suborder Cingulata: armadillos and glyptodonts.
      i. Superfamily Dasypodoidea: armadillos.
      ii. Superfamily Glyptodontoidea: glyptodonts.
14. Order Pholidota: pangolins.
Cohort Glires: rodents and rabbits.
15. Order Rodentia
    A. Suborder Sciuromorpha
      i. Superfamily Ischyromyoidea: basically primitive rodents.
      ii. Superfamily Aplodontoidea: sewellels, related fossils.
      iii. Superfamily Sciuroidea: squirrels, chipmunks, marmots.
      iv. Superfamily Ctenodactyloidea: desert rodents of Africa.
    B. Suborder Theridomyomorpha
      i. Superfamily Theridomyoidea: spring haas, related fossils.
      ii. Superfamily Anomaluroidea: scaly-tailed "squirrels."
    C. Suborder Castorimorpha
      i. Superfamily Castoroidea: beavers.
    D. Suborder Myomorpha
      i. Superfamily Muroidea: rats, mice, muskrats, voles.
      ii. Superfamily Geomyoidea: pocket mice.
      iii. Superfamily Dipodoidea: jumping mice.
      iv. Superfamily Gliroidea: dormice.
    E. Suborder Caviomorpha
      i. Superfamily Octodontoidea: spiny "rats," tucu tucu.
      ii. Superfamily Chinchilloidea: chinchillas.
      iii. Superfamily Cavioidea: guinea pigs, capybaras.
      iv. Superfamily Erethizontoidea: New World porcupines.
    F. Suborder Hystricomorpha
      i. Superfamily Hystricoidea: Old World porcupines.
      ii. Superfamily Thrynomyoidea: bamboo "rats," rock "rats."
    G. Suborder Bathyergomorpha
      i. Superfamily Bathyergoidea: naked "rat."
16. Order Lagomorpha: hares, rabbits, and pikas.
Cohort Mutica: whales, ancient and modern.
17. Order Cetacea: porpoises and whales.
    A. Suborder Archaeoceti: ancient whales.
    B. Suborder Odontoceti: porpoises, dolphins, toothed whales.
    C. Suborder Mysticeti: whalebone whales.
Cohort Ferungulata: carnivores and hoofed mammals.
Superorder Ferae: carnivores or meat-eating mammals.
18. Order Carnivora: all of the carnivores.
    A. Suborder Creodonta: ancient carnivores.
      i. Superfamily Arctocyonoidea: the most primitive creodonts.
      ii. Superfamily Mesonychoidea: large, blunt-toothed creodonts.

iii. Superfamily Oxyaenoidea: progressive creodonts.
B. Suborder Fissipedia: land-living carnivores of modern types.
 i. Superfamily Miacoidea: ancestral fissipeds.
 ii. Superfamily Canoidea: dogs, bears, raccoons, mustelids.
   a. Family Canidae: dogs, wolves, foxes.
   b. Family Ursidae: bears.
   c. Family Procyonidae: raccoons, coatis, kinkajous, pandas.
   d. Family Mustelidae: weasels, mink, otter, badgers, wolverines, skunks.
 iii. Superfamily Feloidea: civets, hyenas, cats.
   a. Family Viverridae: civets.
   b. Family Hyaenidae: hyenas.
   c. Family Felidae: cats, large and small.
C. Suborder Pinnipedia: marine carnivores.
   a. Family Otariidae: eared seals, sea lions.
   b. Family Phocidae: seals, sea elephants.
   c. Family Odobenidae: walruses.
Superorder Protungulata: early ungulates and their descendants.
19. Order Condylarthra: ancestral ungulates.
20. Order Litopterna: South American hoofed mammals.
   a. Family Proterotheriidae: primitive litopterns.
   b. Family Macraucheniidae: progressive and persistent litopterns.
21. Order Notoungulata: South American hoofed mammals.
   A. Suborder Notioprogonia: primitive notoungulates.
   B. Suborder Toxodonta: varied, specialized notoungulates.
   C. Suborder Typotheria: small, rabbit-like notoungulates.
   D. Suborder Hegetotheria: small notoungulates.
22. Order Astrapotheria: South American hoofed mammals.
23. Order Tubulidentata: aardvarks.
Superorder Paenungulata: generally large ungulates, hyracoids, sea cows.
24. Order Pantodonta: large, primitive ungulates, or amblypods.
25. Order Dinocerata: very large, early ungulates, or uintatheres.
26. Order Xenungulata: xenungulates, ancient ungulates of South America.
27. Order Pyrotheria: large ungulates of South America.
28. Order Proboscidea: moeritheres, dinotheres, mastodonts, elephants.
   A. Suborder Moeritherioidea: ancestral proboscideans.
   B. Suborder Deinotherioidea: the dinotheres.
   C. Suborder Elephantoidea: mastodonts and elephants.
     a. Family Gomphotheriidae: long-jawed mastodonts and their descendants.
     b. Family Mastodontidae: crested-toothed mastodonts.
     c. Family Elephantidae: stegodonts, mammoths, elephants.
   D. Suborder Barytherioidea: barytheres.
29. Order Embrithopoda: arsinoitheres of Egypt.

30. Order Hyracoidea: hyraxes.
31. Order Desmostyliformes: desmostylids, large marine waders.
32. Order Sirenia: sea cows.
33. Order Perissodactyla: odd-toed hoofed mammals.
Superorder Mesaxonia: the perissodactyls.
    A. Suborder Hippomorpha: horses, titanotheres, chalicotheres.
      i. Superfamily Equoidea: palaeotheres and horses.
        a. Family Palaeotheriidae: palaeotheres.
        b. Family Equidae: horses.
      ii. Superfamily Brontotherioidea: titanotheres and chalicotheres.
        a. Family Brontotheriidae: titanotheres.
        b. Family Chalicotheriidae: chalicotheres or clawed perissodactyls.
    B. Suborder Ceratomorpha: tapirs and rhinoceroses.
      i. Superfamily Tapiroidea: tapirs.
      ii. Superfamily Rhinocerotoidea: rhinoceroses.
        a. Family Hyrachyidae: ancestral rhinoceroses.
        b. Family Hyracodontidae: early running rhinoceroses.
        c. Family Amynodontidae: aquatic rhinoceroses.
        d. Family Rhinocerotidae: progressive rhinoceroses.
Superorder Paraxonia: the artiodactyls.
34. Order Artiodactyla: the even-toed hoofed mammals.
    A. Suborder Suina: the non-ruminating artiodactyls.
      i. Superfamily Dichobunoidea: ancestral artiodactyls.
      ii. Superfamily Entelodontoidea: entelodonts.
      iii. Superfamily Suoidea: pigs and peccaries.
        a. Family Suidae: Old World pigs.
        b. Family Tayassuidae: New World peccaries.
      iv. Superfamily Anthracotherioidea: anthracotheres to hippopotamuses.
        a. Family Anoplotheriidae: anoplotheres.
        b. Family Anthracotheriidae: anthracotheres.
        c. Family Hippopotamidae: hippopotamuses.
      v. Superfamily Cainotherioidea: caenotheres.
      vi. Superfamily Merycoidodontoidea: the oreodonts.
        a. Family Agriochoeridae: clawed oreodonts.
        b. Family Merycoidodontidae: hoofed oreodonts.
    B. Suborder Tylopoda: xiphodonts and camels.
        a. Family Xiphodontidae: xiphodonts.
        b. Family Camelidae: camels and llamas.
    C. Suborder Ruminantia.
      i. Superfamily Traguloidea: the extinct hypertragulids, protoceratids and modern tragulids.
      ii. Superfamily Cervoidea: deer.
      iii. Superfamily Giraffoidea: giraffes.
      iv. Superfamily Bovoidea: antelopes and cattle.
        a. Family Antilocapridae: the American pronghorn and related fossil forms.
        b. Family Bovidae: antelopes, gazelles, cattle, musk oxen, sheep, goats.

References

This bibliography is made up of a selected list of references that have a bearing upon the subject of vertebrate evolution. The literature on this subject is vast, so that no attempt is made to present a comprehensive list of publications at this place. The bibliographies of vertebrate paleontology, included at the end of this reference list, cite most of the published studies on the fossil vertebrates of North America since the beginning of the science in this country, and of the world since 1928. The bibliography in Alfred S. Romer's *Vertebrate Paleontology* is an excellent selection of significant works on the various groups of fossil vertebrates. The works listed below are those readily available, for the most part, to readers who do not have access to highly specialized libraries of natural history.

Evolution

Since much is being written on this subject at the present time, only a few references of particular importance to the reader interested in the evolution of the vertebrates are listed here. The books by Carter and by Moody and *The Meaning of Evolution*, by Simpson, are excellent discussions of the subject in its general aspects. *Evolution*, by Huxley, and *The Major Features of Evolution*, by Simpson, both very important books, are more extended than the general textbooks.

Carter, George S. 1951. *Animal Evolution, a Study of Recent Views of Its Causes.* London, Sidgwick and Jackson, Ltd. 368 pp.

Gregory, William K. 1951. *Evolution Emerging. A Survey of Changing Patterns from Primeval Life to Man.* New York, The Macmillan Co. Vol. 1, xxvi + 736 pp. (text); vol. 2, viii + 1013 pp. (figures and plates).

Huxley, Julian S. 1942. *Evolution, the Modern Synthesis.* London, George Allen and Unwin, Ltd. 645 pp.

———. 1953. *Evolution in Action.* New York, Harper and Brothers. 182 pp.

Lull, Richard S. 1947. *Organic Evolution,* revised edition. New York, The Macmillan Co. 744 pp.

Moody, Paul A. 1953. *Introduction to Evolution.* New York, Harper and Brothers. 475 pp.

Simpson, George G. 1949. *The Meaning of Evolution.* New Haven, Yale University Press. 364 pp.

———. 1953. *The Major Features of Evolution.* New York, Columbia University Press. 434 pp.

Vertebrate Zoology

Hegner and Stiles, Parker and Haswell, and Storer are all standard textbooks of zoology. The book by Romer is of particular importance in that it is more

than the usual type of comparative anatomy text; it includes extensive consideration of the anatomy in fossil vertebrates. The book by Goodrich also gives
considerable attention to the fossils as they bear upon vertebrate anatomy.
Young's book is an excellent text that deals with many aspects of the structure,
physiology, and evolution of vertebrates, fossil and recent.

De Beer, G. R. 1928. *Vertebrate Zoology.* New York, The Macmillan Co.
505 pp.

Goodrich, Edwin S. 1930. *Studies on the Structure and Development of
Vertebrates.* London, Macmillan and Co., Ltd. 837 pp.

Grassé, Pierre-P. (and collaborators). 1954. *Traité de Zoologie,* Tome XII.
(Comparative Anatomy.) Paris, Masson et Cie. 1145 pp.

Gregory, William K. 1929. *Our Face from Fish to Man.* New York, G. P.
Putnam's Sons. 295 pp.

Hegner, Robert W., and Karl A. Stiles. 1951. *College Zoology,* 6th edition.
New York, The Macmillan Co. 911 pp.

Hyman, Libbie H. 1942. *Comparative Vertebrate Anatomy,* 2nd edition.
Chicago, University of Chicago Press. 544 pp.

Parker, Thomas J., and William A. Haswell. 1940. *A Textbook of Zoology,*
6th edition. London, Macmillan and Co., Ltd. Vol. 1, 725 pp.; vol. 2, 758 pp.

Romer, Alfred S. 1949. *The Vertebrate Body.* Philadelphia, W. B. Saunders
Co. 643 pp.

Storer, Tracy I. 1951. *General Zoology,* 2nd edition. New York, McGraw-Hill
Co. 832 pp.

Young, J. Z. 1950. *The Life of the Vertebrates.* London, Oxford University
Press. 767 pp.

General Works on Vertebrate Paleontology

Vertebrate Paleontology, by Romer, is the outstanding book on this subject
at the present time. It gives a full and well-balanced treatment that contains
virtually all the pertinent information necessary in a general account of the
fossil vertebrates. *Man and the Vertebrates,* by this same author, is a much
more popular account, heavily weighted toward the evolution of man, as illustrated not only by the available fossils but also by the anatomy, racial characters,
and distribution of modern men. Zittel's two volumes are classic handbooks of
paleontology. The books by Boule and Piveteau, by Simpson, and by Swinnerton, though concerned with paleontology as a whole, give considerable space
to the evolution of the vertebrates.

Boule, Marcellin, and Jean Piveteau. 1935. *Les fossiles.* Paris, Masson and Cie.
899 pp.

Camp, Charles L. 1952. *Earth Song.* Berkeley and Los Angeles, University
of California Press. 127 pp.

Kuhn-Schnyder, Emil. 1953. *Geschichte der Wirbeltiere.* Basil, Benno Schwabe
and Co. 156 pp.

Oakley, Kenneth P., and H. M. Muir-Wood. 1948. *The Succession of Life
through Geological Time.* London, British Museum (Natural History). 92 pp.

Peyer, Bernhard. 1950. *Geschichte der Tierwelt.* Zurich, Büchergilde Guten-
berg. 228 pp.

Romer, Alfred S. 1945. *Vertebrate Paleontology,* 2nd edition. Chicago, University of Chicago Press. 687 pp.

Romer, Alfred S. 1941. *Man and the Vertebrates*, 3rd edition. Chicago, University of Chicago Press. 405 pp.

Simpson, George G. 1953. *Life of the Past.* New Haven, Yale University Press. 198 pp.

Swinnerton, H. H. 1947. *Outlines of Paleontology*, 3rd edition. London, Edward Arnold and Co. 393 pp.

Zittel, Karl A. von. 1932. *Textbook of Palaeontology*, revised by A. S. Woodward. London, Macmillan and Co., Ltd. Vol. 2, 464 pp.

——. 1925. *Textbook of Palaeontology*, revised by A. S. Woodward. London, Macmillan and Co., Ltd. Vol. 3, 316 pp.

Fishes

One of the best general accounts of fossil fishes, the book by Dean, has long been out of print. It is nevertheless listed here. A good modern discussion of the subject is Romer's paper in the *Quarterly Review of Biology*. The little book by Moy-Thomas is an excellent treatment of the early fishes that unfortunately is now very difficult to obtain.

Berg, Leo S. 1940. Classification of fishes, both recent and fossil. *Trav. Inst. Zool. Acad. Sci. U.R.S.S.*, vol. 5, pt. II, pp. 85–517. (Lithoprinted by Edwards Brothers, Ann Arbor, Michigan, 1947.)

Dean, Bashford. 1895. *Fishes, Living and Fossil.* New York, The Macmillan Co. 300 pp.

Moy-Thomas, J. A. 1939. *Palaeozoic Fishes.* New York, Chemical Publishing Co. 149 pp.

Norman, John R. 1931. *A History of Fishes.* London, Ernest Benn, Ltd. 463 pp.

Romer, Alfred S. 1946. The early evolution of fishes. *Quar. Rev. Biology*, vol. 21, no. 1, pp. 33–69.

Amphibians and Reptiles

The book by Romer on the osteology of the reptiles is a detailed work on reptilian osteology with particular attention given to the fossil forms. It contains in addition a very complete classification of the reptiles. Volume V of the *Traité de Paléontologie* is a modern, comprehensive survey of fossil amphibians, reptiles and birds. Although the title does not indicate it, the book by Watson is primarily concerned with structure and evolution in late Paleozoic amphibians and reptiles. Swinton's book on dinosaurs, a standard work, is unfortunately now out of print. The book by Colbert, although primarily concerned with dinosaurs, also treats the other fossil reptiles and the amphibians as well. Broom's book, very useful to the advanced student, is largely a series of detailed descriptions of genera and species. The books by Williston, though long out of print, are still useful.

Barbour, Thomas. 1934. *Reptiles and Amphibians, Their Habits and Adaptations.* Boston and New York, Houghton Mifflin Co. 125 pp.

Broom, Robert. 1932. *Mammal-like Reptiles of South Africa.* London, H. F. and G. Witherby. 376 pp.

Colbert, Edwin H. 1951. *The Dinosaur Book,* 2nd edition. New York, Mc-Graw-Hill Book Co. 156 pp.

Ditmars, Raymond L. 1922. *Reptiles of the World.* New York, The Macmillan Co. 373 pp.

von Huene, Friedrich, R. 1956. *Paläontologie und Phylogenie der Niederen Tetrapoden.* Jena, Gustav Fischer Verlag. 716 pp.

Noble, Gladwyn K. 1931. *The Biology of the Amphibia.* New York, McGraw-Hill Book Co. 577 pp.

Piveteau, Jean (and collaborators) 1955. *Traité de Paléontologie.* Tome V. *Amphibiens, Reptiles, Oiseaux.* Paris, Masson et Cie. 1113 pp.

Romer, Alfred S. 1947. Review of the Labyrinthodontia. *Bull. Mus. Comp. Zool.,* vol. 99, no. 1, 368 pp.

——. 1956. *Osteology of the Reptiles.* Chicago, University of Chicago Press. xxi + 772 p.

Swinton, William E. 1934. *The Dinosaurs.* London, Thomas Murby and Co. 233 pp.

Watson, David M. S. 1951. *Paleontology and Modern Biology.* New Haven, Yale University Press. 216 pp.

Williston, Samuel W. 1914. *Water Reptiles of the Past and Present.* Chicago, University of Chicago Press. 251 pp.

——. 1925. *The Osteology of the Reptiles.* Cambridge, Harvard University Press. 300 pp.

Birds

The book by Heilmann is a standard work. The paper by Howard, although particularly concerned with the fossil birds of southern California, gives a brief discussion of avian evolution. An authoritative classification of birds is the paper by Mayr and Amadon, in which some attention is given to a few fossil forms.

Heilmann, Gerhard. 1927. *The Origin of the Birds.* New York, D. Appleton and Co. 210 pp.

Howard, Hildegarde. 1945. Fossil birds. *Los Angeles County Mus. Sci. Ser.,* no. 10, Paleont. no. 6, 40 pp.

Mayr, Ernst, and Dean Amadon. 1951. A classification of recent birds. *Amer. Mus. Novitates,* no. 1496, 42 pp.

Mammals

There are numerous good modern books in English on recent mammals, but nothing at the present time to take the place of *Introduction to the Study of Mammals, Living and Extinct,* by Flower and Lydekker. This is still a useful book, although the paleontology is out of date. Volume XVII (in two parts) of the monumental *Traité de Zoologie* is an authoritative, comprehensive text on fossil and recent mammals. *Die Säugetiere,* by Weber, in two volumes, is also a thorough account of fossil and recent mammals. Simpson's classification of mammals is an outstanding monograph that carries the classification of all mammals, fossil and recent, down to genera. It contains clear and authoritative discussions of mammalian relationships by the leading modern student of fossil mammals. Osborn's *Age of Mammals* and Scott's *History of Land Mam-*

mals in the Western Hemisphere are standard works, widely used. Gregory's *Orders of Mammals* is a basic work on mammalian classification. *Climate and Evolution,* by Matthew, is a classic work, devoted to the geographic history of the mammals. Many books and papers are concerned with various mammalian orders, families, or lesser groups, but the only one that will be listed here is Clark's summary of primate evolution—a subject of particular interest to most of us.

Clark, W. E. LeGros. 1950. *History of the Primates.* London, British Museum (Natural History). 117 pp.

Flower, William H., and Richard Lydekker. 1891. *An Introduction to the Study of Mammals, Living and Extinct.* London, Adam and Charles Black. 763 pp.

Grassé, Pierre-P. (and collaborators) 1955. *Traité de Zoologie.* Tome XVII. *Mammifères.* Paris, Masson et Cie. Pts. I and II, 2300 pp.

Gregory, William K. 1910. The orders of mammals. *Bull. Amer. Mus. Nat. Hist.,* vol. 27, 524 pp.

———. 1922. *The Origin and Evolution of the Human Dentition.* Baltimore, Williams and Wilkins Co. 548 pp.

Matthew, William D. 1939. *Climate and Evolution,* 2nd edition revised. The New York Academy of Science, Special Publications. Vol. 1, 223 pp.

Osborn, Henry F. 1910. *The Age of Mammals in Europe, Asia, and North America.* New York, The Macmillan Co. 635 pp.

Scott, William B. 1937. *A History of Land Mammals in the Western Hemisphere.* New York, The Macmillan Co. 786 pp.

Simpson, George G. 1945. The principles of classification and a classification of mammals. *Bull. Amer. Mus. Nat. Hist.,* vol. 85, 350 pp.

Weber, Max. 1927. *Die Säugetiere.* Jena, Verlag von Gustav Fischer. Vol. 1, 444 pp.

———. 1928. *Die Säugetiere.* Jena, Verlag von Gustav Fischer. Vol. 2, 898 pp.

Geology

Three good modern textbooks of geology are listed here:

Croneis, Carey, and William C. Krumbein. 1943. *Down to Earth, an Introduction to Geology.* Chicago, University of Chicago Press. 501 pp.

Dunbar, Carl O. 1949. *Historical Geology.* New York, John Wiley and Sons. 567 pp.

Moore, Raymond C. 1949. *Introduction to Historical Geology.* New York, McGraw-Hill Book Co. 582 pp.

Past Climates

Brooks, C. E. P. 1949. *Climate through the Ages,* revised edition. London, Ernest Benn, Ltd. 395 pp.

Fossil Plants

Andrews, Henry N. 1947. *Ancient Plants and the World They Lived In.* Ithaca, Comstock Publishing Co. 279 pp.

Bibliographies

As mentioned above, the selected bibliography in Romer's *Vertebrate Paleontology* is a good source for some of the outstanding works on fossil vertebrates. The Hay bibliographies list all papers on the fossil vertebrates of North America up to 1928, and the Camp bibliographies do this on a world-wide basis, from 1928 to the present time. A bibliography by Romer, Edinger, and Wright on fossil vertebrates other than those from North America, and covering the period up to 1928, is now in preparation.

Romer, Alfred S. 1945. *Vertebrate Paleontology,* 2nd edition. Chicago, Chicago University Press. Pp. 628–661.

Hay, Oliver P. 1902. Bibliography and catalogue of the fossil Vertebrata of North America. *Bull. U. S. Geol. Surv.,* no. 179, 868 pp.

—— 1929. *Second Bibliography and Catalogue of the Fossil Vertebrata of North America.* Carnegie Inst. of Washington, Publication no. 390, vol. 1, 916 pp.

——. 1930. *Second Bibliography and Catalogue of the Fossil Vertebrata of North America.* Carnegie Inst. of Washington, Publication no. 390, vol. 2, 1074 pp.

Camp, Charles L., and V. L. Vanderhoof. 1940. *Bibliography of Fossil Vertebrates, 1928–1933.* Geological Society of America, Special Paper no. 27, 503 pp.

Camp, Charles L., D. N. Taylor, and S. P. Welles. 1942. *Bibliography of Fossil Vertebrates, 1934–1938.* Geological Society of America, Special Paper no. 42, 663 pp.

Camp, Charles L., S. P. Welles, and M. Green. 1949. *Bibliography of Fossil Vertebrates, 1939–1943.* Geological Society of America, Memoir 37, 371 pp.

——. 1953. *Bibliography of Fossil Vertebrates, 1944–1948.* Geological Society of America, Memoir 57, 465 pp.

Key to Abbreviations of Bone Names Used in Illustrations

Bones of the Skull and the Lower Jaw

a	articular	m	maxilla
an	angular		
as	alisphenoid	n	nasal
		op [1]	opercular (fish)
bo	basioccipital	op [1] ⎫	
bpt	basipterygoid	opo ⎭	opisthotic (tetrapod)
bs	basisphenoid		
		p	parietal
c	coronoid	pd	predentary
		pf	postfrontal
d	dentary	pl	palatine
		pm	premaxilla
ec	ectopterygoid	pn	postnarial
eo	exoccipital	po	postorbital
ep	epipterygoid	pop	preopercular
esl	lateral extrascapular	pos	postsplenial
esm	medial extrascapular	pp	postparietal
exn	external nares	pq	palatoquadrate
		pr	postrostral
f	frontal	pra	prearticular
		prf	prefrontal
g	gular	pro	prootic
		ps	parasphenoid
hm	hyomandibular	pt	pterygoid
in	internarial	q	quadrate
inn	internal nares	qj	quadratojugal
it	intertemporal		
		sa ⎫	surangular
j [1] ⎫	jugal	san ⎭	
ju ⎭		sm	septomaxilla
		sop	subopercular
l	lacrymal	sor	supraorbital

[1] In spite of every effort to be consistent, a few of these abbreviations got out of hand. The reader's kind indulgence is requested, if he finds two abbreviations being used for a single bone, or, conversely, one abbreviation for two different bones.

sp	splenial		t	tabular
sq	squamosal			
st	supratemporal		v	vomer
sta	stapes		vac	vacuity

Bones of the Postcranial Skeleton

ba	branchial arch		p	pubis
ce	centrale		pc	pleurocentrum
ef	entepicondylar foramen		r	radius
f	fibula		ra	radiale
fi	fibulare		sp	spine
ic	intercentrum		t	tibia
il	ilium		ti	tibiale
in	intermedium			
is	ischium		u	ulna
na	neural arch		ul	ulnare

Sources and Credits for Illustrations

All of the illustrations, with the exception of Figures 18, 42, 48 and 50, are new, and were drawn specifically for this book.

The chapter headings, the restorations, and the phylogenetic diagrams were made by Mrs. Lois Darling under the supervision of the author. The figures in this category, in addition to the chapter headings, are as follows: 4, 7, 11, 13, 14, 16, 19, 24, 26, 31, 38, 41, 45, 49, 52, 54, 55, 59, 62, 63, 64, 65, 66, 68, 75, 76, 78, 80, 82, 83, 85, 87, 88, 89, 90, 93, 94, 95, 96, 100, 101, 102, 109, 110, 111, 112, 113, 114, 115, 116, 118, 119, 120.

Figures 1, 3, 20, 47, 51, and 67 were drawn from original layouts made by the author.

The remaining illustrations, with the exception of Figure 18, also were done under the supervision of the author. Many of them were of necessity based in part upon information from published works. The sources for these figures, and for the four figures noted above are listed below. In this listing, the names of authors, followed by dates, indicate source materials taken from scientific papers or monographs. Sources from copyrighted books are indicated in each case in the usual fashion.

Fig. 2. Adapted from *Animals without Backbones,* by R. Buchsbaum, copyright 1945, by permission of The University of Chicago Press.

Fig. 5. Adapted from *Man and the Vertebrates,* by A. S. Romer, copyright 1941, by permission of The University of Chicago Press.

Fig. 6. After E. A. Stensiö, 1932.

Fig. 8. (*A*) After D. M. S. Watson, 1937. (*B, C*) After T. S. Westoll.

Fig. 9. After D. M. S. Watson, 1937.

Fig. 10. After A. Heintz, 1931.

Fig. 12. (*A, B*) From models in The American Museum of Natural History. (*C*) After J. A. Moy-Thomas, 1940.

Fig. 15. From various sources.

Fig. 17. (*A*) After H. Aldinger, 1937. (*B*) After D. Rayner, 1948.

Fig. 18. From an exhibit in The American Museum of Natural History; courtesy of Bobb Schaeffer.

Fig. 21. (*A*) After D. M. S. Watson, 1921. (*B*) From a model by E. Jarvik.

Fig. 22. (*A*) From a model in The American Museum of Natural History. (*B*) From various sources.

Fig. 23. Adapted from *Vertebrate Paleontology,* by A. S. Romer, copyright 1945, by permission of The University of Chicago Press.

Fig. 25. (*A, C*) Adapted from *Vertebrate Paleontology,* by A. S. Romer, copyright 1945, by permission of The University of Chicago Press. (*B, D*) After E. Jarvik, 1952.

Fig. 27. After E. Jarvik, 1952.

Fig. 28. Adapted from various sources.

Fig. 29. From a skull in The American Museum of Natural History.

Fig. 30. From a skeleton in The American Museum of Natural History.

Fig. 32. (*A*) After E. Jarvik, 1952. (*B, C, D*) After A. S. Romer, 1947.

Fig. 33. (A) After S. W. Williston, 1909. (B) After E. C. Olson, 1951. (C) Adapted from *Evolution Emerging*, by W. K. Gregory, copyright 1951, by permission of The Macmillan Company, New York.

Fig. 34. (A) Adapted from *Man and the Vertebrates*, by A. S. Romer, copyright 1941, by permission of The University of Chicago Press. (B) After A. S. Romer and L. I. Price, 1939.

Fig. 35. After T. E. White, 1939.

Fig. 36. (A) Adapted from *Vertebrate Paleontology*, by A. S. Romer, copyrighted 1945, by permission of The University of Chicago Press. (B) After A. S. Romer, 1946. (C) Adapted from *Evolution Emerging*, by W. K. Gregory, copyright 1951, by permission of The Macmillan Company, New York.

Fig. 37. (A, E) Adapted from *Vertebrate Paleontology*, by A. S. Romer, copyright 1945, by permission of The University of Chicago Press. (B) After C. W. Gilmore, 1905. (C) After C. W. Andrews, 1910–1913. (D) After A. S. Romer and L. I. Price, 1940.

Fig. 39. After E. H. Colbert, 1941.

Fig. 40. (A, B, C, E, F) After A. S. Romer and L. I. Price, 1940. (D) After E. C. Case, 1907.

Fig. 42. From E. H. Colbert, 1948.

Fig. 43. After R. Broom, 1912, 1932.

Fig. 44. (A, B) Adapted from *Vertebrate Paleontology*, by A. S. Romer, copyright 1945, by permission of The University of Chicago Press. (C, D) After W. K. Gregory and C. L. Camp, 1918.

Fig. 46. From a cast in The American Museum of Natural History.

Fig. 48. From E. H. Colbert, 1952.

Fig. 50. From E. H. Colbert (unpublished).

Fig. 53. (A, G) After S. W. Williston, 1914. (B) Adapted from *Textbook of Paleontology*, by K. A. von Zittel, copyright 1932, by permission of Macmillan and Company, Ltd., London. (C) Adapted from *Osteology of the Reptiles*, by S. W. Williston, copyright 1925, by permission of Harvard University Press. (D, E) After F. Broili, 1912. (F) After S. P. Welles, 1952. (H) After B. Peyer, 1941.

Fig. 56. (A) After H. G. Seeley, 1901. (B) After G. F. Eaton, 1910.

Fig. 57. After G. Steinmann and L. Döderlein, 1890.

Fig. 58. From: *The Origin of Birds*, by Gerhard Heilmann. Copyright 1927, D. Appleton and Company. Redrawn and adapted by permission of the publishers, Appleton-Century-Crofts, Inc.

Fig. 60. Adapted from *The Dinosaur Book*, by E. H. Colbert, 1945.

Fig. 61. (A, B, C) After C. W. Gilmore, 1914, 1920, 1925. (D) After R. S. Lull and N. Wright, 1942. (E) After R. S. Lull, 1933.

Fig. 69. (A) After E. H. Colbert and C. C. Mook, 1951. (B) After E. Fraas, 1902. (C, E) Adapted from *Osteology of the Reptiles*, by S. W. Williston, copyright 1925, by permission of Harvard University Press. (D) After C. W. Andrews, 1910–1913.

Fig. 70. (A) Adapted from *Osteology of the Reptiles*, by S. W. Williston, copyright 1925, by permission of Harvard University Press. (B) After H. Gadow, 1909.

Fig. 71. From various sources, including adaptation of a figure by permission from *American Mammals*, by W. J. Hamilton, Jr., copyright 1939. McGraw-Hill Book Company, Inc.

Fig. 72. (A) After H. G. Seeley, 1895. (B, H) After G. G. Simpson, 1929.

Fig. 73. After W. Granger and G. G. Simpson, 1929.

Fig. 74. (A) After W. J. Sinclair, 1906. (B, C, D) Adapted from *Evolution Emerging*, by W. K. Gregory, copyright 1951, by permission of The Macmillan Company,

New York. (*E, G*) Adapted from *Organic Evolution*, by R. S. Lull, copyright 1940, by permission of The Macmillan Company, New York. (*F*) Adapted from *Textbook of Paleontology*, by K. A. von Zittel, copyright 1925, by permission of Macmillan and Company, Ltd., London.

Fig. 77.   After E. H. Colbert, 1939.

Fig. 79.   (*A, D*) After W. K. Gregory and G. G. Simpson, 1926. (*B, C, E, F*) After G. G. Simpson, 1928.

Fig. 81.   (*A, B*) After R. Lydekker, 1894. (*C, D*) After C. Stock, 1925.

Fig. 84.   (*A, B*) After W. K. Gregory, 1921. (*C*) After A. Gaudry, 1862. (*D, E*) Adapted from *Evolution Emerging*, by W. K. Gregory, copyright 1951, by permission of The Macmillan Company, New York.

Fig. 86.   (*A*) After W. D. Matthew, 1910. (*C*) After W. B. Scott, 1905. (*D*) After O. A. Peterson, 1905. Also (*A–D*) adapted from *Vertebrate Paleontology*, by A. S. Romer, copyright 1945, by permission of The University of Chicago Press.

Fig. 91.   (*A, C, G*) After W. D. Matthew, 1935, 1930, 1910. (*B*) After W. B. Scott and G. Jepsen, 1936. (*D*) After J. C. Merriam and C. Stock, 1925. (*E*) After S. H. Reynolds, 1911. (*F*) After O. Zdansky, 1924.

Fig. 92.   (*A, B, G*) After W. D. Matthew, 1935, 1909, 1910. (*C*) After E. H. Colbert, 1933. (*D*) After J. Wortman, 1901. (*E*) After W. B. Scott and G. Jepsen, 1936. (*F*) After J. C. Merriam and C. Stock, 1925. (*H*) After O. Zdansky, 1924.

Fig. 97.   Adapted from *A History of Land Mammals in the Western Hemisphere*, by W. B. Scott, 1937.

Fig. 98.   (*A*) After H. Burmeister, 1866. (*B*) After W. J. Sinclair, 1909. (*C, E*) After W. B. Scott, 1912, 1928. (*D*) After E. S. Riggs, 1935. (*F*) After F. B. Loomis, 1914.

Fig. 99.   (*A–D*) Adapted from *Evolution Emerging*, by W. K. Gregory, copyright 1951, by permission of The Macmillan Company, New York. (*E*) After W. J. Holland and O. A. Peterson, 1913.

Fig. 103.   (*A*) Adapted from *Evolution Emerging*, by W. K. Gregory, copyright 1951, by permission of The Macmillan Company, New York. (*C, E*) After H. F. Osborn, 1918. (*B, D, F*) After W. D. Matthew, 1927.

Fig. 104.   (*A, B*) Adapted from *Evolution Emerging*, by W. K. Gregory, copyright 1951, by permission of The Macmillan Company, New York. (*C, E*) After H. F. Osborn, 1929, 1898. (*D*) After E. M. Schlaikjer, 1937.

Fig. 105.   (*A*) After J. Wortman, 1896. (*B*) After W. D. Matthew, 1927. (*C, E*) After H. F. Osborn, 1929, 1898. (*D*) After E. M. Schlaikjer, 1937.

Fig. 106.   (*A*) After W. B. Scott, 1940. (*B*) Adapted from *Evolution Emerging*, by W. K. Gregory, copyright 1951, by permission of The Macmillan Company, New York. (*C*) Adapted from *Vertebrate Paleontology*, by A. S. Romer, copyright 1945, by permission of The University of Chicago Press. (*D*) After O. A. Peterson, 1904. (*E*) Adapted from *A History of Land Mammals in the Western Hemisphere*, by W. B. Scott, 1937. (*F*) After W. D. Matthew, 1904.

Fig. 107.   (*A*) After W. B. Scott, 1940. (*B*) After S. H. Reynolds, 1922. (*C*) After H. S. Pearson, 1923. (*D*) After W. J. Sinclair, 1914. (*E*) After J. Leidy, 1869. (*F*) After O. A. Peterson, 1904. (*G*) After W. D. Matthew, 1908. (*H*) After R. A. Stirton, 1932. (*I*) After A. Gaudry, 1867.

Fig. 108.   (*A, F, G, H, J*) After F. B. Loomis, 1925. (*B*) Adapted from *Textbook of Paleontology*, by K. A. von Zittel, copyright 1925, by permission of Macmillan and Company, Ltd., London. (*C*) After W. B. Scott, 1940. (*D, I*) After E. H. Colbert, 1935, 1941. (*E*) After O. A. Peterson, 1909. (*K*) After G. Pilgrim, 1937.

Fig. 117.　Adapted from *Evolution Emerging*, by W. K. Gregory, copyright 1951, by permission of The Macmillan Company, New York.

Fig. 121.　After H. F. Osborn, 1936, 1942.

Fig. 122.　After H. F. Osborn, 1936, 1942.

Generic Index

Subject Index